THE NEW BLUE BOOK OF FAVORITE SONGS

THE GOLDEN BOOK OF FAVORITE SONGS
AND
THE GRAY BOOK OF FAVORITE SONGS
COMBINED
WITH AN ENLARGED SUPPLEMENT

---

341 Selections, Complete with Music

Compilers and Editors of "The Golden Book" and "The Gray Book"

JOHN W. BEATTIE

WILLIAM BREACH

MABELLE GLENN

WALTER GOODELL

EDGAR B. GORDON

NORMAN H. HALL

ERNEST G. HESSER

E. JANE WISENALL

Compilers and Arrangers of the Supplement

WALTER GOODELL

FLORENCE M. MARTIN

HALL & McCREARY COMPANY
CHICAGO

NOTICE

All special arrangements and harmonizations, as well as all original matter in PART ONE, *The Golden Book of Favorite Songs*; PART TWO, *The Gray Book of Favorite Songs*, and PART THREE, *The Supplement* are covered by the copyrights which appear on the backs of the title pages of PARTS ONE and TWO and on the front of that of PART THREE; therefore they cannot be reproduced by any process without liability for infringement.

THE BEST
MUSIC
SESAC
IN
AMERICA

Printed in the United States of America P4348

PART ONE

The Golden Book of FAVORITE SONGS

Revised & Enlarged

Responsive Readings

LEADER: *Blessed is the nation whose God is the Lord,*
And the people whom he hath chosen for his own inheritance.

ASSEMBLY: Righteousness exalteth a nation; but sin is a reproach to any people.

LEADER: *When the righteous are in authority the people rejoice; but when the wicked beareth rule, the people mourn.*
If thou hearken diligently unto the voice of the Lord thy God,
The Lord thy God will set thee on high above all nations of the earth.

Psalms

UNISON: We hold these truths to be self-evident:
That all men are created equal;
That they are endowed by their Creator with certain inalienable rights;
That among these are life, liberty, and the pursuit of happiness;
That to secure these rights, governments are instituted among men, deriving their just powers from the consent of the governed.

Thomas Jefferson

Lincoln's Gettysburg Address

LEADER: *Fourscore and seven years ago our fathers brought forth on this continent a new nation, conceived in liberty, and dedicated to the proposition that all men are created equal.*

ASSEMBLY: Now we are engaged in a great civil war, testing whether that nation, or any nation so conceived and so dedicated, can long endure.

LEADER: *We are met on a great battle-field of that war. We have come to dedicate a portion of that field as a final resting-place for those who here gave their lives that that nation might live.*

ASSEMBLY: It is altogether fitting and proper that we should do this. But, in a larger sense we cannot dedicate—we cannot consecrate—we cannot hallow—this ground.

LEADER: *The brave men, living and dead, who struggled here, have consecrated it far above our poor power to add or detract.*

ASSEMBLY: The world will little note nor long remember what we say here, but it can never forget what they did here.

LEADER: *It is for us, the living, rather, to be dedicated here to the unfinished work which they who fought here have thus far so nobly advanced.*

ASSEMBLY: It is rather for us to be here dedicated to the great task remaining before us—that from these honored dead we take increased devotion to that cause for which they gave the last full measure of devotion;

That we here highly resolve that these dead shall not have died in vain; that this nation, under God, shall have a new birth of freedom; and that the government of the people, by the people, for the people, shall not perish from the earth.

Abraham Lincoln

LEADER: *God hath made of one blood all nations of men, and we are his children,—brothers and sisters all.*

ASSEMBLY: We are citizens of these United States, and we believe our Flag stands for self-sacrifice for the good of all the people. We want, therefore, to be true citizens of our great country, and will show our love for her by our works.

LEADER: *Our country does not ask us to die for her welfare; she asks us to live for her, and so to live and so to act that her government may be pure, her officers honest, and every corner of her territory shall be a place fit to grow the best men and women, who shall rule over her.*

Mary McDowell

UNISON: The Flag means universal education—light for every mind, knowledge for every child. We must have but one flag. We must also have but one language. This must be the language of the Declaration of Independence.

Woodrow Wilson

Pledge To The Flag

I pledge allegiance to the Flag of the United States of America and to the Republic for which it stands, One Nation indivisible, with liberty and justice for all.

America
(My Country,'Tis of Thee)

America was written by Rev. Samuel F. Smith, a Baptist minister, who was born in Boston, October 21, 1808, and died November 16, 1895

One of Dr. Smith's friends was Lowell Mason, the eminent musician. A friend had given Mr. Mason a lot of German music books. Being unable to read German the musician took the books to Dr. Smith and asked him to translate some of the songs for him.

Dr. Smith says: "Turning over the leaves of the book one gloomy day in February, 1832, I came across the air, 'God save the King.' I liked the music. I glanced at the German words at the foot of the page. Under the inspiration of the moment I went to work and in half an hour 'America' was the result. It was written on a scrap of paper I picked up from the table and the hymn of today is substantially as it was written that day."

The hymn was first sung at a children's Fourth of July celebration in Park Street Church, Boston. It did not have great popularity until the Civil War. Since then it has become the best known and most frequently sung of any of our national songs. The origin of the music is uncertain. But one writer aptly says. "There certainly must be something more than ordinarily inspiring in an air which has struck the popular heart of two of the great nations of the earth."

SAMUEL FRANCIS SMITH — HENRY CAREY (?)

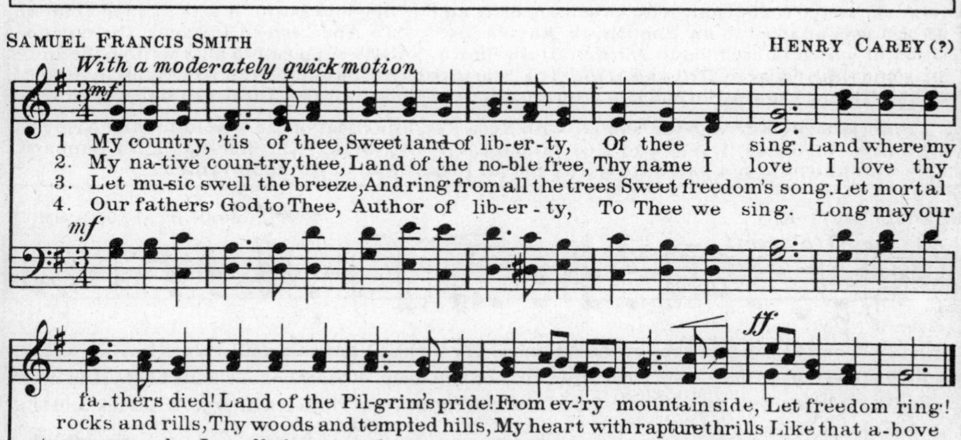
With a moderately quick motion
mf
1 My country, 'tis of thee, Sweet land of lib-er-ty, Of thee I sing. Land where my
2. My na-tive coun-try, thee, Land of the no-ble free, Thy name I love I love thy
3. Let mu-sic swell the breeze, And ring from all the trees Sweet freedom's song. Let mortal
4. Our fathers' God, to Thee, Author of lib-er-ty, To Thee we sing. Long may our
mf
ff
fa-thers died! Land of the Pil-grim's pride! From ev-'ry mountain side, Let freedom ring!
rocks and rills, Thy woods and templed hills, My heart with rapture thrills Like that a-bove
tongues awake, Let all that breathe partake, Let rocks their silence break, The sound prolong.
land be bright With freedom's ho-ly light; Protect us by Thy might, Great God, our King!

God Bless Our Native Land
(Tune — America)

1 God bless our native land,
Firm may she ever stand
Through storm and night!
When the wild tempests rave,
Ruler of wind and wave,
Do thou our country save,
By thy great might!

2 For her our prayers shall rise,
To God above the skies,
On him we wait;
Thou who art ever nigh,
Guarding with watchful eye,
To Thee aloud we cry,
God save the state!

CHARLES T BROOKS AND JOHN S. DWIGHT

The American's Creed

"I believe in the United States of America as a Government of the people, by the people, for the people; whose just powers are derived from the consent of the governed, a democracy in a republic; a sovereign Nation of many sovereign States; a perfect union, one and inseparable; established upon those principles of freedom, equality, justice, and humanity for which American patriots sacrificed their lives and fortunes.

"I therefore believe it is my duty to my country to love it; to support its Constitution; to obey its laws, to respect its flag, and to defend it against all enemies" — William Tyler Page

The Star-Spangled Banner

The "Star-Spangled Banner" was composed under the following circumstances:

It was on the evening of September 13, 1814, during the War of 1812, that a British fleet was anchored in Chesapeake Bay A Dr Beanes, an old resident of Upper Marlborough, Maryland, had been captured by the British and sent as a prisoner to Admiral Cochrane's flag-ship.

Francis Scott Key, a young lawyer of Baltimore, hearing of the misfortune of Dr. Beanes, who was his personal friend, hastened to the British commander to endeavor to have his friend released The enemy was about to attack Fort McHenry, so refused to allow Mr. Key and Dr. Beanes to return until after the fort was captured.

All through the night of September 13th, the bombardment was kept up, and in the light of the "rockets red glare, the bombs bursting in air" they could see the American flag still waving over the old fort. And when, in the first rays of dawn of September 14th, he still beheld the same glorious banner waving from its accustomed place, Francis Scott Key wrote the words of that wonderful song "The Star Spangled Banner."

The next day Key went ashore, and, after copying his poem, showed it to a friend and relative, Judge Nicholson, who saw its worth and at his suggestion it was printed. Soon after it was adapted to an English air known as "To Anacreon in Heaven," the composition of which is credited to John Stafford Smith, who is supposed to have written the music some time between 1770 and 1775. "The Star-Spangled Banner" was first sung in public by Ferdinand Durang, an actor, in a tavern near the Holiday Street Theatre in Baltimore, Md.

Francis Scott Key was the son of John Ross Key, an officer of the Revolutionary Army. He was born August 1, 1779, and died January 11, 1843, leaving "The Star-Spangled Banner" as a monument to his patriotic spirit, and an inspiration to his countrymen.

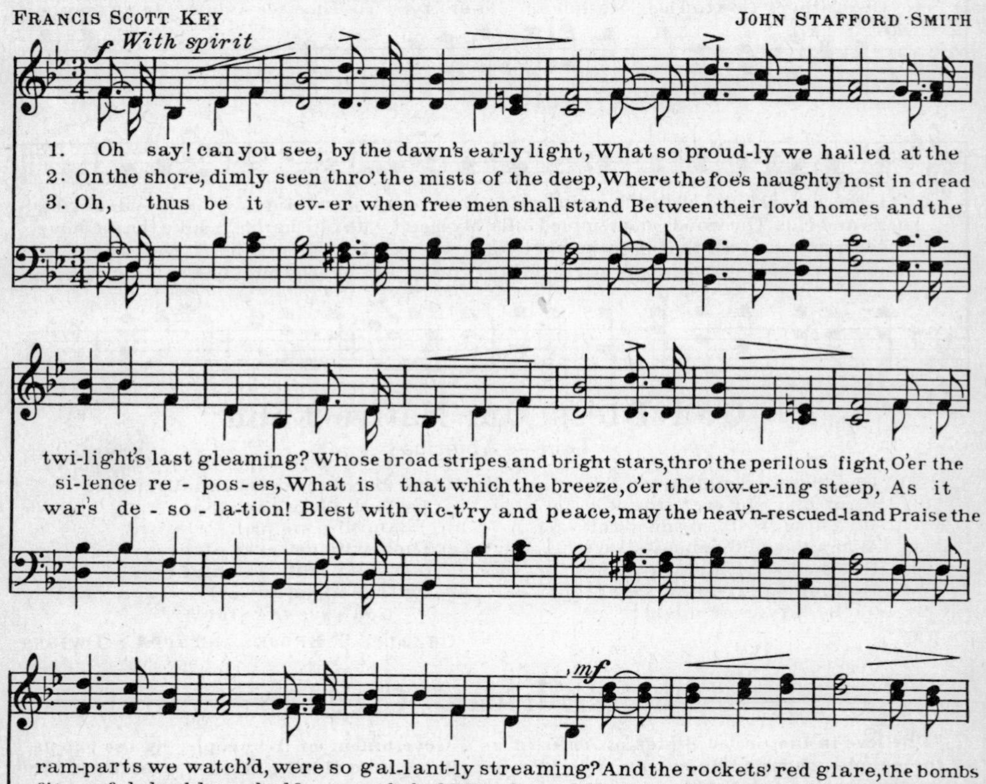
FRANCIS SCOTT KEY
JOHN STAFFORD SMITH
With spirit
1. Oh say! can you see, by the dawn's early light, What so proud-ly we hailed at the
2. On the shore, dimly seen thro' the mists of the deep, Where the foe's haughty host in dread
3. Oh, thus be it ev-er when free men shall stand Be tween their lov'd homes and the
twi-light's last gleaming? Whose broad stripes and bright stars, thro' the perilous fight, O'er the
si-lence re-pos-es, What is that which the breeze, o'er the tow-er-ing steep, As it
war's de-so-la-tion! Blest with vic-t'ry and peace, may the heav'n-rescued-land Praise the
ram-parts we watch'd, were so gal-lant-ly streaming? And the rockets' red glare, the bombs
fit-ful-ly blows, half con-ceals, half dis-clos-es? Now it catch-es the gleam of the
Pow'r that hath made and pre-served us a na-tion! Then con-quer we must, when our

The Star-Spangled Banner—Continued
CHORUS
ff
bursting in air, Gave proof thro' the night that our flag was still there. Oh, say, does that
morning's first beam, In full glory re-flect-ed now shines on the stream; 'Tis the Star-spangled
cause it is just, And this be our mot-to: "In God is our trust!" And the Star-spangled
fff
Star-span-gled Ban-ner yet wave O'er the land of the free and the home of the brave?
Ban-ner, oh, long may it wave O'er the land of the free and the home of the brave!
Ban-ner in triumph shall wave O'er the land of the free and the home of the brave!
Flag Of The Free
UNKNOWN
ARR. FROM WAGNER
Brisk march time
1. Flag of the free, fair-est to see, Borne thro' the strife and the thunder of war;
2. Flag of the brave, long may it wave, Chos-en of God while His might we adore; In
Fine.
Ban-ner so bright with star-ry light, Float ev-er proud-ly from mountain to shore.
Lib - er-ty's van, for manhood of man, Sym-bol of Right thro' the years passing o'er
D.S. While thro' the sky loud rings the cry, Un-ion and Lib - er - ty! one ev - er-more!
D.S.
Emblem of Freedom, hope to the slave, Spread thy fair folds but to shield and to save,
Pride of our country, honored a - far, Scat-ter each cloud that would darken a star,

Columbia, The Gem Of The Ocean

Columbia, the Gem of the Ocean is of uncertain origin. The melody has been claimed as of English composition, under the name of "Brittania, the Pride of the Ocean." The text was written at the request of David T. Shaw for a benefit, by Thomas a'Becket of the Chestnut Street Theatre, who rearranged and added the present beginning and ending to it. The date has been given by the latter as the fall of 1843.

THOMAS A'BECKET
Majestically
1. O Co-lum-bia, the gem of the o-cean, The home of the brave and the free,
2. When war wing'd its wide des-o-la-tion, And threaten'd the land to de-form,
3. The star-spangled banner bring hither, O'er Columbia's true sons let it wave;
The shrine of each patriot's de-vo-tion, A world offers homage to thee.
The ark then of freedom's foundation, Co - lumbia rode safe thro' the storm:
May the wreaths they have won never wither, Nor its stars cease to shine on the brave.
Thy mandates make heroes assemble, When Lib-er-ty's form stands in view;
With her garlands of vic-t'ry a-round her, When so proudly she bore her brave crew;
May thy serv-ice, u - nit - ed ne'er sev-er, But hold to their col-ors so true;
Thy ban-ners make tyr-an-ny tremble, When borne by the red, white, and blue!
With her flag proudly floating before her, The boast of the red, white, and blue!
The ar-my and na - vy for - ev - er, Three cheers for the red, white, and blue!
CHORUS
When borne by the red, white, and blue! When borne by the red, white, and blue!
The boast of the red, white, and blue! The boast of the red, white, and blue!
Three cheers for the red, white, and blue! Three cheers for the red, white, and blue!

Columbia The Gem Of The Ocean—Continued

Thy banners make tyr-an-ny trem-ble, When borne by the red, white, and blue!
With her flag proudly floating be-fore her, The boast of the red, white, and blue!
The ár-my and na-vy for-ev-er, Three cheers for the red, white, and blue!

America, The Beautiful

(Tune—"Materna")

The words of this song were written in the summer of 1893 by Katherine Lee Bates upon her return from her first trip to the summit of Pike's Peak where the opening lines had been inspired by the beautiful view of "spacious skies" and "purple mountain majesties." They were first printed in a magazine on July 4th, 1895 and were soon after set to music. They have been sung to numerous tunes, but the one given below "Materna," by Samuel A. Ward is the best known and the one to which "America the Beautiful" is at present most often sung

KATHERINE LEE BATES — SAMUEL A. WARD

1 O beau-ti-ful for spacious skies, For amber waves of grain, For pur-ple mountain maj-es-ties A-bove the fruit-ed plain. A-mer-i-ca! A-mer-i-ca! God shed His grace on thee, And crown thy good with brotherhood From sea to shining sea.
2. O beau-ti-ful for pil-grim feet Whose stern impassion'd stress A thoroughfare for free-dom beat A-cross the wil-der-ness A-mer-i-ca! A-mer-i-ca! God mend thine ev'ry flaw, Con-firm thy soul in self-con-trol, Thy lib-er-ty in law.
3. O beau-ti-ful for he-roes prov'd In lib-er-at-ing strife, Who more than self their coun-try loved, And mer-cy more than life. A-mer-i-ca! A-mer-i-ca! May God thy gold re-fine Till all suc-cess be no-bleness, And ev'ry gain di-vine.
4. O beau-ti-ful for pa-triot dream That sees beyond the years Thine al-a-bas-ter cit-ies gleam Undimmed by hu-man tears. A-mer-i-ca! A-mer-i-ca! God shed His grace on thee, And crown thy good with brotherhood From sea to shining sea.

Yankee Doodle

When the Revolutionary War began, the colonists had no national hymn. We are told that during the French and Indian War a Dr. Richard Shackburg in a spirit of dirision gave to the poorly clad and awkward colonial soldiers the words and music of "Yankee Doodle", telling them it was a fine martial tune. When they played it the British were greatly amused. Twenty years after these same militiamen marched to victory at Lexington to this much derided tune, while their British teachers skulked behind fences or sought refuge in retreat. And five years after this Cornwallis marched to the same tune at Yorktown to surrender his sword and his army to General Washington.

Little is known of the history of the tune or of the origin of its name. No doubt it is several hundred years old, but authorities disagree as to its origin. One says the tune was commonly used by the Spaniards. Another claims the song was sung by German harvesters who worked in Holland and who sang a harvest song to this well known air, while another tells us that the Puritans of Cromwell's time were ridiculed as "Naukeys" in a stanza adapted to this same tune.

The word "Yankee" is sometimes given as an Indian corruption of the word English Or, as has been said, it was a contemptuous term applied to the Puritans. Others claim it to be a cant word, expressing excellence, which originated in New England, but which finally came to be applied to the people of that region as a derisive epithet. "Doodle," according to the dictionaries, means a trifling or simple fellow

The words which were applied to this tune by the colonists were little more than meaningless doggerel, and are little known now. It is not the lofty sentiment of the words, but the catchy, rollicking tune and the sacred associations, which give this song its place among our national songs.

Dr. SHACKBURG — UNKNOWN

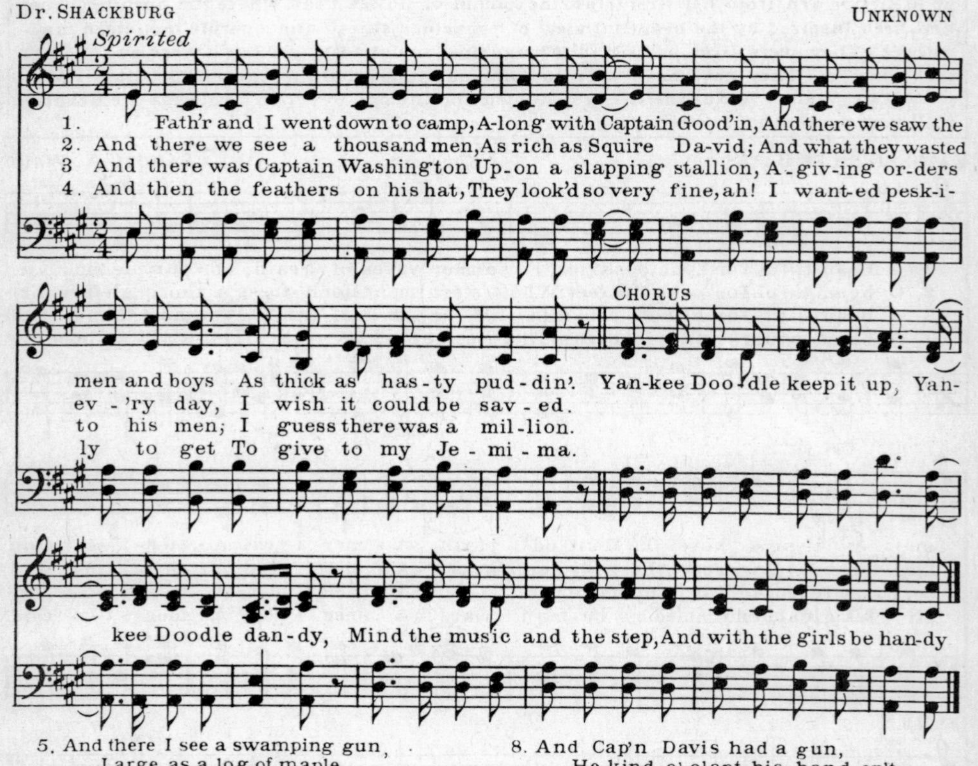
Spirited
1. Fath'r and I went down to camp, A-long with Captain Good'in, And there we saw the men and boys As thick as has-ty pud-din'.
2. And there we see a thousand men, As rich as Squire Da-vid; And what they wasted ev-'ry day, I wish it could be sav-ed.
3 And there was Captain Washington Up-on a slapping stallion, A-giv-ing or-ders to his men; I guess there was a mil-lion.
4. And then the feathers on his hat, They look'd so very fine, ah! I want-ed pesk-i-ly to get To give to my Je-mi-ma.
CHORUS
Yan-kee Doo-dle keep it up, Yan-kee Doodle dan-dy, Mind the music and the step, And with the girls be han-dy

5. And there I see a swamping gun,
Large as a log of maple,
Upon a mighty little cart;
A load for father's cattle.

6. And every time they fired it off,
It took a horn of powder;
It made a noise like father's gun
Only a nation louder.

7. And there I see a little keg,
Its head all made of leather,
They knocked upon't with little sticks,
To call the folks together.

8. And Cap'n Davis had a gun,
He kind o' clapt his hand on't
And stuck a crooked stabbing-iron
Upon the little end on't.

9. The troopers, too, would gallop up
And fire right in our faces;
It scared me almost half to death
To see them run such races.

10. It scared me so I hooked it off,
Nor stopped, as I remember,
Nor turned about till I got home,
Locked up in mother's chamber.

Hail, Columbia!

The music of this song, originally known as "The Washington March", is generally attributed to Philip Phile. It was written in 1789 as an inaugural march for George Washington. The words were written nine years later by Joseph Hopkinson for a special occasion. At the time, England and France were at war and Americans were being divided by their sympathies for one or the other of these countries. No allusion is made in this song to either of the countries but its purpose was to keep Americans united. This sentiment has won for "Hail, Columbia!" a place among our national songs.

JOSEPH HOPKINSON
Attributed to PHILIP PHILE
Majestically
1. Hail, Co-lum-bia, hap-py land! Hail, ye heroes! heav'n-born band! Who fought and bled in
2. Im-mor-tal pa-triots! rise once more, Defend your rights, defend your shore; Let no rude foe with
3. Sound, sound the trump of fame! Let Wash-ington's great name Ring thro' the world with
4. Be-hold the Chief who now commands, Once more to serve his country stands, The rock on which the
Freedom's cause, Who fought and bled in Freedom's cause, And when the storm of war was gone, En-
im - pious hand, Let no rude foe with impious hand, In-vade the shrine where sacred lies, Of
loud applause, Ring thro' the world with loud applause; Let ev-'ry clime to free-dom dear
storm will beat, The rock on which the storm will beat; But armed in virtue, firm and true, His
joyed the peace your val-or won. Let in-de-pen-dence be our boast, Ev - er mind-ful
toil and blood the well earn'd prize. While off'ring peace, sincere and just, In heav'n we place a
Lis - ten with a joy-ful ear. With e-qual skill, with God-like pow'r, He governs in the
hopes are fixed on heav'n and you. When hope was sinking in dismay, When gloom obscur'd Co-
CHORUS
what it cost; Ev-er grate-ful for the prize, Let its al - tar reach the skies.
manly trust, That Truth and Justice will prevail, And ev'ry scheme of bondage fail.
fear-ful hour Of horrid war; or guides with ease The happier times of honest peace. Firm, united,
lumbia's day, His steady mind, from changes free, Resolv'd on death or liber-ty.
let us be, Rallying round our liber-ty; As a band of brothers joined, Peace and safety
we shall find.

Dixie

"Dixie Land," or "Dixie," as it is generally called, the most popular of the songs of the South, was written by Daniel D. Emmett, of Ohio. In 1859, Mr. Emmett was a member of "Bryant's Minstrels," then playing in New York. One Saturday evening he was asked by Mr. Bryant to furnish a new song to be used in the performances the following week On Monday morning Mr. Emmett took to the rehearsal the words and music of "Dixie", The song soon became the favorite all over the land. In 1860, an entertainment was given in New Orleans. The leader had some difficulty in selecting a march for his chorus. After trying several he decided upon. "Dixie." It was taken up by the people, sung upon the streets and soon carried to the battlefields, where it became the great, inspirational song of the Southern Army.

Many different words were written to the tune. Those by Albert Pike, of Arkansas, were much used and are, perhaps, the most worthy of mention

Like "Yankee Doodle," (with which it holds a close place), the original words of "Dixie" voice no great patriotic sentiment, and the music is not of a lofty character. Yet, like its companion, its notes stirred the hearts and crystallized souls who fought for the "Flag of Dixie."

Today, to the music of these two strange songs, there echoes the tread of a united people whose hearts are moved alike by the stirring strains, and who as they listen are ready to say with uplifted hands, bared brows, and reverent lips, We give our heads and our hearts to God, and our Country."

D.D.E.
DAN D. EMMETT
Lively
1. I wish I was in de land ob cot-ton,
2. Dar's buck-wheat cakes an' In-gen bat-ter,
Old times dar am not forgotten, Look a-way! Look a-way! Look a-way! Dixie
Makes you fat, or a lit-tle fatter, Look a-way! Look a-way! Look a-way! Dixie
Land. In Dix-ie Land whar I was born in, Ear-ly on one
Land. Den hoe it down an' scratch your grabble, To Dix-ie Land I'm

Dixie—Continued

frost-y mornin', Look a-way! Look a - way! Look a - way! Dix-ie Land!
bound to trabble, Look a-way! Look a - way! Look a - way! Dix-ie Land!
CHORUS
Den I wish I was in Dix-ie, Hoo-ray! (hooray) Hoo-ray! (hooray) In Dixie Land, I'll
take my stand to lib and die in Dix-ie; A - way, A - way, A -
A - way, a - way,
way down south in Dixie, A - way, A-way, A-way down south in Dixie.
A - way, a - way,

In the chorus of Dixie, where the melody is given to the bass voices, the sopranos may take those notes two octaves higher than written, if it seems best to have the sopranos on the melody throughout the song.

Battle Hymn of the Republic

Julia Ward Howe, the author of this stirring war song, was born in New York, May 27, 1819, and was married to Dr. S. G. Howe in 1843.

In December, 1861, Dr. and Mrs. Howe, with a party of friends, paid a visit to Washington. Everything about the city had a martial aspect. The railroads were guarded by pickets, the streets were full of soldiers and all about could be seen the "watchfires of a hundred circling camps."

One day the party drove several miles from the city to see a review of the Federal soldiers. An attack by the Confederates caused much excitement and delayed their return. Finally they started back to Washington under an escort of soldiers, and to while away the time they sang war songs, among others, "John Brown."

Waking in the gray dawn of the following morning Mrs. Howe found herself weaving together words to the music she had sung the day before. Fearing she might forget the lines if she slept again, she arose and wrote down the verses of the "Battle Hymn of the Republic." The poem was first published in the Atlantic Monthly for February, 1862. The verses were published without the author's name, and she received but five dollars for them.

Of this great hymn a recent writer says, "Unlike many of the songs of the Civil War, it contains nothing sectional, nothing personal, nothing of a temporary character. While we feel the beauty of the lines and their aspiration after freedom, even in the piping times of peace, it is only in the time of storm and stress that their full meaning shines out. Written with intense feeling, they seem to burn and glow when our own emotions are aroused."

JULIA WARD HOWE — WILLIAM STEFFE

Moderate march time
1. Mine eyes have seen the glo-ry of the com-ing of the Lord; He is
2. I have seen Him in the watch-fires of a hun-dred cir-cling camps, They have
3. I have read a fi-ery gos-pel writ in bur-nished rows of steel: "As ye
4. He has sound-ed forth the trumpet that shall nev-er call re-treat; He is
5. In the beau-ty of the lil-ies Christ was born a-cross the sea, With a
tramp-ling out the vint-age where the grapes of wrath are stor'd; He hath loos'd the fateful
build-ed Him an al-tar in the evening dews and damps; I can read His righteous
deal with My con-tem-ners, so with you My grace shall deal:" Let the He-ro born of
sift-ing out the hearts of men be-fore His judgment seat. Oh, be swift, my soul, to
glo-ry in His bos-om that trans-figures you and me; As He died to make men
light-ning of His ter-ri-ble swift sword: His truth is march-ing on.
sen-tence by the dim and flar-ing lamps: His day is march-ing on.
wom-an crush the ser-pent with His heel, Since God is march-ing on.
an-swer Him! be ju-bi-lant, my feet! Our God is march-ing on.
ho-ly let us die to make men free, While God is march-ing on.
CHORUS
Glo-ry, glo-ry, hal-le-lu-jah! Glo-ry, glo-ry, hal-le-lu-jah!

Battle Hymn of the Republic — Continued

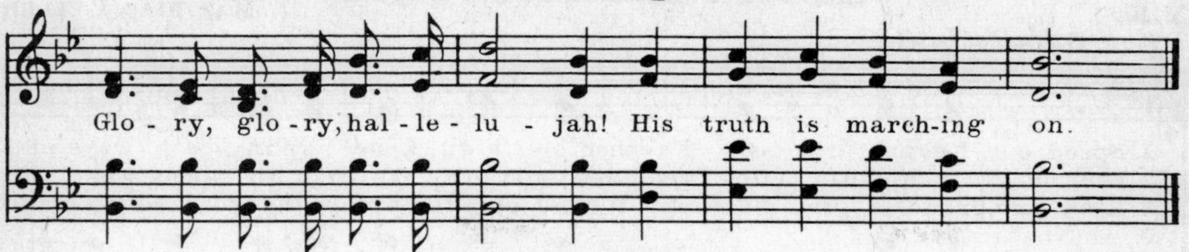
Glo - ry, glo - ry, hal - le - lu - jah! His truth is march-ing on.

John Brown's Body

(Tune–Battle Hymn of the Republic)

1.
John Brown's body lies amould'ring in the grave,
John Brown's body lies amould'ring in the grave,
John Brown's body lies amould'ring in the grave,
His soul goes marching on!
Chorus:

2.
The stars of heaven are looking kindly down,
The stars of heaven are looking kindly down,
The stars of heaven are looking kindly down,
On the grave of old John Brown!
Chorus:

3.
He's gone to be a soldier in the army of the Lord,
He's gone to be a soldier in the army of the Lord,
He's gone to be a soldier in the army of the Lord,
His soul is marching on!
Chorus:

4.
John Brown's knapsack is strapped upon his back,
John Brown's knapsack is strapped upon his back,
John Brown's knapsack is strapped upon his back,
His soul is marching on!
Chorus:

Chorus· Glory, glory, hallelujah! Glory, glory, hallelujah!
Glory, glory, hallelujah! His soul is marching on.

The Vacant Chair

H.S. WASHBURN — GEORGE F ROOT

With feeling

1. We shall meet, but we shall miss him, There will be one vacant chair, We shall linger to ca-
2 At our fire-side, sad and lone-ly, Oft-en will the bosom swell At remembrance of the
3 True, they tell us wreaths of glory Evermore will deck his brow, But this sooth's the anguish

D.C. We shall meet, but we shall miss him, There will be one vacant chair, We shall linger to ca-

Fine.

ress him, When we breathe our ev'ning pray'r. When a year a - go we gather'd, Joy was
sto - ry How our no - ble Wil-lie fell; How he strove to bear our banner Thro' the
on - ly Sweeping o'er our heartstrings now. Sleep to-day, O ear-ly fall-en, In thy

ress him, When we breathe our evening pray'r.

D. C.

in his mild blue eye, But a gold-en cord is severed, And our hopes in ru-in lie
thick-est of the fight, And up-hold our country's honor, In the strength of manhood's might.
green and narrow bed, Dirges from the pine and cypress Mingle with the tears we shed.

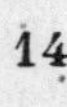

Keller's American Hymn

M.K. MATTHIAS KELLER

f Majestically

1. Speed our Re-pub-lic, O Fa-ther on high, Lead us in path-ways of
2. Fore-most in bat-tle, for Free-dom to stand, We rush to arms when a-
3. Rise up, proud ea-gle, rise up to the clouds, Spread thy broad wing o'er this

p *cresc.*

jus-tice and right; Rul-ers as well as the ruled, one and all,
roused by its call; Still as of yore when George Wash-ing-ton led,
fair west-ern world! Fling from thy beak our dear ban-ner of old!

mf *f*

Gir-dle with vir-tue, the ar-mor of might! Hail! three times hail to our
Thun-ders our war-cry, "We con-quer or fall!" Hail! three times hail to our
Show that it still is for free-dom un-furled! Hail! three times hail to our

Fine. mf *D.S.*

coun-try and flag! Rul-ers as well as the ruled, one and all,
coun-try and flag! Still as of yore when George Wash-ing-ton led,
coun-try and flag! Fling from thy beak our dear ban-ner of old!

Tramp! Tramp! Tramp!

G.F.R. GEORGE F. ROOT

1. In the pris-on cell I sit, Think-ing, Moth-er dear, of you, And our
2. In the bat-tle front we stood, When their fierce-st charge they made, And they
3. So, with-in the pris-on cell, We are wait-ing for the day That shall

bright and hap-py home so far a-way; And the tears they fill my eyes Spite of
swept us off, a hun-dred men or more; But be-fore we reach'd their lines They were
come to o-pen wide the i-ron door; And the hol-low eye grows bright, And the

D. S.—neath the star-ry flag We shall

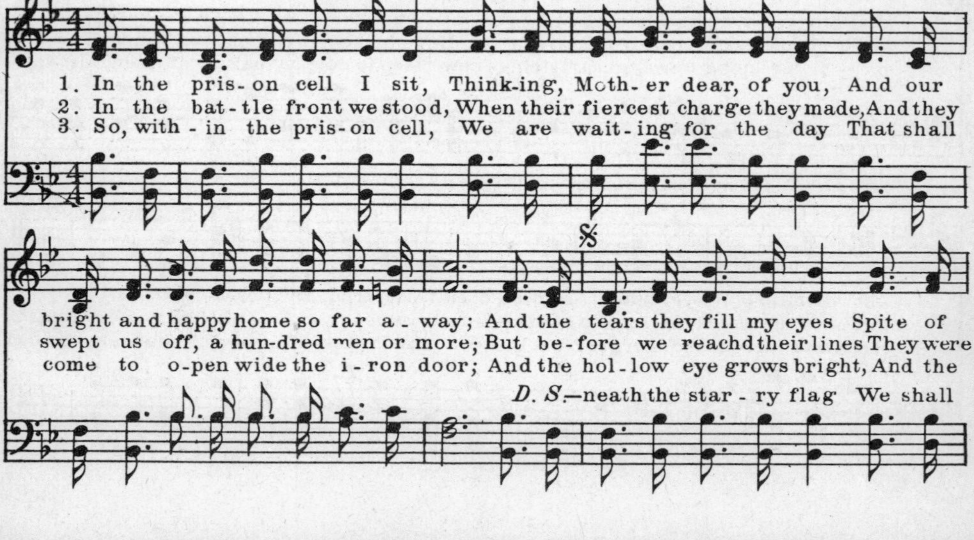

Tramp! Tramp! Tramp!—Continued
Fine.
all that I can do, Though I try to cheer my com-rades and be gay.
beat-en back dis-mayed, And we heard the cry of vic-t'ry o'er and o'er.
poor heart al-most gay, As we think of see-ing home and friends once more.
breathe the air a-gain Of the free-land in our own be-lov-ed home.
CHORUS
D S
Tramp, tramp, tramp, the boys are marching, Cheer up, comrades, they will come, And be-
marching on, O cheer up, com-rades, they will come,
Tenting On The Old Camp Ground
W.K.
Moderately
WALTER KITTREDGE
1. We're tent-ing to night on the old Camp ground, Give us a song to cheer
2. We've been tent-ing to night on the old Camp ground, Thinking of days gone by,
3. We are tired of war on the old Camp ground, Man-y are dead and gone,
4. We've been fight-ing to-day on the old Camp ground, Man-y are ly-ing near,
Our wear-y hearts, a song of home And friends we love so dear
Of the loved ones at home that gave us the hand, And the tear that said, "Good-bye"
Of the brave and true who've left their homes, Oth-ers been wounded long
Some are dead, and some are dy-ing, Man-y are in tears
CHORUS
Man-y are the hearts that are weary to-night, Wishing for the war to cease; Man-y are the hearts that are
looking for the right, To see the dawn of peace. Tenting to-night, Tenting to-night, Tenting on the old camp-ground.

The Battle Cry Of Freedom

G. F. R. GEORGE F. ROOT

1. Yes, we'll ral-ly round the flag boys, we'll rally once again, Shouting the battle cry of
2. We are springing to the call of our brothers gone before, Shouting the battle cry of
3. We will wel-come to our numbers the loyal, true and brave, Shouting the battle cry of
4. So we're springing to the call from the East and from the West, Shouting the battle cry of

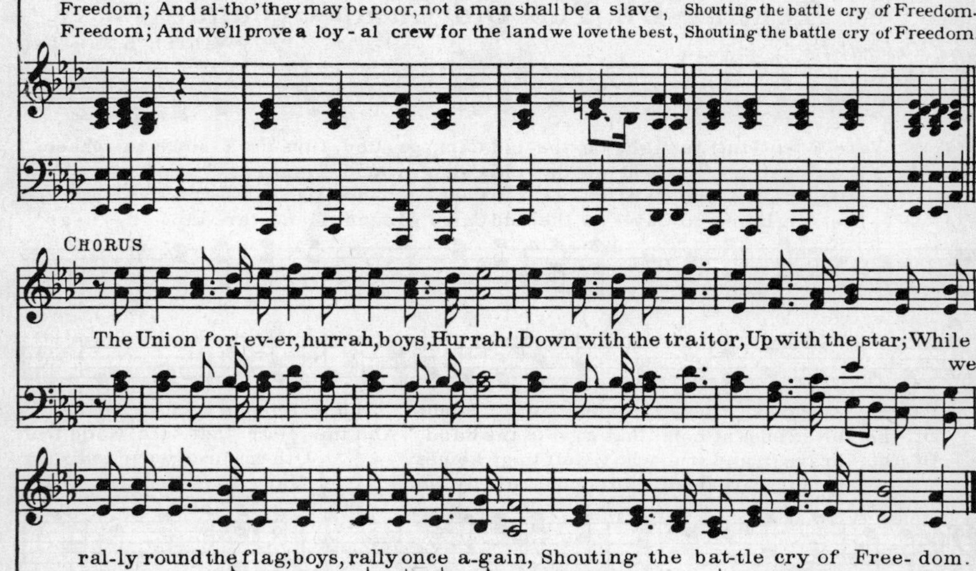
Freedom; We will rally from the hillside, we'll gather from the plain, Shouting the battle cry of Freedom.
Freedom; And we'll fill the vacant ranks with a million free men more, Shouting the battle cry of Freedom.
Freedom; And al-tho' they may be poor, not a man shall be a slave, Shouting the battle cry of Freedom.
Freedom; And we'll prove a loy-al crew for the land we love the best, Shouting the battle cry of Freedom.
CHORUS
The Union for-ev-er, hurrah, boys, Hurrah! Down with the traitor, Up with the star; While we
ral-ly round the flag, boys, rally once a-gain, Shouting the bat-tle cry of Free-dom.

Just Before The Battle, Mother

G. F. R. GEORGE F. ROOT

1 { Just be-fore the bat-tle, Moth-er, I am think-ing most of you,
While up-on the field we're watching, With the en-e-my in view. }

2. { Hark! I hear the bu-gles sounding, 'Tis the sig-nal for the fight;
Now may God pro-tect us, Moth-er, As He ev-er does the right. }

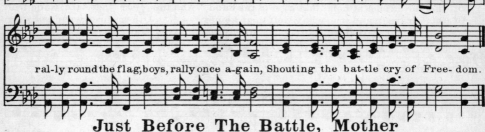

Just Before The Battle, Mother—Continued

Com-rades brave are round me ly-ing, Fill'd with thot's of home and God; For
Hear the "Bat-tle Cry of Free dom;" How it swells up-on the air; Oh,
well they know that on the mor-row Some will sleep be-neath the sod.
yes, we'll ral-ly round the standard, Or we'll per-ish no-bly there.
CHORUS
Fare-well, Moth-er, you may never Press me to your heart a-gain, But
(you may never, Mother,)
oh, you'll not for-get me, Mother, If I'm number'd with the slain.
(you will not forget me)
rit.

Civil War Songs

The nine foregoing songs, and "When Johnny Comes Marching Home," which follows, are among those which came into existence during the Civil War. Because each embodies some typical sentiment of the time, it holds a place among our popular national songs

The stories of "Dixie," "Battle Hymn of the Republic," and "John Brown's Body," have been previously given.

"Keller's American Hymn" attracted little notice during the Civil War but in 1872, at a Peace Festival, it was featured and became well known It stands as a guiding principle of what we would like our country to be.

"Tenting on the Old Camp Ground" was written, composed and first sung by Walter Kittredge as his patriotic contribution after he had failed to pass the physical examination for entrance into the Union Army.

"When Johnny Comes Marching Home" is a stirring number popular ever since the Civil War when it was composed. The name of the author and composer, "Louis Lambert," was a nom de plume used by Patrick S. Gilmore, famous as a band leader and promoter of festivals and jubilees

George F. Root contributed "Tramp! Tramp! Tramp!" "The Battle Cry of Freedom," "Just Before the Battle Mother," and with Henry F. Washburn, he wrote "The Vacant Chair"

All of these songs were written under the influence of emotions excited by the Civil War. Today, after our more recent war experience, they take on a newer and deeper meaning.

When Johnny Comes Marching Home

L.L. SOLO *With spirit* CHORUS SOLO LOUIS LAMBERT

1. When Johnny comes marching home again, Hurrah, hur-rah! We'll give him a heart-y
2. The old church bell will peal with joy, Hurrah, hur-rah! To wel-come home our
3. Get rea-dy for the Ju-bi-lee, Hurrah, hur-rah! We'll give the he-ro

ff *p*

CHORUS SOLO

wel-come then, Hur-rah, hur-rah! The men will cheer, the boys will shout, The
dar-ling boy, Hur-rah, hur-rah! The vil-lage lads and las-sies say, With
three times three; Hur-rah, hur-rah! The lau-rel wreath is rea-dy now To

ff *p*

CHORUS *Repeat at lib.*

la-dies, they will all turn out, And we'll all feel gay, When Johnny comes marching home.
roses they will strew the way, And we'll all feel gay, When Johnny comes marching home.
place up-on his loy-al brow; And we'll all feel gay, When Johnny comes marching home.

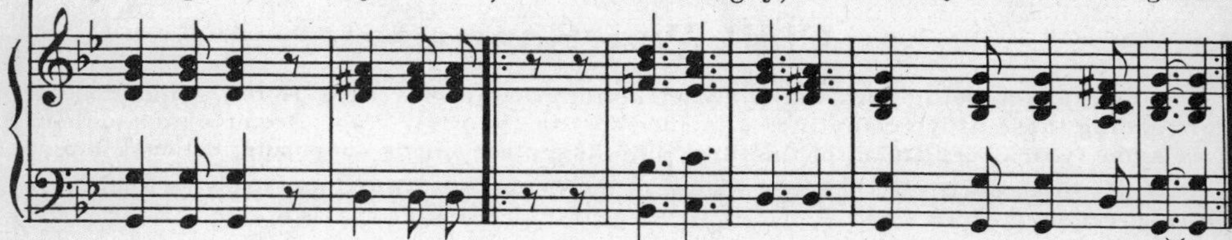

A National Prayer

O God of purity and peace, God of light and freedom, God of comfort and joy, we thank thee for our country, this great land of hope, whose wide doors thou hast opened to so many millions that struggle with hardship and with hunger in the crowded Old World.

We give thanks to the power that has made and preserved us a nation, that has carried our ship of state through storm and darkness and has given us a place of honor and power that we might bear aloft the standard of impartial liberty and impartial law.

May our altars and our schools ever stand as pillars of welfare; may the broad land be filled with homes of intelligent and contented industry, that through the long generations our land may be a happy land and our country a power of good will among the nations. *Amen.*

CHARLES GORDON AMES

Keep The Home Fires Burning

LENA GUILBERT FORD

IVOR NOVELLO

March time

1. They were summon'd from the hill-side, They were call'd in from the glen, And the Country found them ready at the stir-ring call for men (the stir-ring call for men) Let no tears add to their hard-ships, As the sol-diers pass a-long, And al-though your heart is break-ing, Make it sing this cheer-y song.

2. O - ver seas they came a-plead-ing, "Help a na-tion in dis-tress!" And we gave our glo-rious lad-dies; Honor bade us do no less, (and bade us do no less) For no gal-lant son of free-dom To a ty-rant's yoke should bend; And a no-ble heart must an-swer To the sa-cred call of "Friend."

CHORUS

Keep the Home-fires burn-ing While your hearts are yearn-ing, Tho' your lads are far a-way They dream of home.
There's a sil-ver lin-ing Thro' the dark clouds shin-ing, Turn the dark cloud in-side out, Till the boys come home.

Anvil Chorus

(From the opera, Il Trovatore)

GIUSEPPI VERDI

Quickly
FULL CHORUS IN UNISON
God of the na-tions, in glo-ry en-thron-ed, Upon our lov'd country Thy blessings
pour; Guide us and guard us from strife in the future, Let Peace dwell among us for ever-
more!

Anvil Chorus – Continued

CHORUS IN UNISON
ANVILS
Proud - ly our
f
bann - er now gleams with gold - en lus - tre! Bright - er each
star shines in the glo - rious clus - ter! Lib - er -
ty for - ev - er - more! And Peace and Un - ion, And Peace and
Un - ion, throughout our hap - py land. land.
ff
D.C.
1
2

Years Of Peace

SICILIAN MARINERS' AIR

1. Years are com - ing, speed them on - ward!
2. Earth has heard too long of bat - tle,
3. Years are com - ing when for - ev - er,

When the sword shall gath - er rust, And the hel - met,
Heard the trum - pet's voice too long; But an - oth - er
War's dread ban - ner shall be furled, And the an - gel,

lance and fal - chion, Sleep at last in__ si - lent dust!
age ad - van - ces, Seers fore - told in__ an - cient song.
Peace, be wel - comed, Reg - ent of the__ hap - py world.

O God, Beneath Thy Guiding Hand

LEONARD BACON

JOHN HATTON

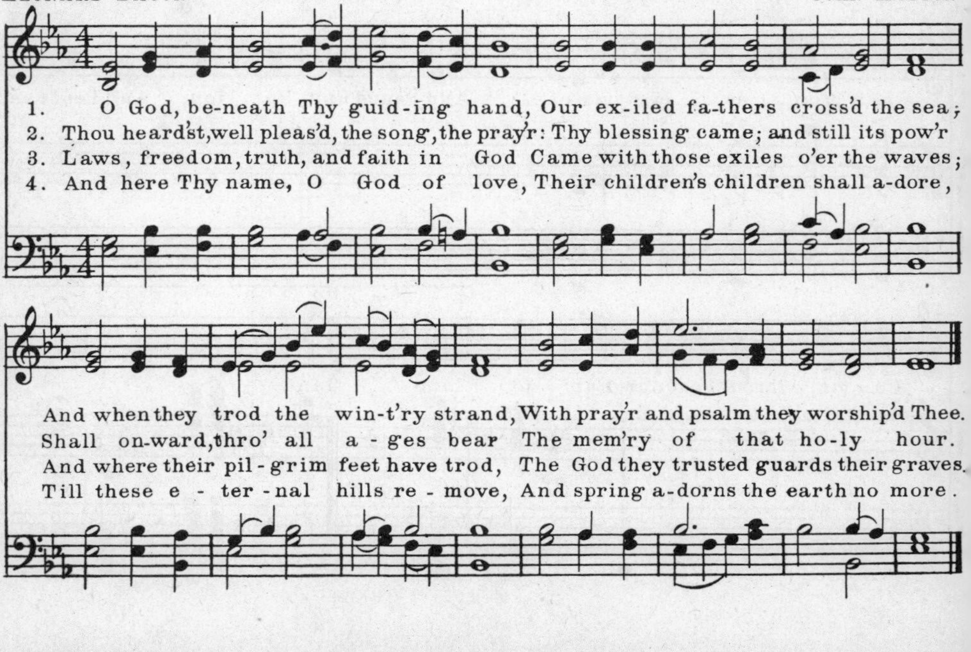

1. O God, be-neath Thy guid-ing hand, Our ex-iled fa-thers cross'd the sea;
2. Thou heard'st, well pleas'd, the song, the pray'r: Thy blessing came; and still its pow'r
3. Laws, freedom, truth, and faith in God Came with those exiles o'er the waves;
4. And here Thy name, O God of love, Their children's children shall a-dore,

And when they trod the win-t'ry strand, With pray'r and psalm they worship'd Thee.
Shall on-ward, thro' all a - ges bear The mem'ry of that ho-ly hour.
And where their pil - grim feet have trod, The God they trusted guards their graves.
Till these e - ter - nal hills re - move, And spring a-dorns the earth no more.

Praise for Peace

ANGUS S. HIBBARD | FRIEDRICH F. FLEMMING

1. Fa - ther in Heav - en, in Thy love a - bound - ing, Hear these Thy chil - dren thro' the world re - sound - ing, Loud in Thy prais - es thanks for peace a - bid - ing, Ev - er a - bid - ing.
2. Filled be our hearts with peace be - yond com - par - ing, Peace in Thy world, joy to all heart's des - pair - ing, Firm is our trust in Thee for peace en - dur - ing, Ev - er en - dur - ing.
3. God of our Fa - thers strength - en ev - 'ry na - tion, In Thy great peace where on - ly is sal - va - tion, So may the world its fu - ture spread be - fore Thee, Thus to a - dore Thee.

Integer Vitae

The Latin words, which are two stanzas from Horace's XXII Ode, may be sung to the music of "Praise for Peace." A rather free translation of the Latin is also given.

Using the Latin words, the song is a very effective number for male voices.

Integer vitae scelerisque purus
Non eget Mauris jaculis, neque arcu,
Neque venenatis gravida sagittis,
Fusce, pharetra;

Sive per Syrtes iter aestuasas,
Sive facturus per inhospitalem
Caucasum, vel quae loca fabulosus
Lambit Hydaspes.

He who is noble, kind in thought and action,
Faithful to duty, pure, and single hearted,
Needs not a weapon, needs not man to guard him,
Virtue defends him.

What though he wander o'er the burning desert?
What though he journey o'er unfriendly mountain?
Sleeping or waking, though by death surrounded,
Virtue defends him.

Home, Sweet Home

While the United States has no great war song which ranks with those of other nations, it has one song of peace that reaches not only the hearts of its own people, but touches a responsive chord in the hearts of the whole world. The song is "Home, Sweet Home."

Its author, John Howard Payne, was born in New York City, June 9, 1792, and died at Tunis, April 10, 1852. Payne's mother died when he was thirteen, and after that the author of the world's home song never knew what it meant to have a home of his own.

At the age of thirteen Payne became a clerk in a mercantile house. At seventeen he went on the stage and achieved great success in the large eastern cities. He was twenty-one when he appeared in Drury Lane Theatre, London. He lived abroad for twenty years, and, altho he seemed to have been diligent and fairly successful, he was poor and often wretched.

He wrote several successful dramas, among them, "Clari, the Maid of Milan." At the suggestion of the manager of Covent Garden Theatre, the play was changed into an opera and the words of "Home, Sweet Home," were introduced into it. The song was a great success and enriched all who handled it except its author He did not even receive the twenty-five pounds which was his share of the proceeds from the sale of the manuscript.

In 1832 Payne returned to America. Later he was appointed consul to Tunis and died there in 1852.

In 1883, through the generosity of W. W. Corcoran, the remains of John Howard Payne were brought to his native land and buried at Oak Hill Cemetary, Washington, D.C.

JOHN HOWARD PAYNE — HENRY R. BISHOP

1. 'Mid pleasures and pal - a - ces though we may roam, Be it ev - er so humble, there's no place like home; A charm from the skies seems to hal-low us there. Which, seek thro' the world, is ne'er met with else-where.
2. I gaze on the moon as I tread the drear wild, And feel that my mother now thinks of her child, As she looks on that moon from our own cottage door, Thro' the wood-bine whose fragrance shall cheer me no more.
3. An ex - ile from home splendor daz - zles in vain; Oh, give me my lowly thatched cottage a - gain; The birds singing gai - ly, that came at my call, Give me them, and that peace of mind dear-er than all.
Home, home, sweet, sweet home,
D.S. There's no place like home, Oh, there's no place like home.
The Bell Doth Toll
(Round)
Slowly
1 The bell doth toll, Its ech - oes roll, I know the sound full well;
2 I love its ring - ing, For it calls to sing - ing, With its
bim, bim, bim, bom, bell,
3 Bim, bom, bim, bom, bell.

Old Black Joe

S. C. F.
STEPHEN C. FOSTER
1. Gone are the days when my heart was young and gay; Gone are my friends from the cot-ton fields a-way; Gone from the earth to a bet-ter land I know,
2. Why do I weep when my heart should feel no pain? Why do I sigh that my friends come not a-gain? Griev-ing for forms now de-part-ed long a-go,
3. Where are the hearts once so hap-py and so free? The chil-dren so dear that I held up-on my knee? Gone to the shore where my soul has long'd to go,
I hear their gen-tle voic-es calling, "Old Black Joe!"
Fine.
mf CHORUS
pp
I'm com-ing, I'm com-ing, For my head is bend-ing low,
D.S. al Fine.

Stephen C. Foster

Stephen Collins Foster, a truly American writer of what may be called the folk-songs of America, was born July 4th, 1826 at Lawrenceburg, Pennsylvania, now a part of Pittsburgh, and died in New York in 1864. From an early age he was interested in music. He often attendend negro camp meetings and there studied the music of the colored people. His first success in composition was "Oh! Susannah" Soon after he produced "My Old Kentucky Home" and "Massa's In The Cold, Cold Ground" which at once became popular.

"The Old Folks At Home" (Way down upon the Swanee River) is his masterpiece. A more tender song of home and its memories has never been written. Another of his songs which achieved great popularity is "Old Black Joe"

Chief among Foster's characteristics was his tenderness. This quality is reflected in all of his songs.

My Old Kentucky Home

S.C.F.
STEPHEN C. FOSTER
Rather slowly
1. The sun shines bright in the old Ken-tuck-y home, 'Tis sum-mer,
young folks roll on the lit-tle cab-in floor, All mer-ry,
2. They hunt no more for the pos-sum and the coon, On the mead-ow,
day goes by like a shadow o'er the heart, With sor-row
3. The head must bow and the back will have to bend, Wher - ev - er
few more days for to tote the wea-ry load, No mat-ter,
the dark-ies are gay; The corn-top's ripe and the mead-ow's in the bloom, While the
all hap-py and bright; By'n by hard times comes a knock-ing at the door, Then my
the hill and the shore; They sing no more by the glim-mer of the moon, On the
where all was de-light; The time has come when the darkies have to part, Then my
the dark-y may go; A few more days, and the trou-ble all will end, In the
'twill nev-er be light; A few more days till we tot-ter on the road, Then my
1. birds make mu-sic all the day; The old Kentuck-y home, good night!
2. bench by the old cab-in door; The old Kentuck-y home, good night!
3. field where the su-gar-canes grow; A old Kentuck-y home, good night!
CHORUS
Weep no more, my la-dy, O weep no more to day! We will
sing one song for the old Ken-tucky home, For the old Kentucky home, far a-way.
rit.

Old Folks At Home

S. C. F.
STEPHEN C. FOSTER
1. 'Way down up-on de Swa-nee Riv-er, Far, far a-way,
All up and down de whole cre-a-tion, Sad-ly I roam,
2. All roun' de lit-tle farm I wan-dered, When I was young;
When I was play-ing with my broth-er, Hap-py was I;
3. One lit-tle hut a-mong de bush-es, One that I love,
When will I see de bees a-hum-ming All roun' de comb?
Fine.
Dere's wha my heart is turn-ing ev-er, Dere's wha de old folks stay.
Still long-ing for de old plan-ta-tion, And for de old folks at home.
Den man-y hap-py days I squander'd, Man-y de songs I sung.
Oh! take me to my kind old moth-er, There let me live and die.
Still sad-ly to my mem-'ry rush-es, No mat-ter where I rove.
When will I hear de ban-jo tum-ming, Down in my good old home?
D.S.—Oh! darkies, how my heart grows weary, Far from de old folks at home.
REFRAIN
D.S.
All de world am sad and drear-y, Ev-'ry-where I roam;
Stars Of The Summer Night
HENRY W. LONGFELLOW
ISAAC B. WOODBURY
1. Stars of the sum-mer night, Far in yon az-ure deeps, Hide, hide your
2. Moon of the sum-mer night, Far down yon west-ern steeps, Sink, sink in
3. Dreams of the sum-mer night, Tell her, her lov-er keeps Watch while, in
gold-en light, She sleeps, my la-dy sleeps; She sleeps, She sleeps, my lady sleeps.
sil-ver light, She sleeps, my la-dy sleeps; She sleeps, She sleeps, my lady sleeps.
slumber light, She sleeps, my la-dy sleeps; She sleeps, She sleeps, my lady sleeps.

Hard Times Come Again No More

S.C.F. STEPHEN C. FOSTER

mf Moderately
1. Let us pause in life's pleasures and count its many tears While we all sup sorrow with the
2. While we seek mirth and beauty and music light and gay There are frail forms fainting at the
poor: There's a song that will linger for-ev-er in our ears, "Oh! Hard Times, come again no more"
door: Tho' their voices are silent, their pleading looks will say: "Oh! Hard Times, come again no more"
CHORUS
'Tis the song, the sigh of the wea - ry; Hard Times, Hard Times, come again no more
slower
Many days you have linger'd a-round my cab-in door, Oh! Hard Times, come again no more
Old Dog Tray
S.C.F. STEPHEN C. FOSTER
Moderately
1. The morn of life is past, And ev'ning comes at last, It brings me a dream of a
2 The forms I call'd my own, Have vanish'd one by one, The loved ones, the dear ones hav
once hap-py day, Of mer-ry forms I've seen Up - on the vil-lage green,
all passed a way, Their happy smiles have flown, Their gentle voices gone; I've

Old Dog Tray—Continued

CHORUS
Sport-ing with my old dog Tray.
noth-ing left but old dog Tray.
Old dog Tray's ever faithful, Grief can-not drive him a-
way, He's gen-tle, he is kind; I'll nev er, nev er find A bet-ter friend than old dog Tray.
Uncle Ned
S.C.F.
STEPHEN C. FOSTER
1. There was an old darkey and his name was Uncle Ned, And he died long ago, long a-go;
2. His fingers were long as the cane in the brake, And he had no eyes for to see;
3. One cold, frost-y morning, old Ned died, Massa's tears they fell like the rain;
He had no wool on the top of his head, In the place where the wool ought to grow.
And he had no teeth for to eat a hoe-cake, So he had to let the hoe-cake be.
For he knew when Ned was laid in the ground, He'd never see his like a - gain.
REFRAIN Bass Solo
Harmony
Then lay down the shov-el and the hoe, Hang up the fid-dle and the bow,
For there's no more work for poor old Ned, He's gone where the good darkies go.

Massa's In The Cold Ground

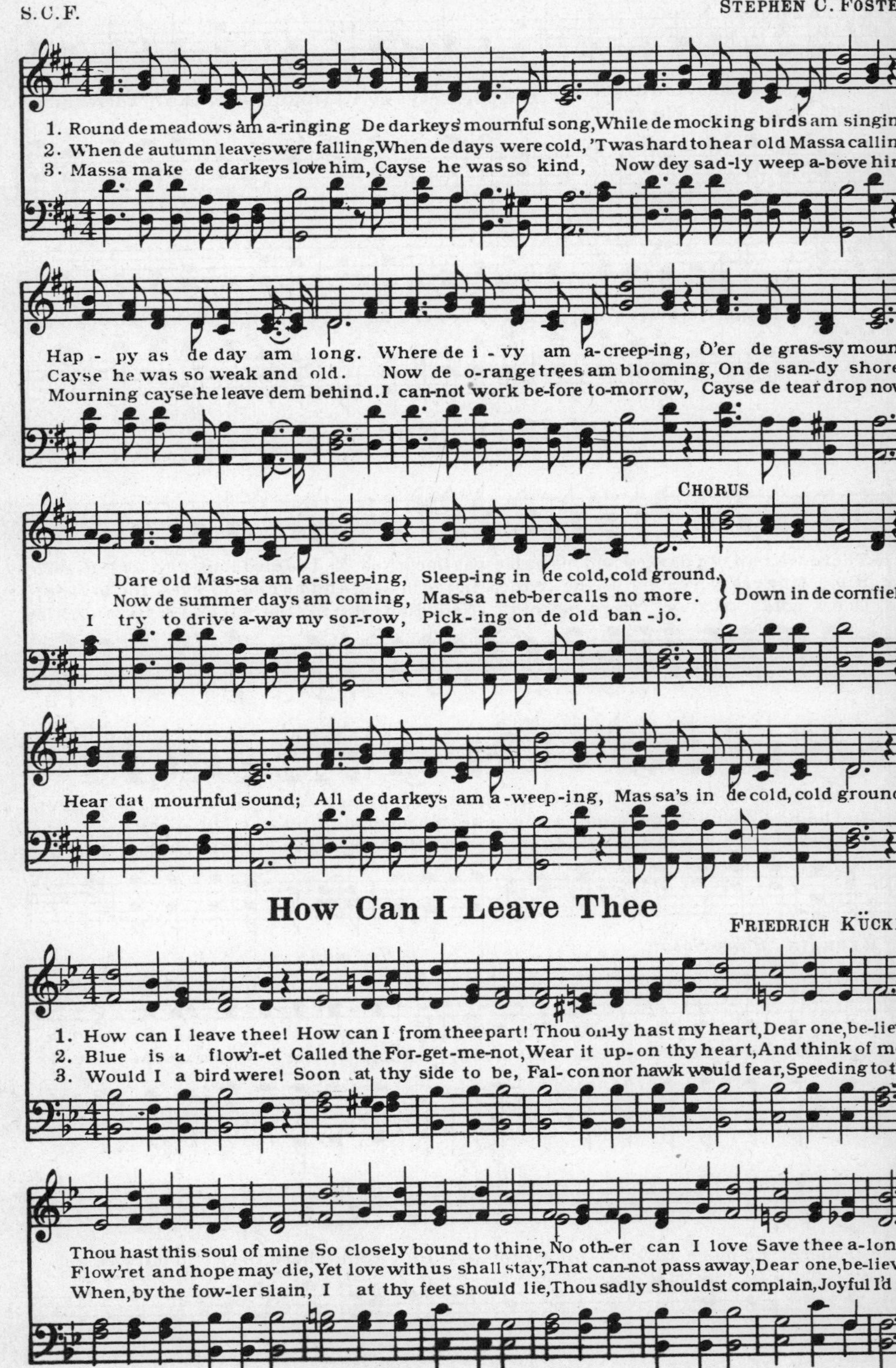
S.C.F.
STEPHEN C. FOSTE
1. Round de meadows am a-ringing De darkeys' mournful song, While de mocking birds am singin
2. When de autumn leaves were falling, When de days were cold, 'Twas hard to hear old Massa callin
3. Massa make de darkeys love him, Cayse he was so kind, Now dey sad-ly weep a-bove hin
Hap - py as de day am long. Where de i - vy am a-creep-ing, O'er de gras-sy moun
Cayse he was so weak and old. Now de o-range trees am blooming, On de san-dy shore
Mourning cayse he leave dem behind. I can-not work be-fore to-morrow, Cayse de tear drop nov
CHORUS
Dare old Mas-sa am a-sleep-ing, Sleep-ing in de cold, cold ground.
Now de summer days am coming, Mas-sa neb-ber calls no more.
I try to drive a-way my sor-row, Pick-ing on de old ban-jo.
Down in de cornfiel
Hear dat mournful sound; All de darkeys am a-weep-ing, Mas-sa's in de cold, cold ground
How Can I Leave Thee
FRIEDRICH KÜCK
1. How can I leave thee! How can I from thee part! Thou on-ly hast my heart, Dear one, be-liev
2. Blue is a flow'r-et Called the For-get-me-not, Wear it up-on thy heart, And think of me
3. Would I a bird were! Soon at thy side to be, Fal-con nor hawk would fear, Speeding to th
Thou hast this soul of mine So closely bound to thine, No oth-er can I love Save thee a-lon
Flow'ret and hope may die, Yet love with us shall stay, That can-not pass away, Dear one, be-liev
When, by the fow-ler slain, I at thy feet should lie, Thou sadly shouldst complain, Joyful I'd

Darling Nelly Gray

B.R.H.

B. R. HANBY

1. There's a low green val-ley on the old Ken-tuck-y shore, Where I've whiled many
2. When the moon had clim'd the mountain, and the stars were shining too, Then I'd take my
3. My eyes are get-ting blinded, And I can-not see my way; Hark! There's some bod-y

hap - py hours a-way, A sit-ting and a-sing-ing by the lit-tle cot-tage door
darl - ing Nel-ly Gray, And we'd float down the riv-er in my lit-tle red ca-noe,
knock-ing at the door, O I hear the an-gels calling, and I see my Nel-ly Gray,

Where lived my darl-ing Nel-ly Gray.
While my ban-jo sweet-ly I would play.
Fare - well to the old Ken-tuck-y shore.

CHORUS

O my poor Nel-ly Gray, they have
O my poor Nel-ly Gray, they have
O my darling Nel-ly Gray, up in

1-2. tak-en you a-way, And I'll nev-er see my darl-ing an-y more; I'm sit-ting by the
3. heaven there, they say, That they'll never take you from me any more; I'm a coming—coming—

riv-er and I'm weeping all the day, For youve gone from the old Kentucky shore.
coming, as the an-gels clear the way, Fare - well to the old Kentucky shore.

Good Night

(Round)

1 Good night to you all, and sweet be thy sleep; 2 May an-gels a - round you their si-lent watch keep, 3 Good night, good night, good night, good night

Carry Me Back To Old Virginny

J. B. JAMES BLAND

1. Car-ry me back to old Vir-ginny, There's where the cotton and the corn and taters grow,
2. Car-ry me back to old Vir-ginny, There let me live till I with-er and de-cay,
p
There's where the birds warble sweet in the spring-time, There's where the old darkey's
Long by the old Dis-mal Swamp have I wan dered, There's where this old darkey's
heart am long'd to go. There's where I la-bored so hard for old Mas-sa,
life will pass a-way. Mas - sa and Mis-sis have long gone be-fore me,
Day af-ter day in the field of yel-low corn, No place on earth do I
Soon we will meet on that bright and golden shore, There we'll be hap-py and
love more sin-cere-ly Than old Vir-gin-ny, the state where I was born.
free from all sor-row, There's where we'll meet and we'll nev- er part no more.
rit.

Carry Me Back To Old Virginny—Concluded

CHORUS
Car - ry me back to old Vir - gin - ny, There's where the
cot - ton and the corn and ta - ters grow There's where the birds war - ble
sweet in the spring-time, There's where the old darkey's heart am long'd to go
When The Corn Is Waving
C. B.
C. BLAMPHIN
1. When the corn is waving, Annie dear, Oh meet me by the stile, To hear thy gentle
2. When the corn is waving, Annie dear, Our tales of love we'll tell Be-side the gen-tle
Fine
voice a-gain And greet thy winning smile; The moon will be at full, love, The stars will brightly
flowing stream That both our hearts know well; Where wild flow'rs in their beauty Will scent the ev'ning
gleam. Oh come, my Queen of night, love, And grace the beauteous scene. When the
breeze, Oh haste, the stars are peep-ing And the moon's behind the trees.

"Carry Me Back To Old Virginny" is a favorite number for male quartets. An excellent effect may be secured by disposing of the parts as follows: Have the second tenor or "lead" sing the soprano part of the chorus, one octave lower than here given; the first tenor takes the alto part, singing it in the register of the alto voice; the first bass or baritone should carry the first line in the bass clef and the second bass, the lower line.

The same disposition of voices will give another fine number for male quartets in the song "When The Corn Is Waving."

T.H.B.
Long, Long Ago
THOMAS H. BAYLY
Moderately
1. Tell me the tales that to me were so dear, Long,long a-go, Long,long a-go;
2. Do you re-mem-ber the path where we met, Long,long a-go, Long,long a-go?
3. Tho' by your kindness my fond hopes were rais'd, Long,long a-go, Long,long a-go,
Fine
Sing me the songs I de-light-ed to hear, Long,long a-go, long a - go.
Ah, yes,you told me you ne'er would for-get, Long,long a-go, long a - go.
You by more el - o-quent lips have been prais'd,Long,long a-go, long a - go.
D.S. Let me be-lieve that you love as you loved, Long, long a-go, long a - go.
D.S. Still my heart treasures the praises I heard, Long, long a-go, long a - go.
D.S. Blest as I was when I sat by your side, Long, long a-go, long a - go.
D.S.
Now you are come, all my grief is re-moved, Let me for-get that so long you have rov'd,
Then,to all oth-ers, my smile you preferr'd, Love,when you spoke,gave a charm to each word,
But by long absence your truth has been tried, Still to your ac-cents I list - en with pride,
G.F.R.
There's Music In The Air
GEORGE F. ROOT
Moderately quick motion
1. There's mu-sic in the air When the in-fant morn is nigh, And faint its blush is seen
2. There's mu-sic in the air When the noontide's sultry beam Reflects a golden light
3. There's mu-sic in the air When the twilight's gentle sigh Is lost on evening's breast,
On the bright and laughing sky. Many a harp's ec-stat - ic sound, With its thrill of
On the distant mountain stream. When beneath some grateful shade, Sorrow's aching
As its pen-sive beauties die. Then,oh,then the loved ones gone Wake the pure ce-
joy pro-found, While we list, en-chant-ed there, To the mu-sic in the air.
head is laid, Sweet-ly to the spir - it there Comes the music in the air.
les-tial song, An-gel voi-ces greet us there, In the mu-sic in the air.

Flow Gently, Sweet Afton

ROBERT BURNS — JAMES E. SPILMAN

Not too slowly
1. Flow gen-tly, sweet Af-ton, a-mang thy green braes; Flow gently, I'll sing thee a
2. How loft - y, sweet Af-ton, thy neighboring hills, Far mark'd with the courses of
3. Thy crys-tal stream, Afton, how love-ly it glides, And winds by the cot where my
song in thy praise; My Ma-ry's a - sleep by thy murmuring stream, Flow gently, sweet
clear winding rills! There daily I wan-der, as morn ris-es high, My flocks and my
Ma - ry re-sides! How wanton thy wa-ters her snowy feet lave, As, gath'ring sweet
Af-ton, dis-turb not her dream. Thou stock-dove, whose ech-o re-sounds from the
Ma-ry's sweet cot in my eye. How pleas-ant thy banks and green val-leys be-
flow'rets, she stems thy clear wave! Flow gen-tly, sweet Af ton, a - mang thy green
hill, Ye wild whistling black-birds in yon thorn-y dell, Thou green crest-ed
low, Where wild in the wood-lands the prim-ros - es blow! There oft, as mild
braes, Flow gen-tly, sweet riv - er, the theme of my lays: My Ma-ry's a
lap-wing, thy screaming for-bear, I charge you, dis-turb not my slum-ber-ing fair
evening creeps o-ver the lea, The sweet scented birk shades my Ma-ry and me
sleep by thy murmuring stream, Flow gen-tly, sweet Af-ton, dis-turb not her dream

Loch Lomond
UNKNOWN
OLD SCOTCH AIR
1. By yon bonnie banks, And by yon bonnie braes, Where the sun shines bright on Loch
2. 'Twas then that we part-ed In yon shad-y glen, On the steep, steep side of Ben
3. The wee bir-dies sing, And the wild flowers spring, And in sunshine the waters are
Lo - mond, Where me and my true love Were ev - er wont to gae, On the
Lo - mond, Where in pur-ple hue The Highland hills we view, And the
sleep - ing, But the broken heart it kens Nae second spring a - gain, Tho' the
Brisker
CHORUS
bonnie, bonnie banks of Loch Lo - mond.
moon coming out in the gloam - ing. Oh! ye'll take the high road, and I'll take the
wae-ful may cease frae their greet - ing.
low road, And I'll be in Scot - land a - fore_ ye, But me and my true love will
nev - er meet a - gain On the bonnie, bon-nie banks of Loch Lo - mond.
Scotland's Burning
(Round)
1
2
3
4
Scotland's burning, Scotland's burning, Look out, look out! Fire, fire, fire, fire! Pour on water, Pour on water.

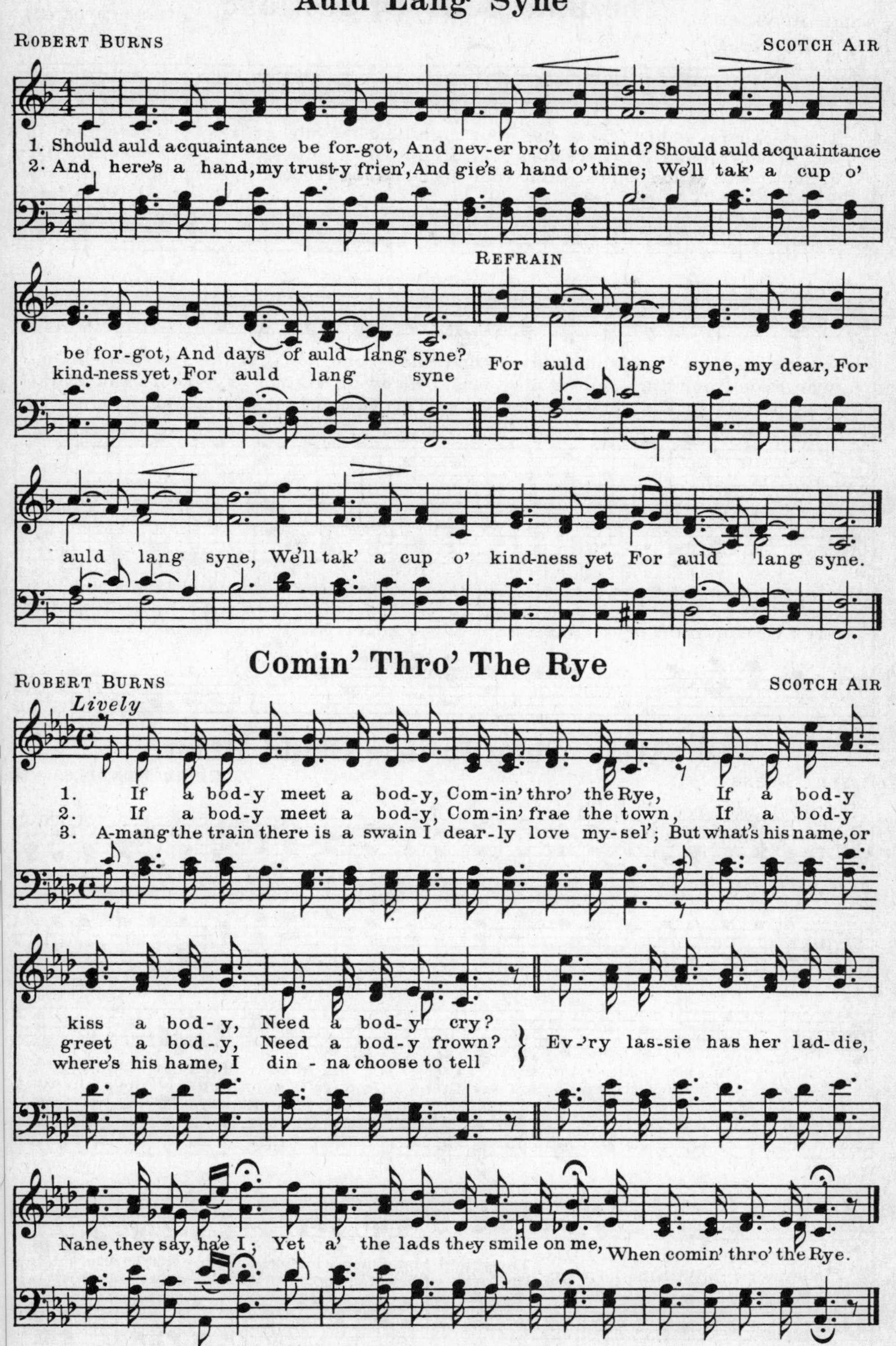
Auld Lang Syne
ROBERT BURNS
SCOTCH AIR
1. Should auld acquaintance be for-got, And nev-er bro't to mind? Should auld acquaintance
2. And here's a hand, my trust-y frien', And gie's a hand o' thine; We'll tak' a cup o'
REFRAIN
be for-got, And days of auld lang syne?
kind-ness yet, For auld lang syne
For auld lang syne, my dear, For
auld lang syne, We'll tak' a cup o' kind-ness yet For auld lang syne.
Comin' Thro' The Rye
ROBERT BURNS
SCOTCH AIR
Lively
1. If a bod-y meet a bod-y, Com-in' thro' the Rye, If a bod-y
2. If a bod-y meet a bod-y, Com-in' frae the town, If a bod-y
3. A-mang the train there is a swain I dear-ly love my-sel'; But what's his name, or
kiss a bod-y, Need a bod-y cry?
greet a bod-y, Need a bod-y frown?
where's his hame, I din - na choose to tell
Ev'ry las-sie has her lad-die,
Nane, they say, ha'e I; Yet a' the lads they smile on me, When comin' thro' the Rye.

The Blue Bells Of Scotland

ANNIE MC VICAR — OLD SCOTCH AIR

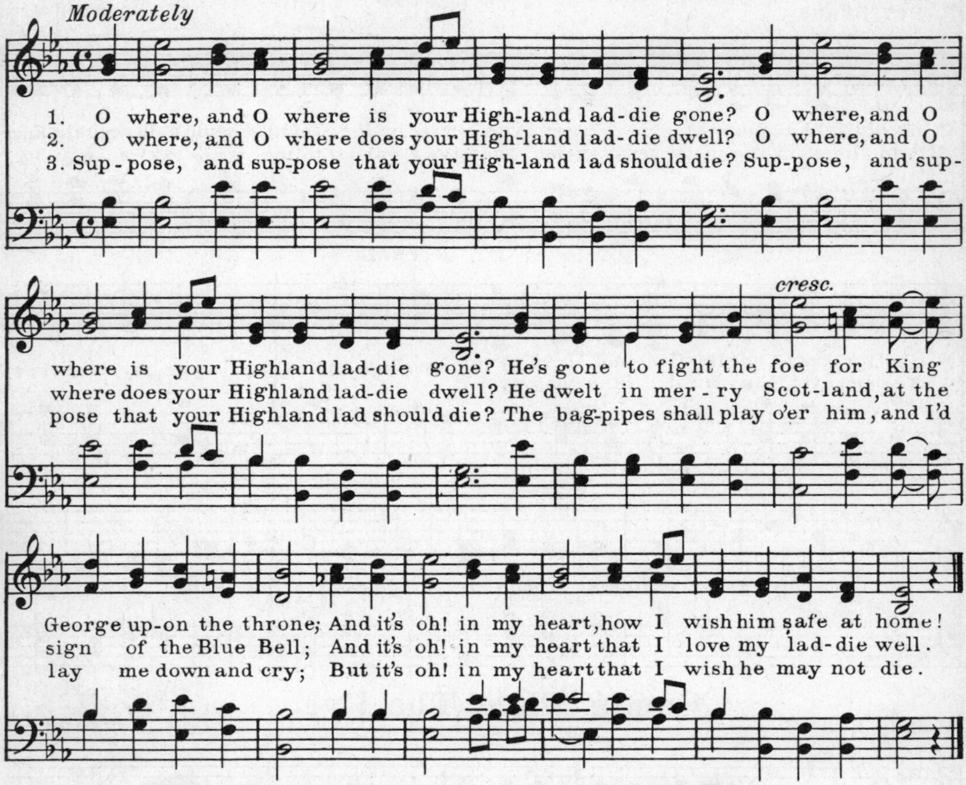

Moderately

1. O where, and O where is your High-land lad-die gone? O where, and O
2. O where, and O where does your High-land lad-die dwell? O where, and O
3. Sup - pose, and sup-pose that your High-land lad should die? Sup-pose, and sup-

where is your Highland lad-die gone? He's gone to fight the foe for King
where does your Highland lad-die dwell? He dwelt in mer - ry Scot-land, at the
pose that your Highland lad should die? The bag-pipes shall play o'er him, and I'd

cresc.

George up-on the throne; And it's oh! in my heart, how I wish him safe at home!
sign of the Blue Bell; And it's oh! in my heart that I love my lad-die well.
lay me down and cry; But it's oh! in my heart that I wish he may not die.

Oh, Wert Thou In The Cauld Blast

ROBERT BURNS — FELIX MENDELSSOHN

1. Oh, wert thou in the cauld blast, On yon-der lea, On yon-der lea, My plaidie to the angry
2. Oh, were I in the wildest waste, Sae bleak and bare, Sae bleak and bare, The desert were a Para-

airt, I'd shel-ter thee, I'd shel-ter thee; Or did mis-for-tune's bit-ter storms A -
dise If thou wert there, If thou wert there; Or were I mon-arch of the globe, With

round thee blaw, A-round thee blaw, Thy shield should be my bosom, To share it a', To share it a'.
thee to reign, With thee to reign, The brightest jewel in my crown Wad be my queen, Wad be my queen.

Annie Laurie
WILLIAM DOUGLASS
LADY JOHN SCOTT
Moderately quick
1. Max-wel-ton's braes are bon-nie, Where ear - ly fa's the dew, And 'twas
2. Her brow is like the snow-drift, Her throat is like the swan; Her
3. Like dew on th' gow-an ly - ing Is th' fa' o'her fair - y feet, And like
there that Annie Lau-rie Gave me her prom-ise true, Gave me her prom-ise true,
face it is the fair-est That e'er the sun shone on; That e'er the sun shone on,
winds in summer sighing, Her voice is low and sweet, Her voice is low and sweet,
Which ne'er forgot will be, And for bon-nie An-nie Lau-rie, I'd lay me doon and dee.
And dark blue is her e'e, And for bon-nie An-nie Lau-rie, I'd lay me doon and dee.
And she's a' the world to me, And for bon-nie An-nie Lau-rie, I'd lay me doon and dee.
Robin Adair
CAROLINE KEPPEL
SCOTCH AIR
1. What's this dull town to me? Ro - bin's not near;
What was't I wished to see, What wish'd to hear?
Where's all the joy and mirth
2. What made th' as-sem-bly shine? Ro-bin A - dair;
What made the ball so fine? Ro bin was there;
What, when the play was o'er,
3. But now thou'rt cold to me, Ro-bin A - dair;
But now thou'rt cold to me, Ro-bin A - dair;
Yet, him I loved so well,
That made this town a heav'n on earth? Oh! they're all fled with thee, Ro-bin A - dair.
What made my heart so sore? Oh! it was part-ing with Ro-bin A - dair.
Still in my heart shall dwell, Oh! I can ne'er for-get Ro-bin A - dair.

Hail To The Chief

SIR WALTER SCOTT — JAMES SANDERSON

f Majestically

1. Hail to the chief, who in triumph ad-van-ces, Hon-ored and bless'd be the ev-ergreen pine!
2. Ours is no sapling, chance-sown by the fountain, Blooming at Beltane, in winter to fade; When the
3. Row, vassals, row for the pride of the Highlands! Stretch to your oars for the evergreen pine!

ff

Long may the tree in his banner that glances, Flourish, the shelter and grace of our line.
whirl-wind has stripp'd ev'ry leaf on the mountain, The more shall Clan-Alpine exult in her shade.
Oh, that the rosebud that graces yon islands, Were wreath'd in a garland around him to twine!

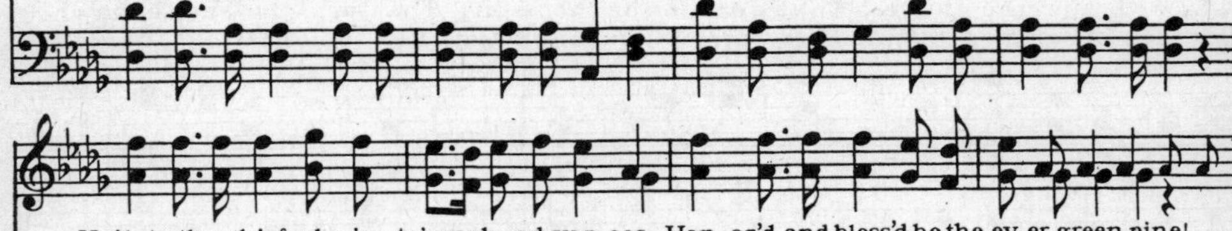

Hail to the chief, who in triumph ad-van-ces, Hon-or'd and bless'd be the ev-er-green pine!
Ours is no sapling, chance-sown by the fountain, Blooming at Beltane, in winter to fade; When the
Row, vassals, row, for the pride of the Highlands! Stretch to your oars for the evergreen pine!

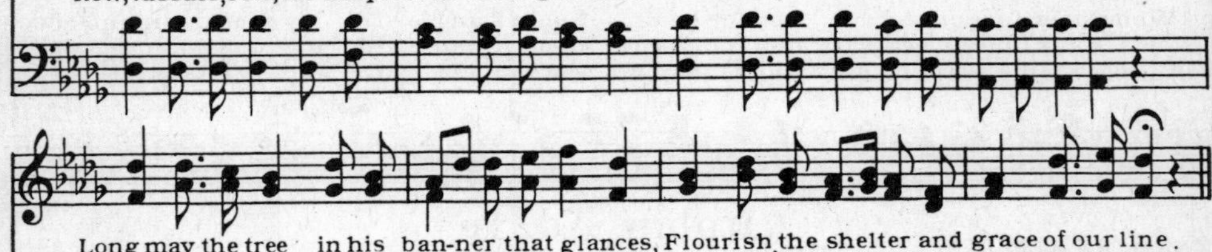

Long may the tree in his ban-ner that glances, Flourish, the shelter and grace of our line.
whirl-wind has stripp'd ev'ry leaf on the mountain, The more shall Clan-Alpine exult in her shade.
Oh, that the rose-bud that graces yon islands, Were wreath'd in a garland around him to twine!

Lively
f

Heav'n send it hap-py dew, Earth lend it sap a-new; Gai-ly to bourgeon and broadly to grow;
Moor'd in the rift-ed rock, Proof to the tempest shock, Firmer he roots him, the ruder it blow;
O, that some seedling gem, Worthy such noble stem, Honor'd and bless'd in their shadow might grow!

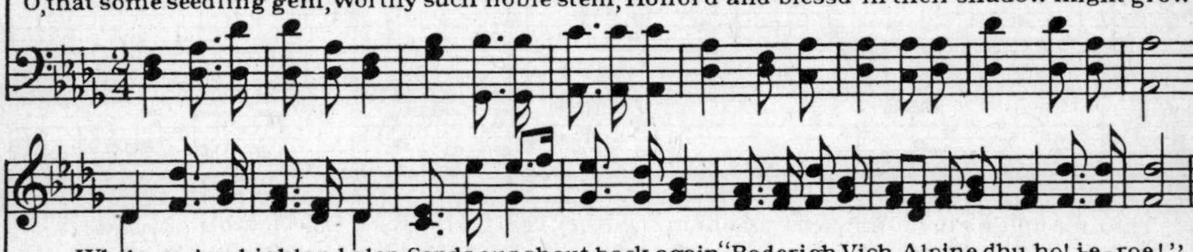

While ev-'ry highland glen, Sends our shout back again, "Roderigh Vich Alpine dhu, ho! i-e-roe!"
Menteith and Breadalbane, then, Echo his praise a-gain, "Roderigh Vich Alpine dhu, ho! i-e-roe!"
Loud should Clan-Alpine then, Ring from her deepmost glen, "Roderigh Vich Alpine dhu, ho! i-e-roe!"

The Last Rose Of Summer

Thomas Moore, the great Irish lyric poet, did for Irish folk songs what Burns did for those of his native land. "The Last Rose of Summer" is among his most famous songs, having achieved great popularity through its interpolation into the ever popular and beautiful opera "Martha" by Flotow, to whom the authorship of the song is sometimes erroneously attributed. The air is an ancient one, called the "Groves of Blarney," which in turn was taken from a more ancient Celtic melody.

THOMAS MOORE
IRISH AIR
1. 'Tis the last rose of summer, Left blooming a - lone;
All her love-ly companions Are fad - ed and gone;
No flower of her kindred
2. I'll not leave thee, thou lone one, To pine on the stem;
Since the love-ly are sleeping, Go sleep thou with them;
Thus kind-ly I scatter
3. So soon may I fol - low, When friend-ships de-cay,
And from love's shining cir-cle The gems drop a - way;
When true hearts lie withered
rit.
No rose-bud is nigh, To re-flect back her blushes, Or give sigh for sigh.
Thy leaves o'er the bed Where thy mates of the garden Lie scent-less and dead.
And fond ones have flown, Oh, who would in - hab-it This bleak world a - lone.
HAROLD BOULTON
All Through The Night
OLD WELSH AIR
Softly
1. Sleep, my child, and peace at-tend thee All thro' the night; Guardian an-gels
2. While the moon her watch is keep-ing All thro' the night; While the wea-ry
God will send thee, All thro' the night, Soft the drow-sy hours are creeping,
world is sleep-ing All thro' the night. O'er thy spir-it gen-tly steal-ing,
Hill and vale in slum-ber steeping, I my loving vig-il keeping All thro' the night.
Visions of de-light re-veal-ing, Breathes a pure and ho-ly feeling, All thro' the night.

Sweet and Low

ALFRED TENNYSON

JOSEPH BARNBY

pp Slowly
1. Sweet and low, sweet and low, Wind of the west - ern sea;
2. Sleep and rest, sleep and rest, Fa - ther will come to thee soon;
sf
p
Low, low, breathe and blow, Wind of the west - ern sea;
Rest, rest, on moth - er's breast, Fa - ther will come to thee soon;
mf
pp
O - ver the roll - ing wa - ters go, Come from the
O - ver the wa - ters go, Come
Fa - ther will come to his babe in the nest, Sil - ver
Fa - ther will come to his babe, Sil - ver
f
dy - ing moon and blow, Blow him a - gain to me,
from the moon and blow,
sails all out of the west, Un - der the sil - ver moon,
sails out of the west,
p
rall. e dim.
pp
While my lit - tle one, while my pret - ty one, sleeps.
Sleep, my lit - tle one, sleep, my pret - ty one, sleep.

M. W. B.

Killarney

MICHAEL W. BALFE

Moderately

1. By Kil-lar-ney's lakes and fells, Em'rald isles and winding bays, Mountain paths and
2. In-nis-fal-len's ruined shrine May suggest a passing sigh; But man's faith can
3. No place else can charm the eye With such bright and varied tints, Ev'ry rock that
4. Music there for e-cho dwells, Makes each sound a harmony; Many-voiced the

woodland dells, Mem'ry ev - er fond-ly strays, Bounteous nature loves all lands,
ne'er de-cline Such God's wonders floating by; Cas-tle Lough and Glena bay;
you pass by, Ver-dure broiders or besprints, Vir-gin there the green grass grows
cho-rus swells, Till it faints in ec-sta-sy. With the charmful tints be - low,

Beau - ty wan - ders ev - 'ry - where, Foot-prints leaves on man-y strands,
Moun-tains Tore and Ea-gle's Nest, Still at Mu-cross you must pray
Ev - 'ry morn springs na-tal day, Bright-hued ber-ries daff the snows,
Seems the heav'n a - bove to vie, All rich col-ors that we know,

rall *dim.* *PP* *a tempo*

But her home is sure-ly there! Angels fold their wings and rest, In that E-den
Tho' the monks are now at rest. Angels wonder not that man There would fain pro-
Smil-ing win-ter's frown a-way. Angels oft-en pausing there, Doubt if E-den
Tinge the cloud-wreaths in that sky. Wings of angels so might shine, Glancing back soft

cresc. *f*

of the West, Beauty's home, Kil - lar - ney, Ev-er fair Kil-lar-ney.
long life's span, Beauty's home, Kil - lar - ney, Ev-er fair Kil-lar-ney.
were more fair, Beauty's home, Kil - lar - ney, Ev-er fair Kil-lar-ney
light di-vine, Beauty's home, Kil - lar - ney, Ev-er fair Kil-lar-ney.

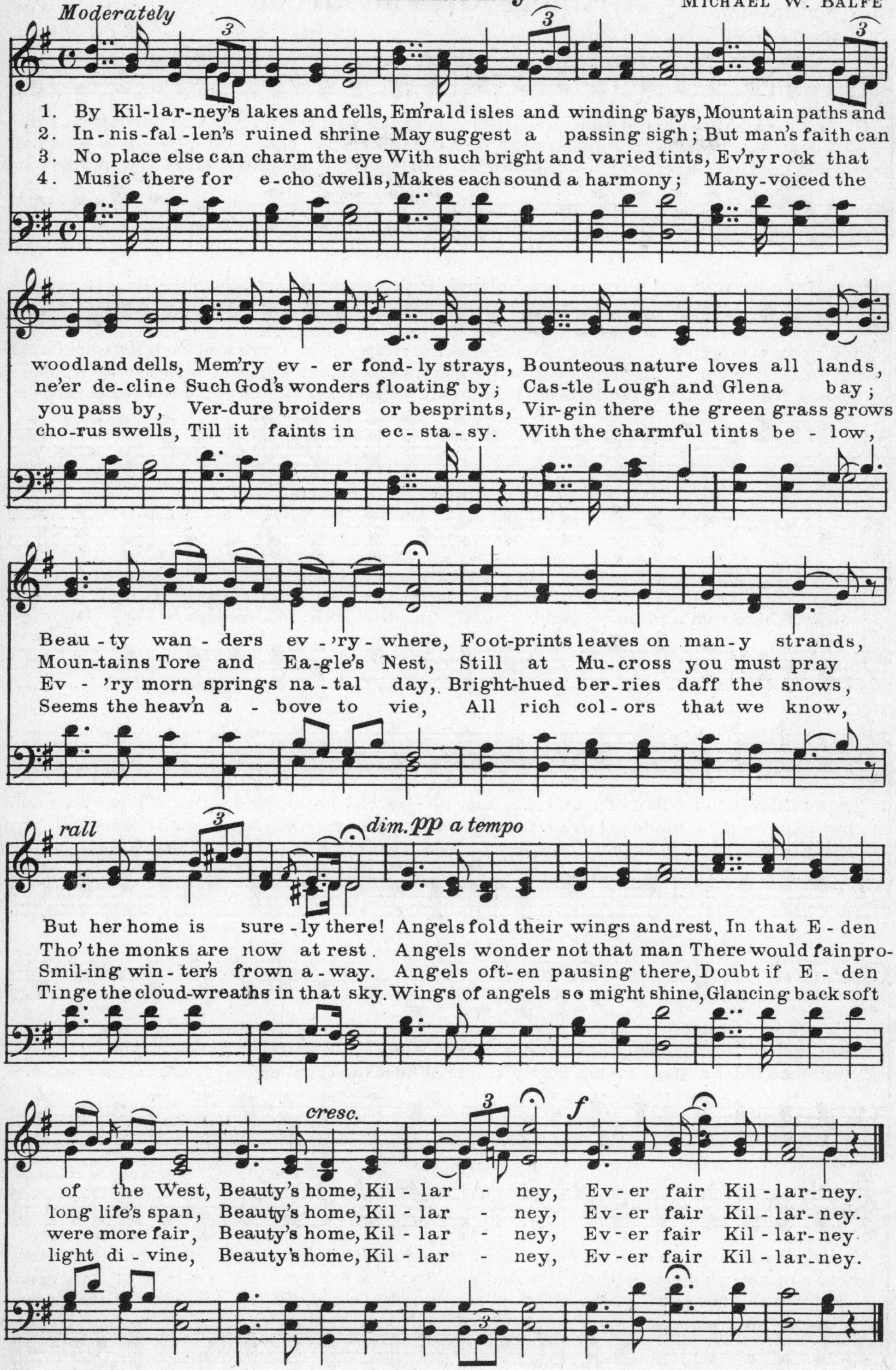

Wearing Of The Green
Dion Boucicault
Irish Air
Moderately
1. Oh! Pad-dy, dear, and did you hear the news that's going round, The shamrock is for -
2. Then since the col-or we must wear, is England's cruel red, Sure Ireland's sons will
3. But if at last our col-or should be torn from Ireland's heart, Her sons with shame and
bid by law to grow on I-rish ground; Saint Patrick's day no more we'll keep, His color can't be
ne'er forget the blood that they have shed; You may take the shamrock from your hat, and cast it on the
sorrow from the dear old soil will part; I've heard whisper of a country that lies far beyant the
seen, For there's a blood-y law a-gin' the Wear-in' o' the Green; I
sod, But 'twill take root and flourish still, tho' un-der-foot 'tis trod; When the
say, Where rich and poor stand e-qual, in the light of freedom's day; Oh,
met with Nap-per Tan-dy and he tuk me by the hand, And he said "How's poor ould
law can stop the blades of grass from growing as they grow, And when the leaves in
E - rin must we lave you, driv-en by the tyrant's hand, Must we ask a moth-er's
Ire-land, and how does she stand?" She's the most dis-tressful country, that
sum-mer time their verdure dare not show; Then I will change the col-or I
welcome from a strange but happy land? Where the cruel cross of England's thraldom
ev-er you have seen; They're hanging men and women there for wearing of the green.
wear in my cau-been, But 'till that day, I'll stick for aye to wearing of the green.
nev-er shall be seen; And where, in peace, we'll live and die, a - wearing of the green.
Repeat as Chorus

Love's Old Sweet Song

G. CLIFTON BINGHAM — J. L. MOLLOY

With a moderately quick motion
1. Once in the dear dead days beyond re-call, When on the world the mists be-gan to
2. E - ven to-day we hear love's song of yore, Deep in our hearts it dwells for-ev-er -
fall, Out of the dreams that rose in hap-py throng, Low to our hearts love sang an
more, Foot-steps may fal - ter, wear-y grow the way, Still we can hear it at the
old sweet song; And in the dusk, where fell the fire-light gleam, Soft - ly it
close of day; So till the end, when life's dim shadows fall, Love will be
wove it-self in-to our dream.
found the sweetest song of all.
REFRAIN
Just a song at twi-light, when the lights are low,
And the flick'ring shadows softly come and go; Tho' the heart be weary, sad the day and
long, Still to us at twi-light comes love's old song, Comes love's old sweet song.

Because "Just a Song at Twilight" brings joy to the weary soul, wouldn't it be thoughtful of you to send a copy of this book, full of inspiration and happiness, to that friend who needs a little help from you? It will cost you but a few cents but will mean much to the friend.

Drink To Me Only With Thine Eyes

BEN JONSON
OLD ENGLISH AIR
1. Drink to me on - ly with thine eyes, And I will pledge with mine;
2. I sent thee late a ro - sy wreath, Not so much hon'ring thee
Or leave a kiss with - in the cup, And I'll not ask for wine; The
As giv - ing it a hope that there It could not withered be; But
thirst that from the soul doth rise, Doth ask a drink di - vine;
thou there - on didst on - ly breathe, And sent'st it back to me,
But might I of Jove's nec - tar sip, I would not change for thine.
Since when it grows and smells, I swear, Not of it - self, but thee.
Believe Me, If All Those Endearing Young Charms
THOMAS MOORE
IRISH AIR
Moderately slow
1. Be - lieve me, if all those en - dearing young charms, Which I gaze on so
2. It is not while beauty and youth are thine own, And thy cheeks unpro-
fond - ly to - day, Were to change by to - mor - row, and fleet in my arms, Like
faned by a tear, That the fer - vor and faith of a soul can be known, To which

Believe Me, If All Those Endearing Young Charms—Conc.

fair - y gifts, fad - ing a - way, Thou wouldst still be a - dored — as this
time will but make thee more dear! No, the heart that has tru - ly loved
moment thou art, Let thy love - li - ness fade as it will; And a - round the dear
nev - er for - gets, But as tru - ly loves on to the close; As the sun - flow - er
ru - in, each wish of my heart Would en - twine it - self ver - dant - ly still!
turns on her god, when he sets, The same look which she turn'd when he rose!
The Harp That Once Through Tara's Halls
THOMAS MOORE
SIR JOHN STEVENSON
1. The harp that once thro' Tara's halls The soul of music shed; Now hangs as mute on
2. No more to chiefs and ladies bright The harp of Tara swells; The chord a - lone that
Ta - ra's walls As tho' that soul were fled So sleeps the pride of former days, So
breaks at night Its tale of ru - in tells. Thus Freedom now so seldom wakes; The
glo - ry's thrill is o'er, And hearts that once beat high for praise Now feel that pulse no more.
on - ly throb she gives Is when some heart, in - dignant, breaks, To show that still she lives.

Kathleen Mavourneen

Mrs. JULIA CRAWFORD | FREDERICK N. CROUCH

Moderately quick
1. Kathleen Ma-vourneen, the gray dawn is breaking, The horn of the hun-ter is
2. Kathleen Ma-vourneen, a - wake from thy slumbers; The blue mountains glow in the
Small notes to be sung for 2d V.
heard on the hill; The lark from her light wing the bright dew is shak - ing;
sun's golden light; Ah! where is the spell that once hung on my numbers? A -
Kathleen Mavour-neen, what! slumb'ring still? Kathleen Mavourneen, what!
rise in thy beauty, thou star of my night; A-rise in thy beau-ty, thou
slum - b'ring still? Or hast thou for-got-ten how soon we must sev-er? Oh!
star of my night! Ma-vour-neen, Ma-vour-neen, my sad tears are falling, To
hast thou for-gotten this day we must part?
think that from E-rin and thee I must part!
It may be for years, and it
may be for ev-er; Then why art thou si-lent, thou voice of my heart? It may be for
semplice

Kathleen Mavourneen—Continued

mf
mf
mf
years, and it may be for ev er; Then why art thou si-lent, Kathleen Ma-vourneen?
The Heart Bowed Down
M.W.B.
(From "The Bohemian Girl")
MICHAEL Wm. BALFE
Moderately slow
1. The heart bow'd down by weight of woe, To weak-est hopes will cling, To
2. The mind will in its worst de-spair, Still pon-der o'er the past, On
thought and im-pulse while they flow, That can no com - fort bring, that can, that
mo - ments of de - light that were Too beauti-ful to last, that were too
can no com - fort bring; To those ex-cit-ing scenes will blend, O'er
beau-ti - ful to last; To long de-part-ed years ex-tend, Its
pleasure's pathway thrown; But mem'ry is the on - ly friend That grief can call its
vi-sions with them flown; For mem'ry is the on - ly friend That grief can call its
own, That grief can call its own, ___ That grief can call its own

When You And I Were Young, Maggie

GEORGE W. JOHNSON
J. A. BUTTERFIELD
1. I wan-dered to-day to the hill, Maggie, To watch the scene be - low, The creek and the old rust-y mill, Maggie, Where we sat in the long, long a-go.
2. A cit - y so si-lent and lone, Maggie, Where the young and the gay and the best, In polish'd white mansions of stone, Maggie, Have each found a place of rest,
3. They say I am fee-ble with age, Maggie, My steps are less spright-ly than then; My face is a well-written page, Maggie, But time a - lone was the pen.
The green grove is gone from the hill, Maggie, Where first the dai - sies sprung; The old rust - y mill is still, Mag-gie, Since you and I were young.
Is built where the birds used to play, Maggie, And join in the songs that were sung, For we sang just as gay as they, Mag-gie, When you and I were young.
They say we are a - ged and gray, Maggie, As spray by the white breakers flung, But to me you're as fair as you were, Mag-gie, When you and I were young.
D.S. And now we are a - ged and gray, Maggie, The tri - als of life near-ly done, Let us sing of the days that are gone, Mag-gie, When you and I were young.
D.S.
Row, Row, Row Your Boat
(Round)
E. O. LYTE
1
2
3
4
Row, row, row your boat Gent - tly down the stream; Mer-ri - ly, mer-ri - ly, mer-ri - ly, mer-ri - ly, Life is but a dream.

THOMAS MOORE

The Minstrel Boy

IRISH AIR

Lively

1. The min - strel boy___ to the war is gone, In the
2. The min - strel fell,___ but the foe - man's chain Could not

ranks of death___ you'll find___ him; His fa - ther's sword he hath
bring that proud___ soul un - der; The harp he lov'd ne'er

gird - ed on, And his wild harp slung___ be - hind him.
spoke a - gain, For he tore its chords___ a - sun - der, And

"Land of song!" said the war - rior bard, "Tho' all the world be - trays thee, One
said, "No chain shall sul - ly thee, Thou soul of love and brav - 'ry! Thy

sword at least thy rights shall guard, One faith-ful harp shall praise thee."
songs were made for the pure and free, They shall nev - er sound in slav - 'ry."

Moore, Jonson, and Burns

Thomas Moore, the great Irish poet, was born in Dublin in 1779 and died in 1852. As a song writer, Moore is one of the greatest; he is excellent alike in verse, romance and satire.

Ben Jonson, (1573-1637), famous among English dramatists and poets, is noted for his charmingly beautiful work. His poems are many and varied; they are full of grace and are classical in form and phraseology. After three centuries his, "Drink To Me Only With Thine Eyes," which is on page 46 is still popular.

Robert Burns, the national poet of Scotland was born in a little clay cottage near Ayr in 1759. At the time of his death in 1796 he was recognized for his great genius but he died in penury. It was his custom to write his poems to existing Scotch airs and to this habit we owe some of the greatest lyrics in the language.

Juanita

"Juanita," for many years a favorite, was written by the granddaughter of Richard Brinsley Sheridan, the Irish wit and playwright. The Honorable Mrs. Norton, as she was called, adapted her text to an old Spanish air, and rearranged it much in its present form.

Mrs. CAROLINE NORTON
SPANISH AIR
1. Soft o'er the foun-tain, lin-g'ring falls the southern moon; Far o'er the mountain,
2. When in thy dream ing Moons like these shall shine again, And daylight beaming,
Breaks the day too soon! In thy dark eyes, splendor, Where the warm light loves to dwell,
Prove thy dreams are vain, Wilt thou not, re lent ing, For thine absent lov er sigh?
Wear-y looks, yet ten-der, Speak their fond fare-well. Ni ta! Jua ni ta!
In thy heart con sent ing To a pray'r gone by? Ni ta! Jua ni ta!
Ask thy soul if we should part! Ni-ta! Jua - ni-ta! Lean thou on my heart.
Let me lin-ger by thy side! Ni-ta! Jua - ni-ta! Be my own Fair Bride.
3
3
The Dearest Spot
W. T. W.
W. T. WRIGHTON
1. The dear-est spot on earth to me Is home, sweet home; The fair - y land I've
2. I've taught my heart the way to prize My home, sweet home; I've learn'd to look with
D.C. The dear-est spot on earth to me Is home, sweet home; The fair - y land I've
Fine.
long'd to see Is home, sweet home; There how charm'd the sense of hearing, There where hearts are
lover's eyes On home, sweet home; There where vows are tru - ly plighted, There where hearts are
long'd to see Is home, sweet home.

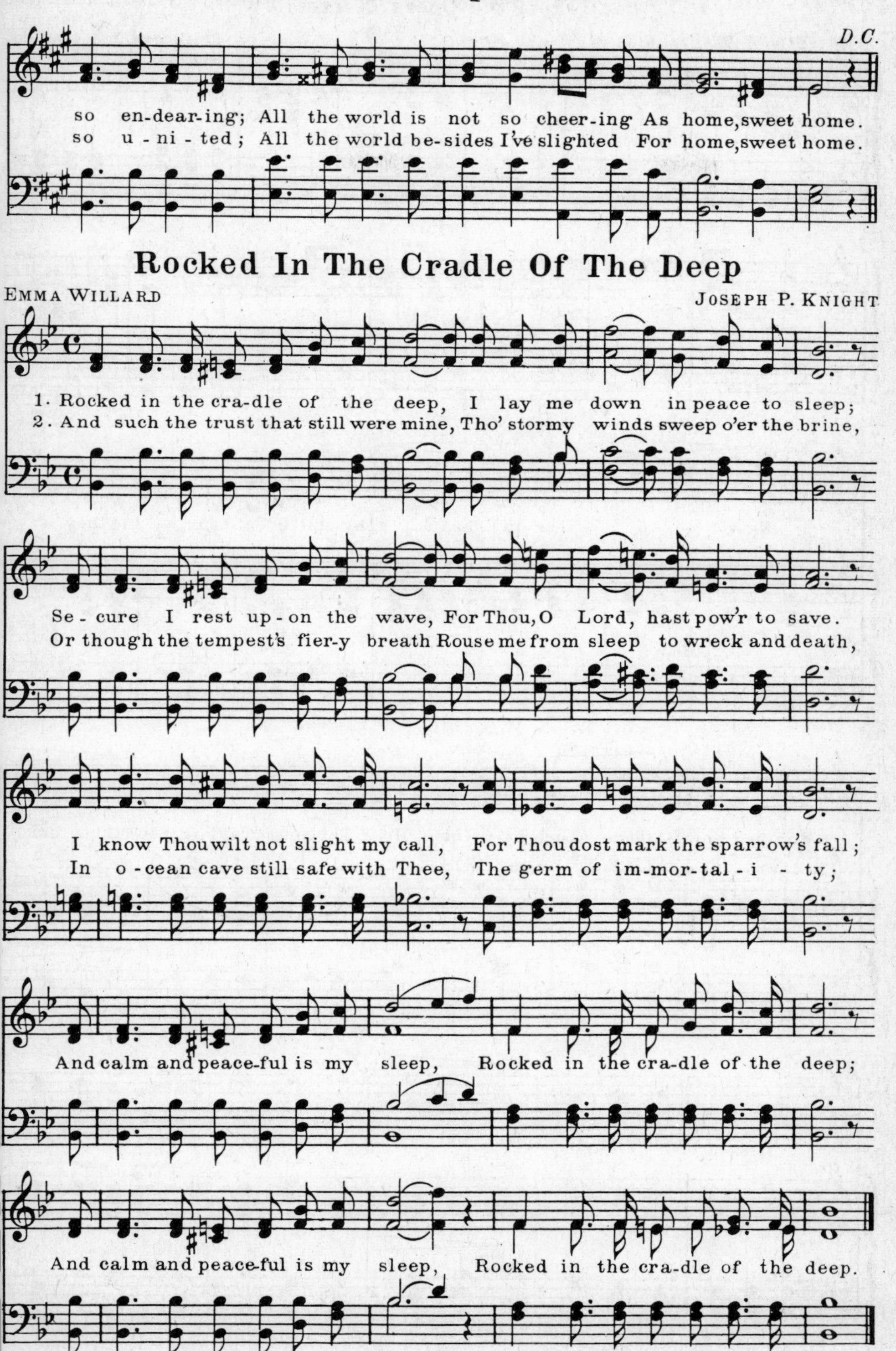
D.C.
so en-dear-ing; All the world is not so cheer-ing As home, sweet home.
so u-ni-ted; All the world be-sides I've slighted For home, sweet home.
Rocked In The Cradle Of The Deep
EMMA WILLARD
JOSEPH P. KNIGHT
1. Rocked in the cra-dle of the deep, I lay me down in peace to sleep;
2. And such the trust that still were mine, Tho' stormy winds sweep o'er the brine,
Se-cure I rest up-on the wave, For Thou, O Lord, hast pow'r to save.
Or though the tempest's fier-y breath Rouse me from sleep to wreck and death,
I know Thou wilt not slight my call, For Thou dost mark the sparrow's fall;
In o-cean cave still safe with Thee, The germ of im-mor-tal-i-ty;
And calm and peace-ful is my sleep, Rocked in the cra-dle of the deep;
And calm and peace-ful is my sleep, Rocked in the cra-dle of the deep.

Largo

(From the Opera, Xerxes)

THOMAS WILLIAMS | GEORGE FRIEDRICH HANDEL

Very slowly
Fa - - ther in heav'n, Thy chil-dren hear, As they a -
dor-ing bow, O Thou Al-might-y One, Hear Thou our pray'r; Streng-then our
faith; With hope in - spire our hearts, Flaming our souls with love

Largo– Continued

pp

Like un - to Thine. Then ___ shall Thy works a-bound, Men shall pro -

f

claim that God our Lord ___ is God a-lone, And ho - ly,

p

ho-ly is His name, ___ And ho - ly is His name;

ff

God our Lord is God a-lone, And ho - ly, ho-ly is His name.

God our Lord is God a-lone, And ho - ly, ho-ly is His name.

Holy, Holy, Holy

REGINALD HEBER
JOHN B. DYKES
1. Ho-ly, ho-ly, ho-ly! Lord God Al-migh-ty! Ear-ly in the
2. Ho-ly, ho-ly, ho-ly! all the saints a-dore Thee, Cast-ing down their
3. Ho-ly, ho-ly, ho-ly! though the dark-ness hide Thee, Though the eye of
4. Ho-ly, ho-ly, ho-ly! Lord God Al-migh-ty! All Thy works shall
morn-ing our song shall rise to Thee. Ho-ly, ho-ly, ho-ly,
golden crowns a-round the glas-sy sea; Cher-u-bim and Sera-phim
sin-ful man Thy glo-ry may not see, On-ly Thou art ho-ly!
praise Thy name in earth, and sky, and sea. Ho-ly, ho-ly, ho-ly!
mer-ci-ful and migh-ty, God in three per-sons, bless-ed Trin-i-ty!
fall-ing down be-fore Thee, Which wert, and art, and ev-er-more shalt be.
there is none be-side Thee, Per-fect in pow'r, in love, and pu-ri-ty.
mer-ci-ful and migh-ty, God in three per-sons, bless-ed Trin-i-ty!
Come, Thou Almighty King
(Italian Hymn)
CHARLES WESLEY
GIARDINI
1. Come, Thou al-might-y King, Help us Thy name to sing, Help us to praise! Fa-ther all-
2. Come, Thou in-car-nate Word, Gird on Thy might-y sword, Our pray'r attend! Come, and Thy
3. Come, Ho-ly Com-fort-er, Thy sacred wit-ness bear, In this glad hour! Thou, who al-
glo-ri-ous, O'er all vic-to-ri-ous, Come and reign o-ver us, An-cient of days!
peo-ple bless, And give Thy word success: Spir-it of ho-li-ness, On us de-scend!
might-y art, Now rule in ev'ry heart, And ne'er from us depart, Spir-it of pow'r!

Onward, Christian Soldiers

In 1865, the Rev. Sabine Baring-Gould was Curate of the Horbury Bridge School in a small English village. A school festival was to be given for which a suitable song was desired but he could find no song in his books which he considered suitable to the occasion. To supply the necessity he wrote this now famous processional hymn which is the most universally sung of the hymns of today.

The spirited music written for it by Sir Arthur Seymour Sullivan has doubtless added to the enthusiasm with which it is always sung.

SABINE BARING-GOULD
SIR ARTHUR SEYMOUR SULLIVAN
1. On-ward, Christian sol-diers! Marching as to war, With the cross of Je - sus
2. Like a might-y ar - my Moves the Church of God; Brothers, we are tread-ing
3. Crowns and thrones may perish, Kingdoms rise and wane, But the Church of Je - sus
4. On-ward, then, ye peo - ple! Join our hap-py throng, Blend with ours your voices
Go - ing on be-fore. Christ, the roy-al Mas - ter, Leads a-gainst the foe;
Where the saints have trod; We are not di - vid - ed, All one bod - y we,
Con-stant will re-main; Gates of hell can nev - er 'Gainst that Church pre-vail;
In the tri-umph song; Glo - ry, laud, and hon - or Un - to Christ the King.
Forward in to bat - tle, See, His ban-ners go!
One in hope and doc - trine One in char-i - ty.
We have Christ's own promise, And that can-not fail.
This thru countless a - ges Men and an-gels sing.
CHORUS
Onward, Christian soldiers!
Marching as to war, With the cross of Je-sus Go-ing on be-fore.

Now the Day Is Over

SABINE BARING-GOULD

JOSEPH BARNBY

1. Now the day is o-ver, Night is drawing nigh, Shadows of the ev'ning Steal across the sky.
2. Jesus, give the weary Calm and sweet repose With Thy tend'rest blessing, May our eyelids close.
3. When the morning wakens, Then may we arise Pure and fresh and sinless In Thy holy eyes.

Work, for the Night Is Coming
ANNIE L. WALKER-COGHILL
LOWELL MASON
1. Work, for the night is com - ing, Work thro' the morn-ing hours;
2. Work, for the night is com - ing, Work thro' the sun - ny noon;
3. Work, for the night is com - ing, Un - der the sun - set skies;
Fine.
Work, while the dew is spark - ling, Work 'mid spring-ing flow'rs;
Fill bright - est hours with la - bor, Rest comes sure and soon.
While their bright tints are glow - ing, Work, for day - light flies,
D.S. Work, for the night is com - ing, When man's work is done.
D.S. Work, for the night is com - ing, When man works no more.
D.S. Work while the night is dark'n - ing When man's work is o'er.
cresc.
D.S.
Work, when the day grows bright - er, Work in the glow-ing sun;
Give ev - 'ry fly - ing min - ute, Some-thing to keep in store;
Work till the last beam fad - eth, Fad - eth to shine no more;
Jesus, Tender Shepherd, Hear Me
CLARIBEL
Mrs. CHARLES BARNARD (CLARIBEL)
1. Je - sus, ten - der Shep-herd, hear me; Bless Thy lit - tle lamb to - night;
2. All this day Thy hand has led me, And I thank Thee for Thy care;
3. Let my sins be all for - giv - en; Bless the friends I love so well;
Thro' the dark - ness be Thou near me, Keep me safe till morn - ing light.
Thou hast clothed me, warmed and fed me, List - en to my eve - ning pray'r!
Take me, when I die, to heav - en, Hap - py there with Thee to dwell.

The Twenty-third Psalm

The Lord is my shepherd; I shall not want. He maketh me to lie down in green pastures: he leadeth me beside the still waters. He restoreth my soul: he leadeth me in the paths of righteousness for his name's sake. Yea, though I walk through the valley of the shadow of death, I will fear no evil, for thou art with me; thy rod and thy staff they comfort me Thou preparest a table before me in the presence of mine enemies: thou anointest my head with oil; my cup runneth over. Surely goodness and mercy shall follow me all the days of my life; and I will dwell in the house of the Lord for ever.

My Faith Looks Up to Thee

RAY PALMER — LOWELL MASON

1. My faith looks up to Thee, Thou Lamb of Cal-va-ry,
Savior di-vine! Now hear me while I pray, Take all my
guilt a-way, O, let me from this day Be whol-ly Thine.

2. May Thy rich grace im-part Strength to my faint-ing heart,
My zeal in-spire; As Thou hast died for me, O, may my
love to Thee Pure, warm and changeless be, A liv-ing fire.

3. When ends life's tran-sient dream, When death's cold, sul-len stream
Shall o'er me roll, Blest Sav-ior then, in love, Fear and dis-
trust re-move; O, bear me safe a-bove, A ran-somed soul.

Abide with Me

HENRY F. LYTE — WILLIAM H. MONK

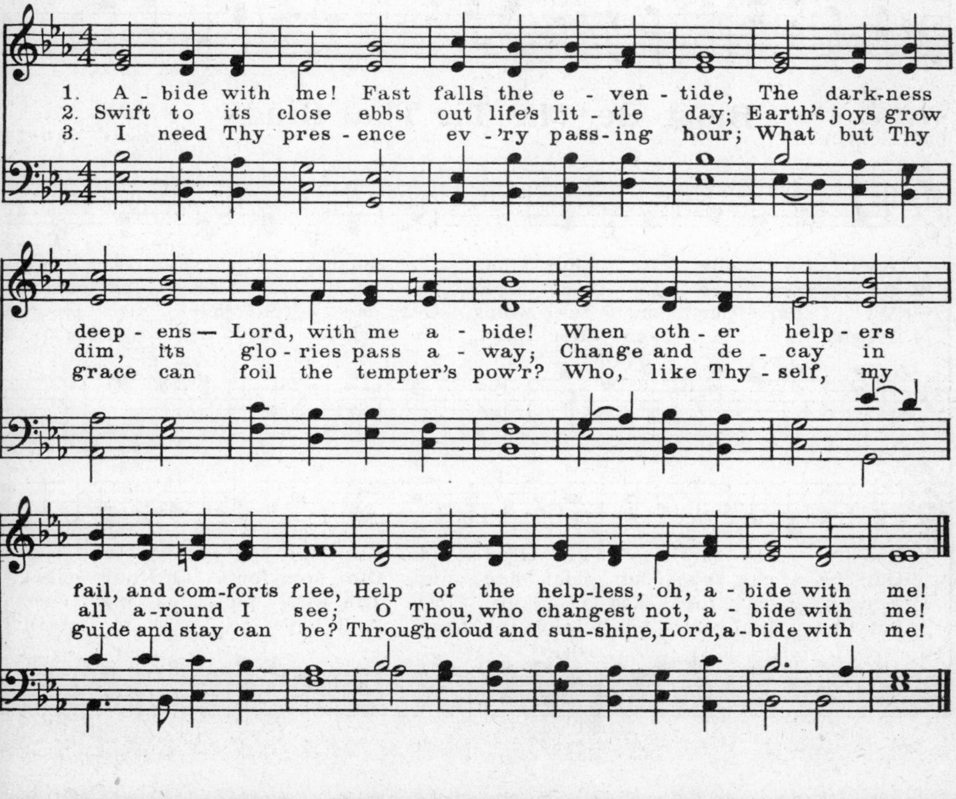

1. A-bide with me! Fast falls the e-ven-tide, The dark-ness
deep-ens— Lord, with me a-bide! When oth-er help-ers
fail, and com-forts flee, Help of the help-less, oh, a-bide with me!

2. Swift to its close ebbs out life's lit-tle day; Earth's joys grow
dim, its glo-ries pass a-way; Change and de-cay in
all a-round I see; O Thou, who changest not, a-bide with me!

3. I need Thy pres-ence ev-'ry pass-ing hour; What but Thy
grace can foil the tempter's pow'r? Who, like Thy-self, my
guide and stay can be? Through cloud and sun-shine, Lord, a-bide with me!

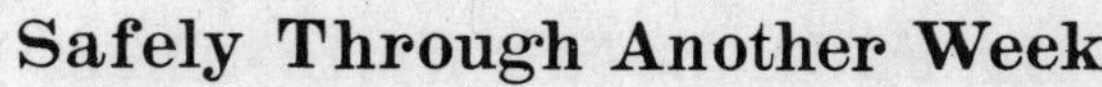

Safely Through Another Week

JOHN NEWTON — LOWELL MASON

1. Safe-ly thro' an-oth-er week God has bro't us on our way; Let us now a bless-ing
2. While we pray for pard'ning grace, Thro' the dear Redeemer's name, Show Thy rec-on-cil-ed
3. May Thy gos-pel's joyful sound Conquer sinners, comfort saints; May the fruits of grace a-

seek, Wait-ing in His courts to - day; Day of all the week the best, Em-blem
face, Take a - way our sin and shame; From our worldly cares set free, May we
bound, Bring re-lief for all com-plaints: Thus may all our Sabbaths prove Till we

of e-ter-nal rest, Day of all the week the best, Em-blem of e-ter-nal rest.
rest this day in Thee; From our worldly cares set free, May we rest this day in Thee.
join the Church above; Thus may all our Sabbaths prove Till we join the Church a-bove.

Blest Be the Tie That Binds

JOHN FAWCETT — HANS G. NAGELI

1. Blest be the tie that binds Our hearts in Christ - ian love;
2. Be - fore our Fa - ther's throne, We pour our ar - dent pray'rs;
3. We share our mu - tual woes, Our mu - tual bur - dens bear;
4. When we a - sun - der part, It gives us in - ward pain;

The fel - low-ship of kin - dred minds Is like to that a - bove.
Our fears, our hopes, our aims are one, Our com-forts and our cares.
And oft - en for each oth - er flows The sym - pa - thiz - ing tear.
But we shall still be joined in heart, And hope to meet a - gain.

Jesus, Lover of My Soul

In the foremost ranks of the composers of immortal lyric verse stands Charles Wesley. Several stories are told of the circumstances under which he wrote these beautiful stanzas but whatever the inciting cause, it resulted in inspiring one of the noblest songs of modern times. It is a song of comfort and of refuge, one that has brought peace and contentment to vast multitudes.

CHARLES WESLEY
SIMEON B. MARSH
1. Je - sus lov - er of my soul, Let me to Thy bo - som fly
While the near - er wa - ters roll, While the tempest sill is high;
2. Oth - er ref - uge have I none, Hangs my help - less soul on Thee;
Leave, oh, leave me not a - lone, Still sup - port and com - fort me.
3. Thou, O Christ, art all I want, More than all in Thee I find;
Raise the fall - en, cheer the faint, Heal the sick and lead the blind.
Hide me, O my Sav - ior, hide, Till the storm of life is past;
All my trust on Thee is stayed, All my help from Thee I bring;
Just and ho - ly is Thy name; I am all un - righteous - ness;
Safe in - to the ha - ven guide, Oh, re - ceive my soul at last.
Cov - er my de - fence - less head With the shad - ow of Thy wing.
Vile and full of sin I am, Thou art full of truth and grace.
Nearer, My God, to Thee
SARAH F. ADAMS
LOWELL MASON
Slowly
1. Near - er, my God, to Thee, Near - er to Thee! E'en tho' it be a cross
2. Tho' like the wan - der - er, The sun gone down, Dark - ness be o - ver me,
3. There let the way ap - pear Steps un - to heav'n; All that Thou sendest me
4. Or if on joy - ful wing Cleav - ing the sky, Sun, moon, and stars forgot,
D.S. Near - er, my God, to Thee,
Fine.
D.S.
That rais - eth me, Still all my song shall be, Near - er, my God, to Thee,
My rest a stone, Yet in my dreams I'd be, Near - er, my God, to Thee,
In mer - cy giv'n; An - gels to beck - on me, Near - er, my God, to Thee,
Up - ward I fly, Still all my song shall be, Near - er, my God, to Thee,
Near - er to Thee.

God Be with You Till We Meet Again

JEREMIAH E. RANKIN — WILLIAM G. TOMER

1. God be with you till we meet a-gain, By His coun-sels guide, up-hold you,
2. God be with you till we meet a-gain, 'Neath His wings pro-tect-ing hide you,
3. God be with you till we meet a-gain, When life's per-ils thick con-found you,
4. God be with you till we meet a-gain, Keep love's ban-ner float-ing o'er you,
With His sheep se-cure-ly fold you, God be with you till we meet a-gain.
Dai-ly man-na still pro-vide you, God be with you till we meet a-gain.
Put His arms un-fail-ing 'round you, God be with you till we meet a-gain.
Smite death's threat'ning wave before you, God be with you till we meet a-gain.
Till we meet, till we meet, Till we meet at Je-sus' feet;
Till we meet, till we meet, till we meet, Till we meet
Till we meet, till we meet, God be with you till we meet a-gain.
Till we meet, till we meet, till we meet,
I Think, When I Read That Sweet Story
JEMIMA T. LUKE
ENGLISH AIR
1. I think when I read that sweet sto-ry of old, When
2. I wish that His hands had been placed on my head, That His
3. Yet still to His foot-stool in pray'r I may go, And

Je - sus was here a-mong men, How He called lit-tle chil-dren like
arms had been thrown a-round me, That I might have seen His kind
ask for a share in His love; And if I thus ear-nest-ly
lambs to His fold, I should like to have been with Him then.
look when He said, "Let the lit-tle ones come un-to Me."
seek Him be-low, I shall see Him and hear Him a-bove.
Jesus Loves Me
ANNA B. WARNER
WILLIAM B. BRADBURY
1. Je-sus loves me! this I know, For the Bi-ble tells me so;
2. Je-sus loves me! He who died Heav-en's gates to o-pen wide;
3. Je-sus loves me! He will stay Close be-side me all the way;
Lit-tle ones to Him be-long; They are weak, but He is strong.
He will wash a-way my sin, Let His lit-tle child come in.
If I love Him, when I die, He will take me home on high.
REFRAIN
Yes, Je-sus loves me! Yes, Je-sus loves me! Yes, Je-sus loves me! The Bi-ble tells me so.

Lead, Kindly Light

On June 16, 1833, John Henry Newman, was on a ship becalmed in the Straits of Bonifacio where he was traveling because of impaired health. At the same time he was being torn by the current spiritual unrest. It was under these conditions that he wrote this noble hymn which invoked aid in solving his great problem and which has since voiced the heartfelt prayers of thousands, for spiritual guidance.

The music was composed by John B. Dykes as he walked through the Strand, one of the busiest thoroughfares of London; a circumstance in striking contrast to that under which the words were written.

JOHN HENRY NEWMAN
JOHN B. DYKES
1. Lead, kind-ly Light, a-mid th'en-cir-cling gloom, Lead Thou me on! The night is dark, and I am far from home; Lead Thou me on! Keep Thou my feet; I do not ask to see___ The dis-tant scene; one step e-nough for me.
2. I was not ev-er thus, nor pray'd that Thou Shouldst lead me on; I loved to choose and see my path; but now Lead Thou me on! I loved the gar-ish day, and, spite of fears,_ Pride ruled my will. Re-mem-ber not past years!
3. So long Thy pow'r hath blest me, sure it still Will lead me on O'er moor and fen, o'er crag and tor-rent, till The night is gone, And with the morn those an-gel fa-ces smile___ Which I have loved long since, and lost a-while.
p
cresc.
Holy Ghost! with Light Divine
ANDREW REED
L. M. GOTTSCHALK
Arr. by H. P. Main
1. Ho-ly Ghost! with light di-vine, Shine up-on this heart of mine; Chase the shades of night a-way, Turn my dark-ness in-to day.
2. Ho-ly Ghost! with pow'r di-vine, Cleanse this guil-ty heart of mine; Long hath sin with-out con-trol Held do-min-ion o'er my soul.
3. Ho-ly Ghost! with joy divine, Cheer this sad-den'd heart of mine; Bid my man-y woes de-part, Heal my wound-ed bleed-ing heart.
4. Ho-ly Spir it! all divine, Dwell with-in this heart of mine; Cast down ev-'ry i-dol throne, Reign su-preme, and reign a-lone.

Now Thank We All Our God
Martin Rinkart
Johann Crüger
1. Now thank we all our God, With heart and hands and voi - ces,
2. O may this bounteous God, Through all our life be near us,
3. All praise and thanks to God, The Fa - ther, now be giv - en,
Who won-drous things hath done, In whom His earth re - joi - ces:
With ev - er joy - ful hearts, And bless - ed peace to cheer us,
The Son and Him who reigns, With them in high - est Heav - en;
Who from our moth - ers' arms Hath blessed us on our way
And keep us in His grace And guide us when per - plexed,
The one e - ter - nal God, Whom earth and Heav'n a - dore;
With count - less gifts of love, And still is ours to - day.
And free us from all ills, In this world and the next.
For thus it was, is now, And shall be ev - er - more!
Praise God, from Whom All Blessings Flow
(Old Hundredth—The Doxology)
Thomas Ken
Louis Bourgeois
Praise God, from whom all blessings flow; Praise Him, all creatures here be-low;
Praise Him a-bove, ye heav'n-ly host; Praise Fa-ther, Son, and Ho-ly Ghost.

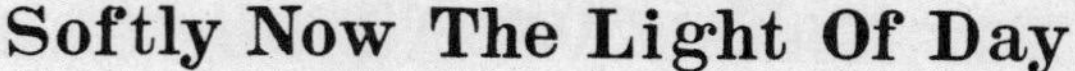

Softly Now The Light Of Day

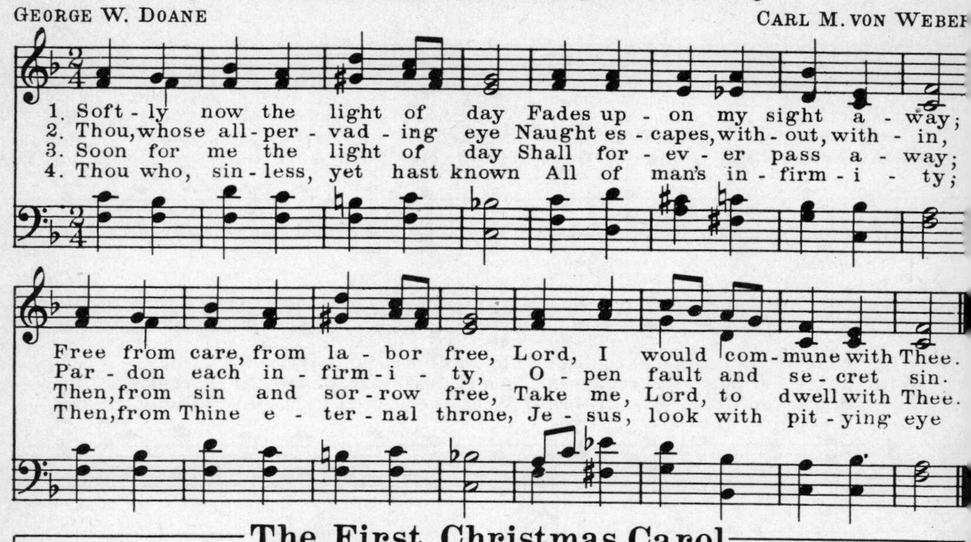
George W. Doane
Carl M. von Weber
1. Soft-ly now the light of day Fades up-on my sight a-way;
2. Thou, whose all-per-vad-ing eye Naught es-capes, with-out, with-in,
3. Soon for me the light of day Shall for-ev-er pass a-way;
4. Thou who, sin-less, yet hast known All of man's in-firm-i-ty;
Free from care, from la-bor free, Lord, I would com-mune with Thee.
Par-don each in-firm-i-ty, O-pen fault and se-cret sin.
Then, from sin and sor-row free, Take me, Lord, to dwell with Thee.
Then, from Thine e-ter-nal throne, Je-sus, look with pit-ying eye

The First Christmas Carol

Fear not: for, behold, I bring you good tidings of great joy, which shall be to all people For unto you is born this day in the city of David a Saviour, which is Christ the Lord. And this shall be a sign unto you; ye shall find the babe wrapped in swaddling clothes lying in a manger. CHORUS: Glory to God in the highest, and on earth peace, good will toward men. — St. Luke's Gospel.

Deck The Halls

OLD WELSH AIR

1. Deck the halls with boughs of hol-ly, Fa la la la la, la la la la.
'Tis the sea-son to be jol-ly, Fa la la la la, la la la la.
Don we now our gay ap-par-rel, Fa la la la la la la,
Troll the an-cient Yule-tide car-ol, Fa la la la la, la la la la.

2. See the blaz-ing Yule be-fore us, Fa la la la la, la la la la.
Strike the harp and join the cho-rus, Fa la la la la, la la la la.
Fol-low me in mer-ry measure, Fa la la la la la la,
While I tell of Yule-tide treas-ure, Fa la la la la, la la la la.

3. Fast a-way the old year pass-es, Fa la la la la, la la la la.
Hail the new, ye lads and lass-es, Fa la la la la, la la la la.
Sing we joy-ous all to-geth-er, Fa la la la la la la,
Heed-less of the wind and weath-er, Fa la la la la, la la la la.

The First Noel

The term Noel is a French word meaning Christmas and is derived from the Latin "natalis" meaning birthday. The songs sung during the Christmas season were known as "Noels," "Nowels" or "Nowells," these names being equivalent to "Carols" in English.

TRADITIONAL TRADITIONAL

mf

1. The first No - el the an-gel did say Was to cer-tain poor shepherds in fields as they lay:
2. They look-ed_ up and_ saw_ a star Shining in_ the East_ beyond them far,
3. This star drew nigh to the north-west, O'er_ Beth - le-hem_ it took_ its rest,
4. Then en-ter'd in there Wise-men three, Full_ rev - 'rent - ly_ up - on their knee,

mf

In fields where they lay keeping their sheep On a cold winter's night that was so deep.
And_ to_ the earth it gave great light, And so it con - tinued both day and night.
And there it_ did both stop and stay Right o-ver the place where Je - sus lay.
And of - fer'd there in His_ pres-ence, Their gold and myrrh and frank-incense.

CHORUS
ff
No - el, No - el, No - el, No - el,_ Born is the King of Is - ra - el.
ff

Silent Night

JOSEPH MOHR FRANZ GRUBER

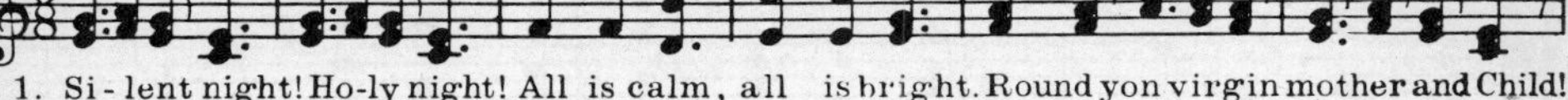
pp

1. Si - lent night! Ho-ly night! All is calm, all is bright. Round yon virgin mother and Child!
2. Si - lent night! Ho-ly night! Shepherds quake at the sight! Glories stream from Heaven a-far,
3. Si - lent night! Ho-ly night! Son of God, love's pure light Radiant beams from Thy holy face,

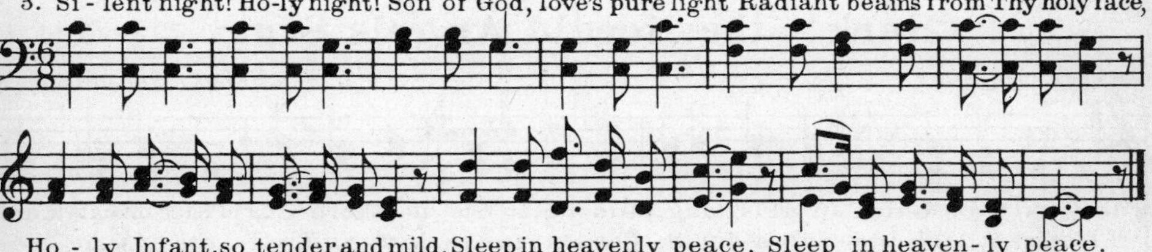

Ho - ly Infant, so tender and mild, Sleep in heavenly peace, Sleep in heaven - ly peace.
Heav'nly hosts sing Al-le-lu-ia, Christ, the Savior, is born! Christ, the Savior, is born!
With the dawn of redeeming grace, Je - sus, Lord, at Thy birth, Je - sus, Lord, at Thy birth.

It Came upon the Midnight Clear

EDWIN H. SEARS
RICHARD S. WILLIS
p
1. It came up-on the mid-night clear, That glo-rious song of old,
2. Still thro' the clo-ven skies they come, With peace-ful wings un-furled;
3. For lo! the days are has-t'ning on, By proph-ets seen of old,
From an-gels bend-ing near the earth, To touch their harps of gold:
And still their heav'n-ly mu-sic floats O'er all the wea-ry world:
When with the ev-er-cir-cling years Shall come the time fore-told,
mf
"Peace on the earth, good-will to men From heav'n's all-gra-cious King;"
A-bove its sad and low-ly plains They bend on hov-'ring wing,
When the new heav'n and earth shall own The Prince of Peace their King,
pp
The world in sol-emn still-ness lay To hear the an-gels sing.
And ev-er o'er its Ba-bel sounds The bless-ed an-gels sing.
And the whole world send back the song Which now the an-gels sing.
Hark! the Herald Angels Sing
CHARLES WESLEY
FELIX MENDELSSOHN
1. Hark! the her-ald an-gels sing, "Glo-ry to the new-born King! Peace on earth, and
2. Christ, by high-est heav'n a-dored; Christ, the ev-er-last-ing Lord; Late in time be-
3. Hail! the heav'n-born Prince of Peace! Hail! the Son of Right-eousness! Light and life to

Hark! the Herald Angels Sing—Concluded

mer-cy mild, God and sin-ners re-con-ciled." Joy-ful, all ye na-tions, rise,
hold Him come, Off-spring of the fa-vored one. Veiled in flesh, the God-head see;
all He brings, Ris'n with heal-ing in His wings. Mild He lays His glo-ry by,
Join the tri-umph of the skies; With th'an-gel-ic host proclaim, "Christ is born in
Hail th'in-car-nate De-i-ty Pleased, as man with men to dwell, Je-sus, our Im-
Born that man no more may die: Born to raise the sons of earth, Born to give them
Beth-le-hem."
man-u-el!
sec-ond birth
Hark! the herald an-gels sing, "Glo-ry to the new-born King!"
Glad Christmas Bells
TRADITIONAL
TRADITIONAL
1. Glad Christmas bells, your mu-sic tells The sweet and pleasant sto-ry;
2. No pal-ace hall its ceil-ing tall His king-ly head spread o-ver,
3. Nor rai-ment gay, as there He lay, A-dorn'd the in-fant stranger;
4. But from a-far, a splendid star The wise men westward turning;
How came to earth, in low-ly birth, The Lord of life and glo-ry.
There on-ly stood a sta-ble rude The heav-enly Babe to cov-er.
Poor, hum-ble Child of moth-er mild, She laid Him in a man-ger.
The live-long night saw pure and bright, A-bove His birth place burn-ing.

From Every Spire on Christmas Eve

ELEANOR A. HUNTER — GEORGE COLES

1. From ev -'ry spire on Christ-mas Eve, The Christmas bells ring clearly out
2 A thousand bless-ed mem'ries throng, The stars are ho - ly signs to them,
3 To whom that sto - ry, old and sweet, Is but a fa - ble at the best,
4. That they, at last, may see the light Which shines from Bethl'hem, and un-fold
Their message of good-will and peace, With man-y a call and sil-ver shout.
And from the eyes of ev -'ry child Looks forth the Babe of Beth-le - hem;
The Christmas mu-sic mocks their ears, And life has naught of joy or rest
For Christ the treasures of their hearts, Rich-er than spi - cer - y or gold.
For faith-ful hearts, the an-gels' song Still ech-oes in the frost - y air,
But there are oth - ers, not like these, Whose brows are sad, whose hopes are cross'd
Oh! for an an-gel's voice to pierce The clouds of grief that o'er them rise,
Hope of the a - ges, draw Thou near, Till all the earth shall own Thy sway,
And by the al - tar low they bow, In ad - o - ra - tion and in pray'r.
To whom the sea- son brings no cheer, And life's most gracious charm is lost.
The mists of doubt and un - be-lief That veil the blue of Christmas skies.
And when Thou reign'st in ev -'ry heart It will, in-deed, be Christmas day.
Lovely Evening
(Round)
1. Somewhat quickly
2.
Oh, how love - ly is the eve - ning, is the eve - ning, When the bells are
3.
sweet - ly ring - ing, sweet - ly ring - ing! Ding, dong, ding, dong, ding, dong

Joy to the World!

ISAAC WATTS

GEORGE F. HANDEL
Arr. by Lowell Mason

1. Joy to the world! The Lord is come; Let earth re-ceive her King;— Let
2. Joy to the world! The Sav-ior reigns; Let men their songs em-ploy;—While
3. No more let sin and sor-row grow, Nor thorns in-fest the ground;— He
4. He rules the world with truth and grace, And makes the na-tions prove— The

ev-'ry heart pre-pare Him room, And heav'n and nature sing, And
fields and floods, rocks, hills and plains, Re-peat the sounding joy, Re-
comes to make His bless-ings flow Far as the curse is found, Far
glo-ries of His righteous-ness, And wonders of His love, And

And heav'n, and heav'n and nature

heav'n and na-ture sing, And heav'n, and heav'n and na-ture sing.
peat the sounding joy, Re-peat, re-peat the sounding joy.
as the curse is found, Far as, far as the curse is found.
won-ders of His love, And wonders, and won-ders of His love.

sing, And heav'n and nature sing,

I Heard the Bells on Christmas Day

HENRY W. LONGFELLOW

J. BAPTISTE CALKIN

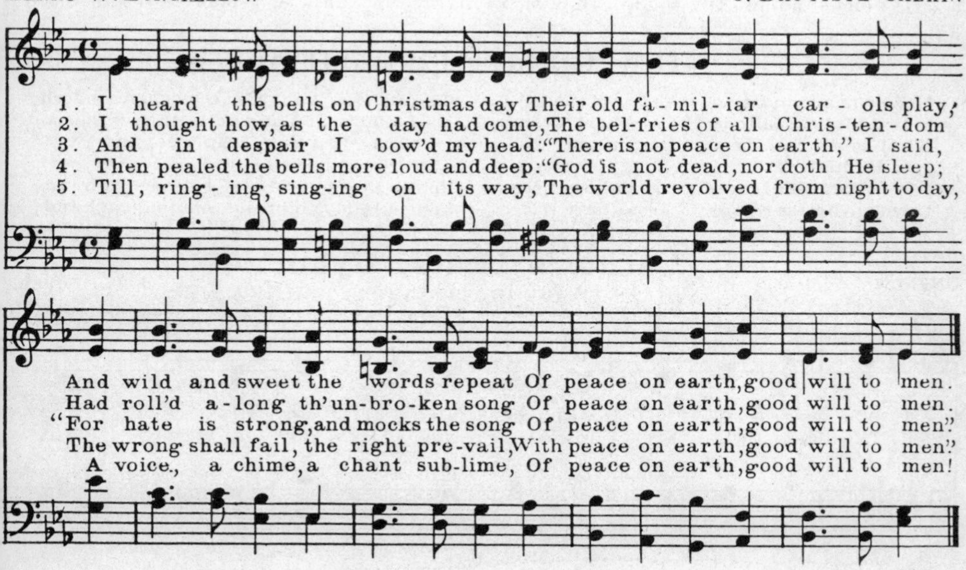

1. I heard the bells on Christmas day Their old fa-mil-iar car-ols play,
2. I thought how, as the day had come, The bel-fries of all Chris-ten-dom
3. And in despair I bow'd my head: "There is no peace on earth," I said,
4. Then pealed the bells more loud and deep: "God is not dead, nor doth He sleep;
5. Till, ring-ing, sing-ing on its way, The world revolved from night to day,

And wild and sweet the words repeat Of peace on earth, good will to men.
Had roll'd a-long th'un-bro-ken song Of peace on earth, good will to men.
"For hate is strong, and mocks the song Of peace on earth, good will to men."
The wrong shall fail, the right pre-vail, With peace on earth, good will to men."
A voice, a chime, a chant sub-lime, Of peace on earth, good will to men!

O Come, All Ye Faithful

(Adeste Fideles)

This hymn is supposed to have been written during the 13th century. It is one of the most popular of the old Latin Hymns and is used in all Christian Churches especially at Christmas. The author of the words is unknown. It was translated by F. Oakley, in 1841. The music is supposed to have been written by John Reading, an English organist of the 18th century.

1. O come, all ye faith-ful, Joy-ful and tri-umphant, O come ye, O come ye to
2. Sing, choirs of An-gels, Sing in ex-ul - ta-tion, — Sing, — all ye cit-i-zens of

A-des-te, fi - de-les, Læ-ti tri-um-phan-tes, Ve-ni - te, ve - ni - te in

Beth-le-hem. Come and be-hold Him, Born the King of Angels: O come, let us a-
heav'n a-bove: Glo - ry to God —— In the highest, glo-ry! O come let us a-

Beth-le-hem. Na-tum vi - de - te, Re-gem an-ge - lo-rum Ve-ni-te, a-do-

dore Him, O come, let us a-dore Him, O come, let us a - dore Him, Christ the Lord.

remus, Ve-ni-te, a - do - re-mus, Ve-ni-te, a - do - re - mus Do - mi-num.

How Firm a Foundation

1. How firm a foundation, ye saints of the Lord,
Is laid for your faith in His excellent Word!
What more can He say than to you
He hath said,
To you, who for refuge to Jesus have fled?
To you, who for refuge to Jesus have fled?

Fear not, I am with thee, O be not dismayed,
For I am thy God and will still give thee aid;
I'll strengthen thee, help thee, and
cause thee to stand,
Upheld by My righteous, omnipotent hand,
Upheld by My righteous, omnipotent hand.

Luther's Cradle Hymn

(Away in a Manger)

UNKNOWN

J. B. HERBERT
Arr. by J.W.B.

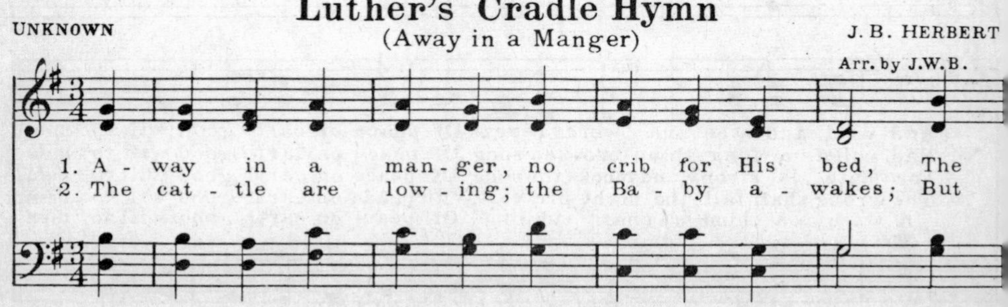
1. A - way in a man - ger, no crib for His bed, The
2. The cat - tle are low - ing; the Ba - by a - wakes; But

Luther's Cradle Hymn—Continued
lit-tle Lord Je-sus lay down His sweet head. The stars in the heav-ens Looked
lit-tle Lord Je-sus no cry-ing He makes. I love Thee, Lord Je-sus Look
down where He lay, The lit-tle Lord Je-sus a-sleep on the hay.
down from the sky, And stay by my cra-dle till morn-ing is nigh.
O, Little Town of Bethlehem
PHILLIPS BROOKS
LEWIS H. REDNER
1. O lit-tle town of Beth-le-hem, How still we see thee lie;
2. For Christ is born of Ma-ry; And gath-ered all a-bove,
3. How si-lent-ly, how si-lent-ly, The Won-drous Gift is giv'n!
4. O ho-ly Child of Beth-le-hem, De-scend to us, we pray;
A-bove thy deep and dream-less sleep The si-lent stars go by:
While mor-tals sleep, the an-gels keep Their watch of wond'ring love.
So God im-parts to hu-man hearts The bless-ings of His heav'n.
Cast out our sin, and en-ter in, Be born in us to-day.
Yet in thy dark streets shin-eth The ev-er-last-ing Light;
O morn-ing stars, to-geth-er Pro-claim the ho-ly birth;
No ear may hear His com-ing, But in this world of sin,
We hear the Christ-mas an-gels The great glad tid-ings tell;
The hopes and fears of all the years Are met in thee to-night.
And prais-es sing to God the King, And peace to men on earth.
Where meek souls will re-ceive Him, still The dear Christ en-ters in.
O come to us, a-bide with us, Our Lord E-man-u-el.

While Shepherds Watched Their Flocks

NAHUM TATE — ARR. FROM GEORGE F. HANDEL

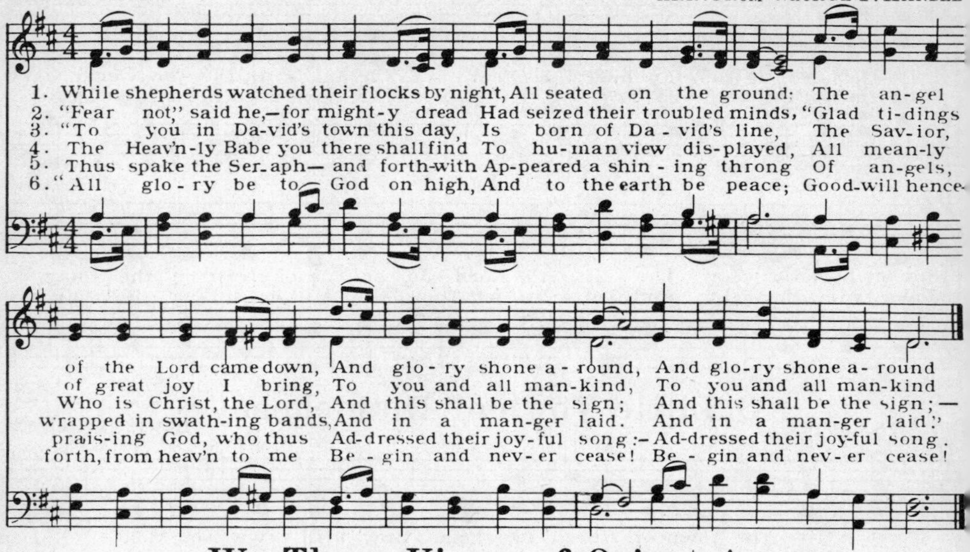

1. While shepherds watched their flocks by night, All seated on the ground; The an-gel
2. "Fear not," said he,—for might-y dread Had seized their troubled minds, "Glad ti-dings
3. "To you in Da-vid's town this day, Is born of Da-vid's line, The Sav-ior,
4. The Heav'n-ly Babe you there shall find To hu-man view dis-played, All mean-ly
5. Thus spake the Ser-aph— and forth-with Ap-peared a shin-ing throng Of an-gels,
6. "All glo-ry be to God on high, And to the earth be peace; Good-will hence-

of the Lord came down, And glo-ry shone a-round, And glo-ry shone a-round
of great joy I bring, To you and all man-kind, To you and all man-kind
Who is Christ, the Lord, And this shall be the sign; And this shall be the sign;—
wrapped in swath-ing bands, And in a man-ger laid. And in a man-ger laid."
prais-ing God, who thus Ad-dressed their joy-ful song:— Ad-dressed their joy-ful song.
forth, from heav'n to me Be-gin and nev-er cease! Be-gin and nev-er cease!"

We Three Kings of Orient Are

J.H.H. — JOHN H. HOPKINS

1. We three kings of O-ri-ent are, Bear-ing gifts we trav-erse a-far
2. Born a babe on Beth-le-hem's plain, Gold we bring to crown Him a-gain;
3. Frank-in-cense to of-fer have I; In-cense owns a De-i-ty nigh,
4. Myrrh is mine; its bit-ter per-fume Breathes a life of gath-'ring gloom;
5. Glo-rious now be-hold—Him rise, King and God and Sac-ri-fice;

Field and foun-tain, moor and moun-tain, Fol-low-ing yon-der Star.
King for-ev-er, ceas-ing nev-er, O-ver us all to reign.
Pray'r and prais-ing all men rais-ing, Wor-ship God on high.
Sorr'wing, sigh-ing, bleed-ing, dy-ing, Sealed in the stone-cold tomb.
Heav'n sings "Hal-le-lu-jah!" "Hal-le-lu-jah!" earth re-plies.

CHORUS

Oh, star of won-der, star of might, Star with roy-al beau-ty bright,
West-ward lead-ing, still pro-ceed-ing, Guide us to the per-fect light.

Jolly Old Saint Nicholas

TRADITIONAL TRADITIONAL

1. Jol-ly old Saint Ni-cho-las, Lean your ear this way! Don't you tell a
2. When the clock is striking twelve, When I'm fast a-sleep, Down the chimney
3. John-ny wants a pair of skates; Su-sy wants a dol-ly; Nel-lie wants a
sin-gle soul What I'm going to say; Christmas Eve is com-ing soon;
broad and black, With your pack you'll creep; All the stock-ings you will find
sto-ry book; She thinks dolls are fol-ly; As for me, my lit-tle brain
Now, you dear old man, Whisper what you'll bring to me; Tell me if you can.
Hang-ing in a row; Mine will be the short-est one, You'll be sure to know.
Is-n't ver-y bright; Choose for me, old San-ta Claus, What you think is right.
Up On The House-Top
B.R.H.
B.R. HANBY
1. Up on the house-top rein-deer pause, Out jumps good old San-ta Claus;
2. First comes the stocking of lit-tle Nell; Oh, dear San-ta, fill it well;
3. Next comes the stocking of lit-tle Will; Oh, just see what a glorious fill!
Down thro' the chimney with lots of toys, All for the lit-tle ones, Christmas joys.
Give her a dol-lie that laughs and crys—One that will open and shut her eyes.
Here is a ham-mer and lots of tacks, Al-so a ball and a whip that cracks.
CHORUS
Ho, ho, ho! who would-n't go! Ho, ho, ho! who would-n't go!
Up on the house-top, click, click, click, Down thro' the chimney with good Saint Nick.

The six following Nursery Rhymes, which all children know and love, date back so many years that their origin is more or less obscure. The verses in the form used here probably came from England and most of the settings are by J.W. Elliott.

Baa! Baa! Black Sheep
Lively
Baa! Baa! Black sheep, have you an - y wool? Yes, sir,
yes, sir! Three bags full, One for my mas - ter, and one for my
dame, But none for the naughty boy that cries in the lane.
Hey, Diddle, Diddle
Lively
Hey, diddle, diddle, The cat and the fiddle, The cow jump'd o-ver the moon; The
lit-tle dog laughed To see such sport, And the dish ran af-ter the spoon.
Dickory, Dickory, Dock
Lively
Dick-o - ry, dick-o - ry, dock; The mouse ran up the clock; The
clock struck "one," The mouse ran down; Dick-o-ry, dick-o - ry, dock.

Little Jack Horner
Lively
Lit-tle Jack Horner sat in a cor-ner, Eat-ing a Christmas pie, He
put in his thumb, And pulled out a plum, And said "What a good boy am I."
Little Bo-Peep
Moderately
mf
Lit-tle Bo-Peep has lost her sheep, And can't tell where to find them,
Leave them a-lone, and they'll come home, Wagging their tails be-hind them.
See-Saw, Margery Daw
Lively
mf
See-saw, Mar-ge-ry Daw, Jack shall have a new mas-ter,
He shall have but a pen-ny a day, Be-cause he won't work any fast-er.

Indian Lullaby

HENRY W. LONGFELLOW — WALTER H. AIKEN

Dreamily
p
1. Rock-a-bye, my
2. Hush-a-bye, my
3. Sleep, O sleep, my
lit-tle ow-let, In thy mos-sy, sway-ing nest,
lit-tle ow-let, Ma-ny voic-es sing to thee,
lit-tle ow-let, Thro' our tent the moon shines bright,
With thy lit-tle wood-land broth-ers, Close thine eyes and
"Hush-a-bye," the wa-ter whis-pers, "Hush!" re-plies the
Like a great eye it will watch thee, Sleep till comes the
take thy rest.
tall pine tree.
morning light.
To whoo, to whoo, to whoo, to

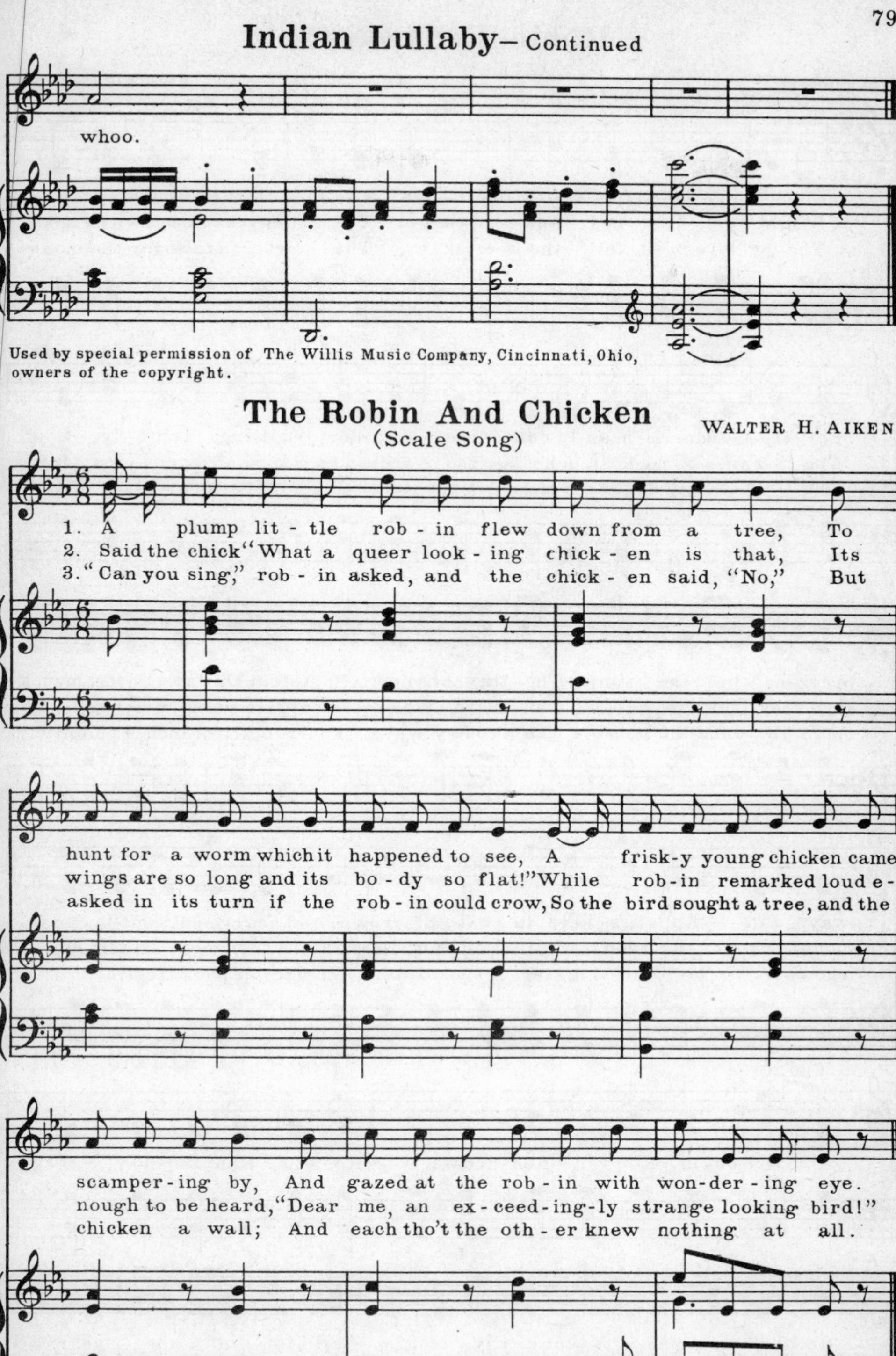
Indian Lullaby—Continued
whoo.
Used by special permission of The Willis Music Company, Cincinnati, Ohio, owners of the copyright.
The Robin And Chicken
(Scale Song)
WALTER H. AIKEN
1. A plump lit - tle rob - in flew down from a tree, To
2. Said the chick "What a queer look - ing chick - en is that, Its
3. "Can you sing," rob - in asked, and the chick - en said, "No," But
hunt for a worm which it happened to see, A frisk-y young chicken came
wings are so long and its bo - dy so flat!" While rob-in remarked loud e -
asked in its turn if the rob - in could crow, So the bird sought a tree, and the
scamper-ing by, And gazed at the rob - in with won-der - ing eye.
nough to be heard, "Dear me, an ex - ceed - ing - ly strange looking bird!"
chicken a wall; And each tho't the oth - er knew nothing at all.

Robin Redbreast

ALLINGHAM
FRIEDRICH KÜCKEN
1. Good - bye, good-bye to Sum-mer, For the Sum-mer's nearly done,
2. Bright yel - low, red and or - ange, The leaves come down in hosts,
3. The fire-side for the crick-et, The wheat-stack for the mouse,
For the Summer's near-ly done; The gar-den smil-ing faint-ly, Cool
The leaves come down in hosts, The trees are In - dian prin - ces, But
The wheat-stack for the mouse, When trembling night-winds whistle And
breez-es in the sun; The thrushes now are si-lent, Our swallows flown a-
soon they'll turn to ghosts; The leath'ry pears and apples Hang russet on the
moan all round the house; The frost-y ways, like i-ron, The branches, plum'd with
way, But Rob-in's here in coat of brown, And scar-let breast-knot gay.
bough; 'Tis Au - tumn, Au - tumn, Au-tumn, late, 'Twill soon be Win - ter now.
snow, A - las! in Win-ter dead and dark, Where can poor Rob-in go?
CHORUS
O Rob-in, Rob-in Red-breast, O Rob-in, Rob-in dear, O
Rob-in sings so sweet - ly in the fall - ing of the year.

Cradle Song

KARL SIMROCK
Translated by Arthur Westbrook

JOHANNES BRAHMS

1. Lul-la - by and good night! With
2. Lul-la - by and good night! Those
ro - ses be - dight,— Creep in - to thy bed, There pil - low thy
blue eyes close tight,— Bright an-gels are near, So sleep with-out
head If God will thou shalt wake, When the morn - ing doth
fear. They will guard thee from harm, With fair dream-land's sweet
break, If God will thou shalt wake, When the morn-ing doth break.
charm, They will guard thee from harm, With fair dream-land's sweet charm.

Singing In The Rain
ELIZABETH AKERS ALLEN
FRANZ JOSEPH HAYD
1.Where the elm-tree branches By the rain are stirr'd,Careless of the show-er
2.From their heavy frin-ges, Pour their drops a-main, Still the bird is sing-ing
3.Cheerful summer prophet! List'ning to thy song, How my faint ing spir-it
Swings a lit-tle bird: Clouds may frown and darken,Drops may fall in vain,
Sing-ing in the rain. O thou hope-ful sing-er, Whom my faith perceives
Grow-eth glad and strong. Let the black clouds gather, Let the sunshine wane,
Lit-tle heeds the warbler Sing-ing in the rain. Dimmer fall the shad-ows,
To a dove transfigured, Bring-ing ol-ive leaves; Ol-ive leaves of prom-ise,
If I may but join thee, Sing-ing in the rain. Let the black clouds gather,
Mist-ier grows the air, Still the black clouds gather, Dark'ning here and there.
Types of joy to be; How in doubt and tri-al Learns my heart of thee.
Let the sunshine wane, If I may but join thee, Sing-ing in the rain.
Good Morning To You
PATTI S. HILL
MILDRED HIL
Brightly
Good morn-ing to you, Good morn-ing to you,

Good Morning To You—Continued

Good - morn - ing, dear chil - dren, Good - morn - ing to all.
Used by permission. Copyright by Clayton F. Summy Co.
Waiting To Grow
WALTER H. AIKEN
1. Lit - tle white snow-drop, just wak - ing up, Vi - o - let, dai - sy and sweet but - ter - cup; Un - der the leaves and the ice and the snow, Wait - ing, wait - ing, Wait - ing to grow.
2. Think what a host of queer lit - tle seeds, Of flow-ers and mos - ses and ferns and weeds Are un - der the leaves and the ice and the snow, Wait - ing, wait - ing, Wait - ing to grow.

Twinkle, Little Star

JANE TAYLOR
Not too slowly
1. Twin-kle, twin-kle, lit - tle star; How I won-der what you are,
2. When the blaz-ing sun is gone, When he noth-ing shines up - on,
3. Then the trav'ller in the dark Thanks you for your ti - ny spark;
4. In the dark blue sky you keep, While you thro' my win - dow peep,
Up a - bove the world so high, Like a dia-mond in the sky!
Then you show your lit - tle light, Twin-kle, twin-kle all the night.
He could not see where to go, If you did not twinkle so.
And you nev - er shut your eye, Till the sun is in the sky.
Twin-kle, twin-kle, lit - tle star, How I won-der what you are.
A Little Man
FOLK SONG
sung in Hansel and Gretel
HUMPERDINCK
Moderately quick
mf
A ti-ny lit-tle man stands in for - est dim, A cunning lit-tle
man-tle he wears on him, Who can this fig-ure be, stand-ing 'neath a
ritard
for-est tree, With the man-tle hang-ing down to his knee?

85
I Will Sing A Lullaby
17th Century
ENGLISH CRADLE SONG
Somewhat slowly
p
1. Gold-en slumbers kiss your eyes, Smiles awake you when you rise; Sleep, pretty lov'd ones,
2. Care is heav-y, there-fore sleep, Mother here safe watch will keep; Sleep, pretty lov'd ones,
do not cry, And I will sing a lul-la-by,
do not cry, And I will sing a lul-la-by,
p
Lul-la-by, lul-la-by, lul - la - by.
The Cuckoo
GERMAN FOLK SONG
1. Cuck - oo, cuck - oo, wel-come thy song! Win - ter is go - ing,
2. Cuck - oo, cuck - oo, war - ble a - way; Bring the sweet flow - ers,
Soft breez - es blow - ing, Spring time, spring time, soon will be here.
Sun - shine and show - ers, Spring time, spring time, do not de - lay.
Hop, Hop, Hop!
GERMAN FOLK SONG
1. Hop, hop, hop! Nim-ble as a top, Where 'tis smooth and where 'tis stony,
2. Whoa, whoa, whoa! How like fun you go! Ver - y well, my lit - tle po - ny,
3. Here, here, here! Yes, my po - ny dear; Now with oats and hay I'll treat you,
Trudge a-long, my lit - tle po - ny, Hop, hop, hop, hop, hop! Nim - ble as a top.
Safe's our jaunt tho' rough and stony, Spare, spare, spare, spare, spare! Sure enough we're there.
And with smiles will ev - er greet you, Po - ny, po - ny dear! Yes my po - ny dear.

Lightly Row

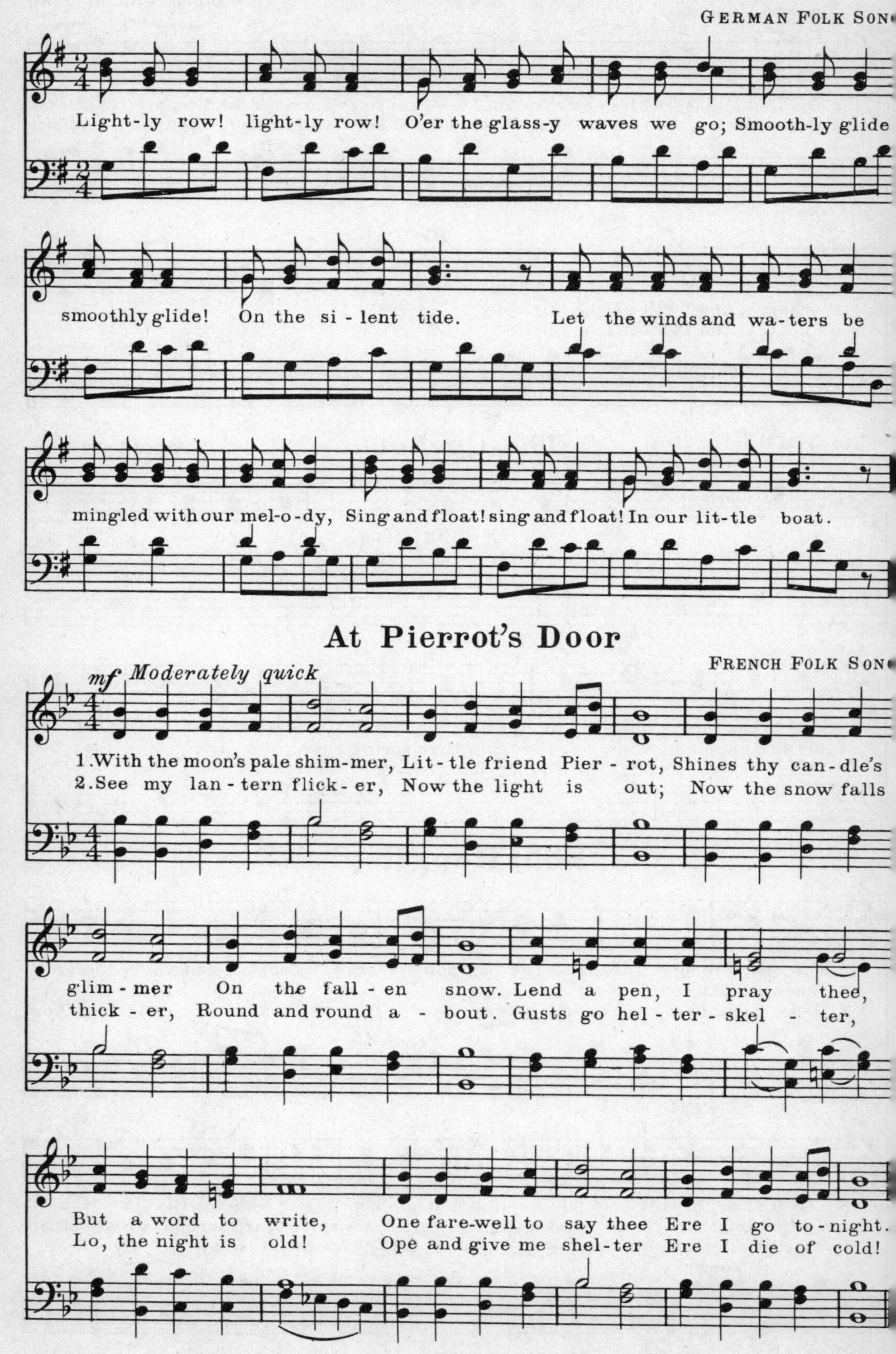
GERMAN FOLK SONG
Light-ly row! light-ly row! O'er the glass-y waves we go; Smooth-ly glide
smoothly glide! On the si - lent tide.
Let the winds and wa-ters be
mingled with our mel-o-dy, Sing and float! sing and float! In our lit-tle boat.
At Pierrot's Door
FRENCH FOLK SONG
mf Moderately quick
1.With the moon's pale shim-mer, Lit-tle friend Pier-rot, Shines thy can-dle's
2.See my lan-tern flick-er, Now the light is out; Now the snow falls
glim-mer On the fall-en snow. Lend a pen, I pray thee,
thick-er, Round and round a-bout. Gusts go hel-ter-skel-ter,
But a word to write, One fare-well to say thee Ere I go to-night.
Lo, the night is old! Ope and give me shel-ter Ere I die of cold!

When I Was A Lady

Waltz time

ENGLISH SINGING GAME

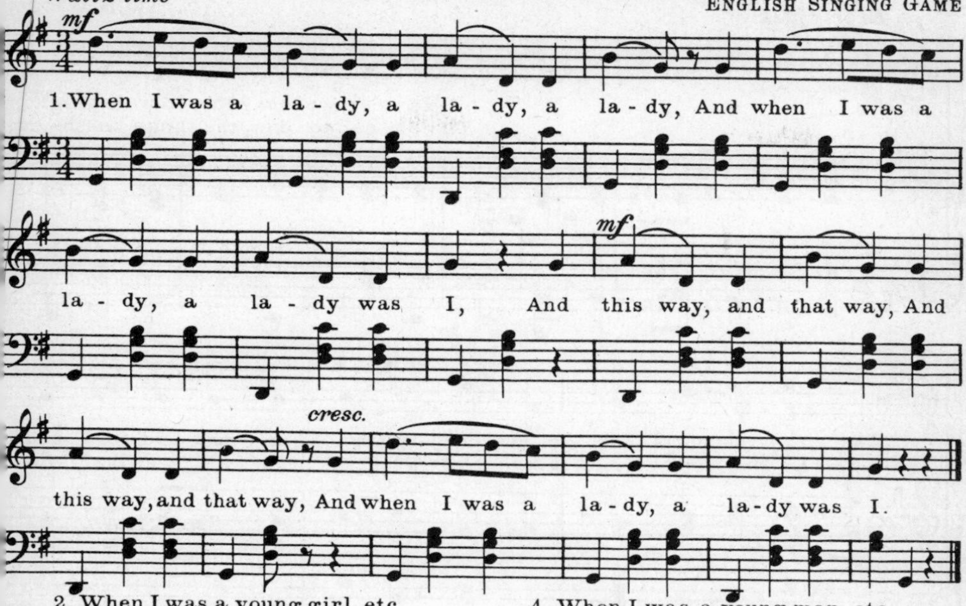

mf

1. When I was a la - dy, a la - dy, a la - dy, And when I was a la - dy, a la - dy was I, *mf* And this way, and that way, And this way, and that way, *cresc.* And when I was a la - dy, a la - dy was I.

2. When I was a young girl, etc.
3. When I was a dancer, etc.
4. When I was a young man, etc.
5. When I was a soldier, etc.

For this motion song a leader is chosen who, while the first verse is being sung, imitates the actions of a lady, curtseying first to the left then to the right. Another leader is chosen for each of the characters in the other verses. The other children imitate the motions of the leader.

Susy, Little Susy

TRANSLATION

FOLK SONG
sung in Hansel and Gretel
HUMPERDINCK

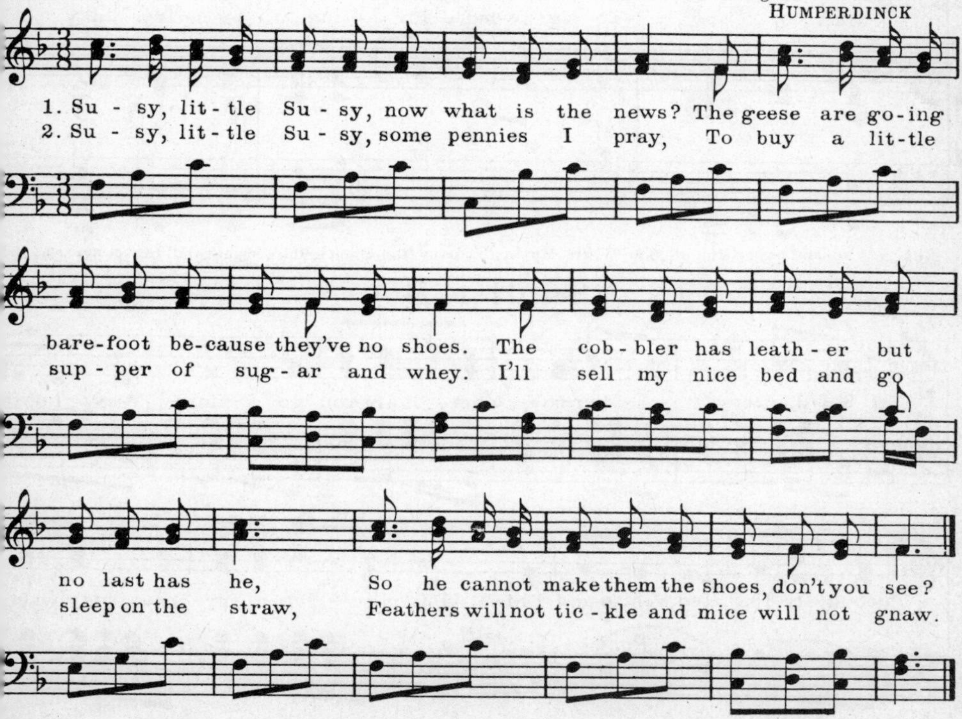

1. Su - sy, lit - tle Su - sy, now what is the news? The geese are go - ing bare-foot be-cause they've no shoes. The cob - bler has leath - er but no last has he, So he cannot make them the shoes, don't you see?
2. Su - sy, lit - tle Su - sy, some pennies I pray, To buy a lit - tle sup - per of sug - ar and whey. I'll sell my nice bed and go sleep on the straw, Feathers will not tic - kle and mice will not gnaw.

Morning Prayer

K. D. WIGGIN[S]

Reverently

1. Fa-ther, we thank Thee for the night, And for the pleas-ant morn-ing light; For rest and food and lov-ing care, And all that makes the world so fair.
2. Help us to do the things we should; To be to oth-ers kind and good; In all we do, in work or play, To grow more lov-ing ev-'ry day.

Soldier Boy

Quickly
f
1. Sol-dier boy, sol-dier boy, where are you go-ing, Wav-ing so
proud-ly the Red, White and Blue? I'm go-ing to my coun-try where

Soldier Boy—Continued
cresc.
du - ty is call - ing, If you'll be a sol-dier boy, you may come too.
The Robin
WALTER H. AIKEN
1. Dear lit-tle rob-in perch'd up in a tree, Chirp - ing and hop-ping so
2. Ver - y well, rob-in, since you will not play, I shall not with you one
hap-py and free; Come in, dear rob-in, and play with me! Rob - in!
moment more stay; Rude lit-tle rob-in, pray, hear what I say! Rob - in!
rob - in! play with me; Rob - in! rob - in! play with me.
rob - in! rob-in, good-day; Rob - in! rob - in! rob - in, good - day!

January and February
JANE B. WALTERS
GERMAN FOLK SONG
1. When Jan u-ar-y days are here, The air is crisp, the sky is clear, Come join our outdoor
2. When Feb-ru-ary north winds blow, Lake, h'll and road are heaped with snow, Come join our in-door
plays, Come join our out-door plays. For o'er the ice we're glid - ing, Or
plays, Come join our in-door plays. Like lit-tle gob-lins hop-ping The
down the hill we're sliding, Or in a bob-sled rid-ing In Jan-u-ar-y days.
feath-ery corn is popping In salt-y pan soon dropping, In Feb-ru-ar-y days.
'Tis Springtime
JANE B. WALTERS
SÜSSMAYER
1. 'Tis spring time, 'tis spring time, Cold win-ter is past; Warm breez-es are
2. 'Tis spring time, 'tis spring time, All na-ture's re-born; Shy flow-ers, fresh
blow-ing And May's here at last; The birds are re-turn-ing, Their
grass-es The hill-sides a-dorn; The or-chards and wood-lands With
songs fill the air; And mea-dows are smil-ing With blossoms so fair.
col-ors are gay, The glad earth re-joic-es Through all the bright day.

Farewell To Summer

JANE B. WALTERS — SWABIAN FOLK SONG

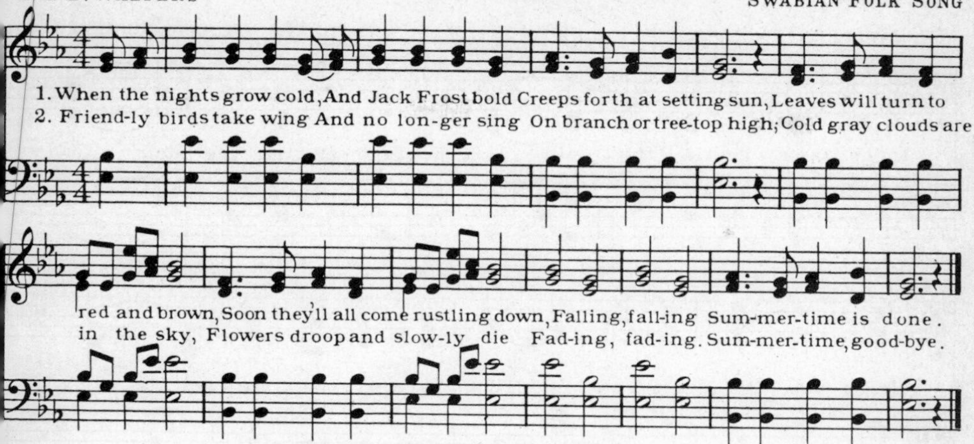

1. When the nights grow cold, And Jack Frost bold Creeps forth at setting sun, Leaves will turn to red and brown, Soon they'll all come rustling down, Falling, fall-ing Sum-mer-time is done.
2. Friend-ly birds take wing And no lon-ger sing On branch or tree-top high; Cold gray clouds are in the sky, Flowers droop and slow-ly die Fad-ing, fad-ing. Sum-mer-time, good-bye.

The Birds' Return

JANE B. WALTERS — BOHEMIAN FOLK SONG

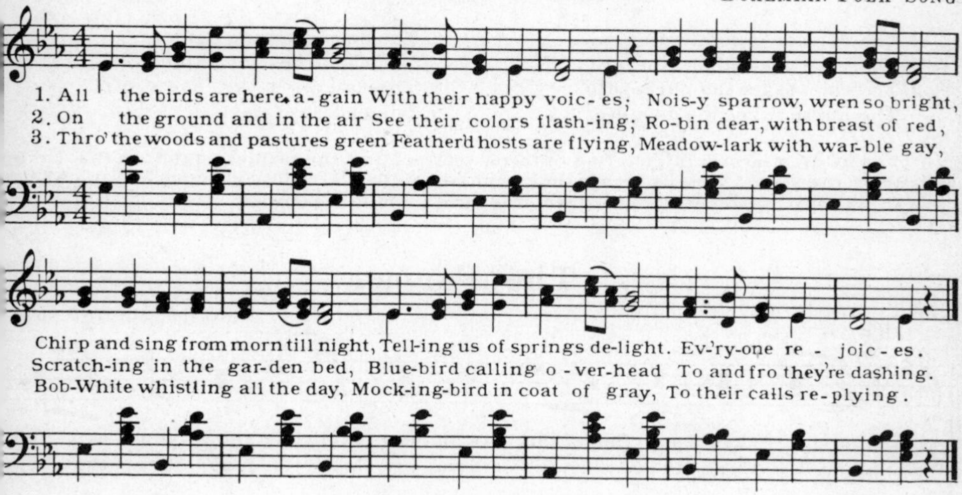

1. All the birds are here a-gain With their happy voic-es; Nois-y sparrow, wren so bright, Chirp and sing from morn till night, Tell-ing us of springs de-light. Ev-'ry-one re-joic-es.
2. On the ground and in the air See their colors flash-ing; Ro-bin dear, with breast of red, Scratch-ing in the gar-den bed, Blue-bird calling o-ver-head To and fro they're dashing.
3. Thro' the woods and pastures green Featherd hosts are flying, Meadow-lark with war-ble gay, Bob-White whistling all the day, Mock-ing-bird in coat of gray, To their calls re-plying.

Slumber Song

TRANSLATION — FRANZ SCHUBERT

1. Slum-ber, slum-ber, ten-der lit-tle flower, Mother's loving care doth around thee twine; Sweet and rest-ful be this hour— Sooth-ing fall this lull-a-by of mine.
2. Slum-ber, slum-ber, lit-tle fad-ed flower, Still doth mother's love around thee glow; Strong-er is it than earth-ly pow'r Guarding thee where e'er thy spir-it go.

The Farmer In The Dell

ENGLISH SINGING GAME

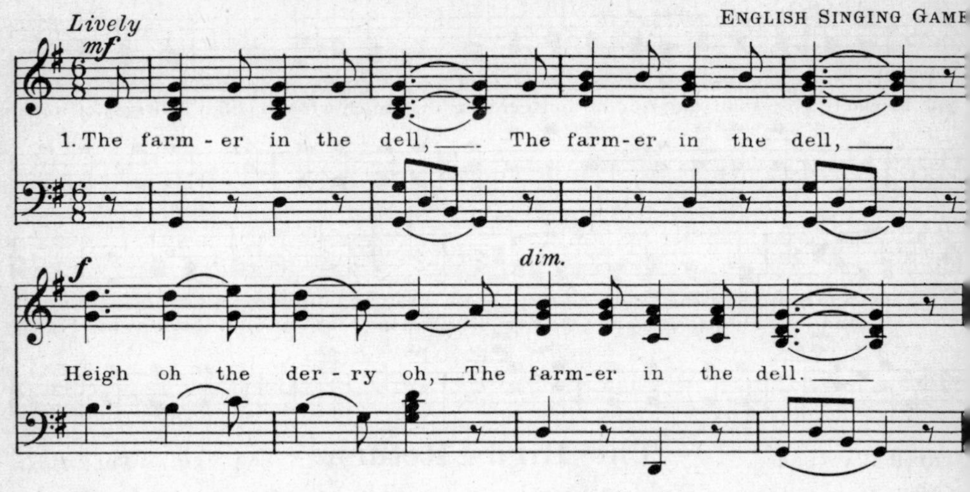
Lively
mf
1. The farm - er in the dell, ___ The farm - er in the dell, ___
f
dim.
Heigh oh the der - ry oh, ___ The farm - er in the dell. ___

2. The farmer takes a wife, etc.
3. The wife takes the child, etc.
4. The child takes the nurse, etc.
5. The nurse takes the dog, etc.
6. The dog takes the cat, etc.
7. The cat takes the rat, etc.
8. The rat takes the cheese, etc.
9. The cheese stands alone, etc.

The children form a circle. One of them, representing the farmer, stands in the center and while the second verse is being sung, chooses "a wife." This one chooses "the child" and so on until "the cheese" is selected when the game is repeated.

The Farmer

ENGLISH SINGING GAME

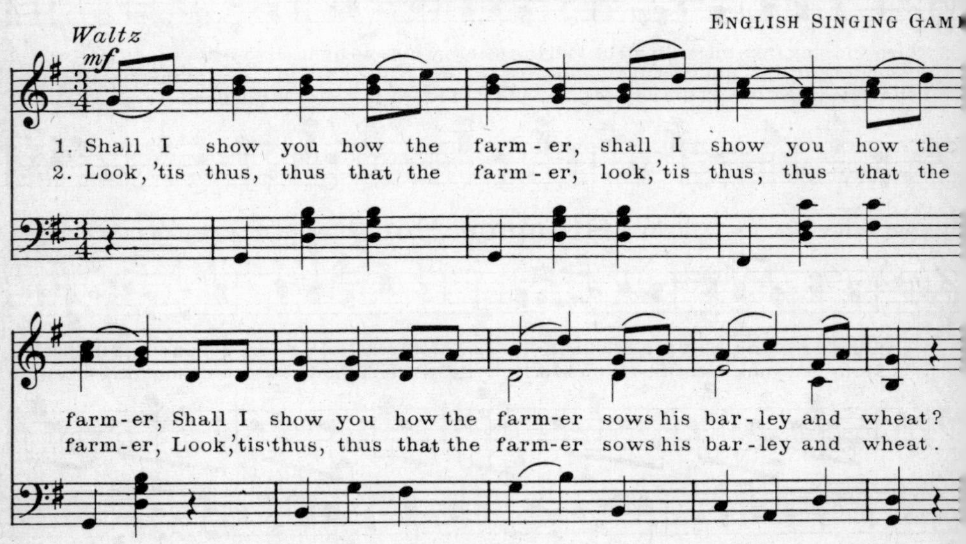
Waltz
mf
1. Shall I show you how the farm - er, shall I show you how the farm-er, Shall I show you how the farm-er sows his bar - ley and wheat?
2. Look, 'tis thus, thus that the farm - er, look, 'tis thus, thus that the farm-er, Look, 'tis thus, thus that the farm-er sows his bar - ley and wheat.

3. Shall I show you how the farmer, etc.
Reaps his barley and wheat.

4. Look 'tis thus, thus that the farmer, etc.
Reaps his barley and wheat.

5. Shall I show you how the farmer, etc.
Threshes barley and wheat.

6. Look 'tis thus, thus that the farmer, etc.
Threshes barley and wheat.

As this song is sung, the children imitate the farmer sowing, reaping and threshing his wheat.

The Farmyard

OLD LONDON FOLK SONG
Lively
mf
1. Up was I on fa - ther's farm On a May - day morn - ing
Feed-ing of my fa - ther's cows On a May - day morn - ing
2. Up was I on fa - ther's farm On a May - day morn - ing
Feed-ing of my fa - ther's goats On a May - day morn - ing
1 (Omit second time)
2
ear - ly, ear - ly. With a moo, moo here, and a moo, moo there,
ear - ly, ear - ly. With a nan, nan here, and a nan, nan there,
Here a moo, there a moo, here a pret-ty moo;
Here a nan, there a nan, here a pret-ty nan;
Six pret-ty maids, come
gang a-long o' me To the mer-ry green fields and the farm - yard.

This song may be continued by using the names of other animals and the sounds they make as sheep (baa-baa),
cks (quack - quack)

A Capital Ship

Spirited
OLD ENGLISH FOLK SON
1. A cap-i-tal ship for an o - cean trip Was the Walloping Win-dow Blind! No
2. The bo'-swain's mate was ver-y se-date, Yet fond of a-muse-ment too; He
3. The cap-tain sat on the commodore's hat, And dined in a roy - al way, Off
4. All nau-ti-cal pride we laid a-side, And we ran the ves-sel a - shore On the
5. On Rug - bug bark, from morn till dark, We dined till we all had grown Un -
wind that blew dis - mayed her crew, Or trou-bled the cap - tain's mind The
play'd hop-scotch with the starboard watch, While the captain tickled the crew And the
toast- ed pigs and pickles and figs, And gun-ner-y bread each day And the
Gul-i-by Isles where the Poo-poo smiles, And the rub - bly Up - dugs roar And we
commonly shrunk, when a Chinese junk Came up from the Tor-ri-bly zone She wa
man at the wheel was made to feel Con - tempt for the wild-est blow-ow-ow, Tho' it
gun-ner we had was ap-par-ent-ly mad, For he sat on the aft-er rai-ai-ail, And
cook was Dutch and be-haved as such, For the di - et he gave the crew-ew-ew, Was a
sat on the edge of a sand - y ledge And shot at the whistling bee-ee-ee; And the
chubby and square, but we didn't much care, So we cheer-i-ly put out to sea-ea-ea; And we
of - ten ap-peared, when the gale had clear'd, That he'd been in his bunk be - low.
fired sa - lutes with the cap - tain's boots, In the teeth of the boom-ing gale!
number of tons of hot cross buns Served up with sug-ar and glue.
cin-na-mon bats wore wa-ter proof hats As they dipped in the shin - y sea.
left all the crew of the junk to chew On the bark of the Rug - bug tree.

A Capital Ship—Continued

CHORUS

Then blow, ye winds, heigh ho! A-rov-ing I will go! I'll stay no more on Eng-land's shore, So let the mu-sic play-ay-ay! I'm off for the morn-ing train! I'll cross the raging main! I'm off to my love with a box-ing glove, Ten thousand miles a-way!

Swing Low, Sweet Chariot

NEGRO "SPIRITUAL"

hm ——— Swing low sweet chariot,

CHORUS Com-in' fo' to car-ry me home;

LEADER Swing low sweet chariot, hm ——— hm ———

CHORUS Com-in' fo' to car-ry me home. *Fine.*

LEADER
1. I looked o-ver Jordan and what did I see,
2. If you get there be - fore, I do,
3. The brightest day that ev-er I saw,
4. I'm some-times up and some-times down,

CHORUS Comin' fo' to car-ry me home,

LEADER
A band of angels com-in' after me,
Tell all my friends I'm com - in' too,
When Jesus wash'd my sins a - way,
But still my soul feels heav'n-ly bound,

CHORUS Comin' fo' to car-ry me home.

TRANSLATION
The Little Dustman
FOLK SONG
OF THE NETHERLANI
Arr. by JOHANNES BRAHM
Moderately quick
1. The flow'rets all sleep sound-ly Beneath the moon's bright ray; They nod their heads t
2. Now see, the lit-tle dust-man At the window shows his head And looks for an-y
geth - er And dream the night away. The rust'ling trees wave to and fro, And murmur soft
chil-dren Who ought to be in bed; And as each weary one he spies, Throws dust into hi
p
low. Sleep on, sleep on, Sleep on, my lit-tle one.
eyes. Sleep on, sleep on, Sleep on, my lit-tle one.
1
2
Adapted by
JANE B. WALTERS
The Patriots
THURINGIAN FOLK SON
1. 'Tis here we are pledging with heart and with hand, Full measure of de - vo-tion to
2. Now all join the cho - rus, let u - nion a - bide, The flag is waving o'er us for
3. O star-ry Old Glo - ry of red, white and blue! We love thy honored sto-ry; to
thee, our na-tive land; Full measure of de - vo - tion to thee, our na-tive land.
which our fa-thers died; The flag is waving o'er us for which our fa-thers died.
thee we'll e'er be true; We love thy honored sto - ry; to thee we'll e'er be true.

I Ain't Gwine Study War No More
NEGRO "SPIRITUAL"
LEADER
Down
Down!
1. Gwine to lay down my bur - den, Down by the riverside, Down by the river side, Down by the
2. Gwine to lay down my sword an' shiel', Down by the riverside, Down by the river side, Down by the
3. Gwine to try on my long white robe Down by the riverside, Down by the river side, Down by the
4. Gwine to try on my star - ry crown, Down by the riverside, Down by the river side, Down by the
LEADER
Down!
riv-er side; Gwine to lay down my bur - den, Down by the river side, to study war no more.
riv-er side; Gwine to lay down my sword an' shiel' Down by the river side, to study war no more
riv-er side; Gwine to try on my long white robe, Down by the river side, to study war no more.
riv-er side; Gwine to try on my star-ry crown, Down by the river side, to study war no more.
I ain't gwine study war no more, Ain't gwine study war no more, Ain't gwine study war no more,
study war no more,
Ain't gwine study war no more, Ain't gwine study war no more, Ain't gwine study war no more!
no more!
Go Down, Moses
NEGRO "SPIRITUAL"
LEADER
CHORUS
LEADER
CHORUS
1. When Israel was in Egypt's land, Let my people go! Oppress'd so hard they could not stand, Let my people
2. Thus saith the Lord, bold Moses said, Let my people go! If not I'll smite your first born dead, Let my people
go! Go down, Moses, Way down in Egypt's land; Tell old Pharoah, Let my peo-ple go!
go! Go down, Moses, Way down in Egypt's land; Tell old Pharoah, Let my peo-ple go!

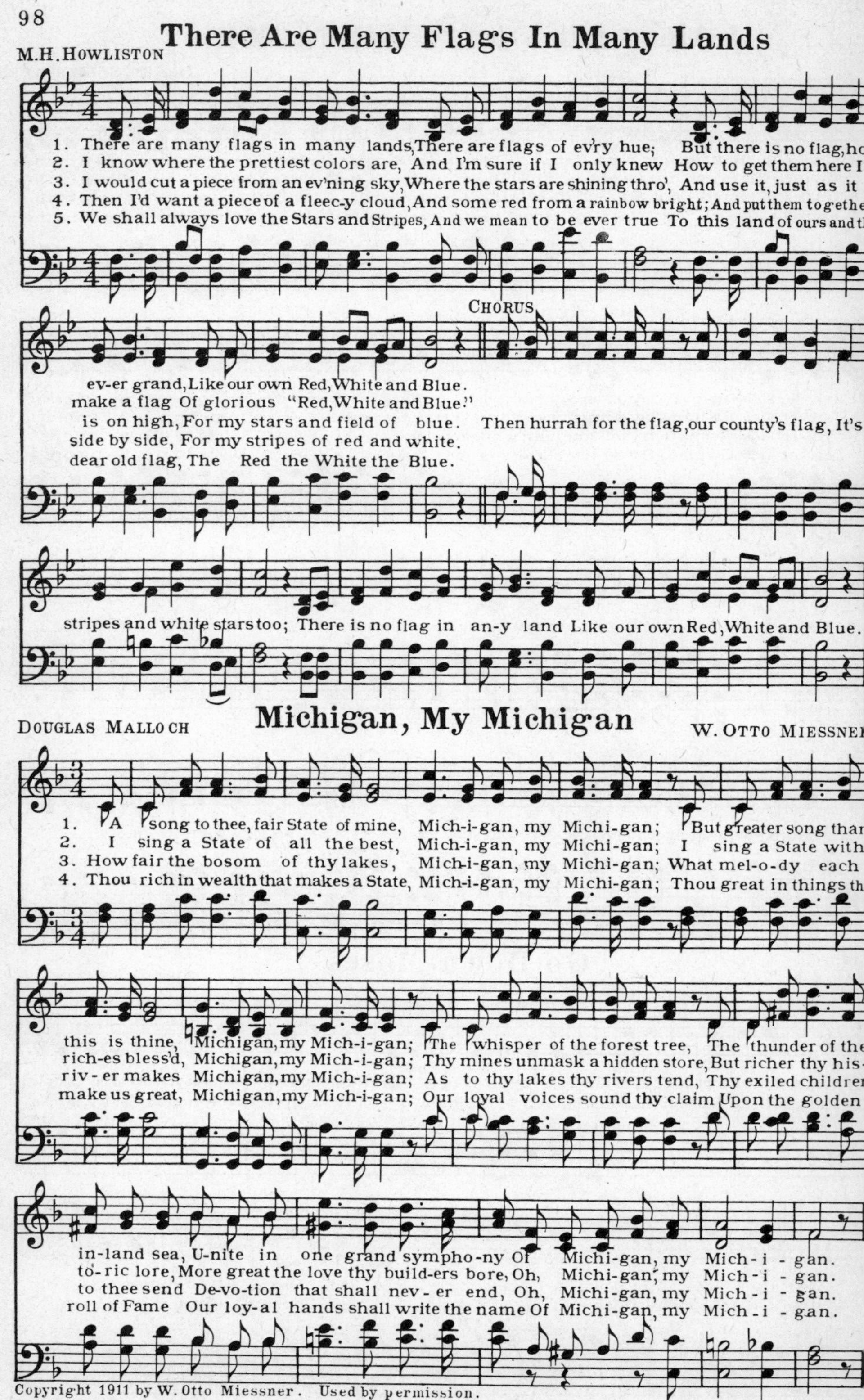
There Are Many Flags In Many Lands
M.H. HOWLISTON
1. There are many flags in many lands, There are flags of ev'ry hue; But there is no flag, ho
2. I know where the prettiest colors are, And I'm sure if I only knew How to get them here I
3. I would cut a piece from an ev'ning sky, Where the stars are shining thro', And use it, just as it
4. Then I'd want a piece of a fleec-y cloud, And some red from a rainbow bright; And put them to-gethe
5. We shall always love the Stars and Stripes, And we mean to be ever true To this land of ours and t
ev-er grand, Like our own Red, White and Blue.
make a flag Of glorious "Red, White and Blue."
is on high, For my stars and field of blue.
side by side, For my stripes of red and white.
dear old flag, The Red the White the Blue.
CHORUS
Then hurrah for the flag, our county's flag, It's
stripes and white stars too; There is no flag in an-y land Like our own Red, White and Blue.
Michigan, My Michigan
DOUGLAS MALLOCH
W. OTTO MIESSNE
1. A song to thee, fair State of mine, Mich-i-gan, my Michi-gan; But greater song thar
2. I sing a State of all the best, Mich-i-gan, my Michi-gan; I sing a State with
3. How fair the bosom of thy lakes, Mich-i-gan, my Michi-gan; What mel-o-dy each
4. Thou rich in wealth that makes a State, Mich-i-gan, my Michi-gan; Thou great in things th
this is thine, Michigan, my Mich-i-gan; The whisper of the forest tree, The thunder of the
rich-es bless'd, Michigan, my Mich-i-gan; Thy mines unmask a hidden store, But richer thy his-
riv-er makes Michigan, my Mich-i-gan; As to thy lakes thy rivers tend, Thy exiled childre
make us great, Michigan, my Mich-i-gan; Our loyal voices sound thy claim Upon the golden
in-land sea, U-nite in one grand sympho-ny Of Michi-gan, my Mich-i-gan.
to-ric lore, More great the love thy build-ers bore, Oh, Michi-gan, my Mich-i-gan.
to thee send De-vo-tion that shall nev-er end, Oh, Michi-gan, my Mich-i-gan.
roll of Fame Our loy-al hands shall write the name Of Michi-gan, my Mich-i-gan.
Copyright 1911 by W. Otto Miessner. Used by permission.

Illinois

(May also be sung to tune "Baby Mine".)
C. H. CHAMBERLAIN
WALTER HOWE JONES
1. By thy rivers gen-tly flow-ing Il-li-nois, Il-li-nois, O'er thy prairies verdant grow-ing, Il-li-nois, Il-li-nois, Comes an ech-o on the breeze, Rus-tling thro' the leaf-y trees, And its mel-low tones are these, Il-li-nois, Il-li-nois.
2. From a wil-der-ness of prairies Il-li-nois, Il-li-nois, Straight thy way and never var-ies, Il-li-nois, Il-li-nois, Till up-on the in-land sea, Stands thy great commer-cial tree, Turn-ing all the world to thee, Il-li-nois, Il-li-nois.
3. Not with-out thy wondrous sto-ry Il-li-nois, Il-li-nois, Can be writ the nation's glo-ry, Il-li-nois, Il-li-nois; On the rec-ord of thy years, A-b'ram Lin-coln's name appears, Grant and Lo-gan, and our tears, Il-li-nois, Il-li-nois.
Copyright 1901 by Walter Howe Jones. Copyright 1914 by The U of I Supply Store Champaign, Ill.
Used by permission
Reuben and Rachel
MODIFIED BY N. H. H.
1. Reu-ben, Reu-ben, I've been think-ing, What a grand world this would be If the men were all trans-port-ed Far be-yond the North-ern Sea.
O! my goodness, gra-cious Ra-chel, What a queer world this would be If the men were all trans-port-ed Far be-yond the North-ern Sea.
2. Reu-ben, Reu-ben, I've been think-ing, What a gay life girls would lead, If they had no men a-bout them, None to tease them, none to heed.
Ra-chel, Ra-chel, I've been think-ing, Men would have a mer-ry time, If at once they were transport-ed Far be-yond the salt-y brine.
3. Reu-ben, Reu-ben, stop your teas-ing, If you've an-y love for me, I was on-ly just a-fool-ing, As I thought of course you'd see.
Ra-chel, if you'll not transport us, I will take you for my wife, And I'll split with you my mon-ey Ev-'ry pay-day of my life.

NOTE: Reuben and Rachel may be used as a duet number, the girls or women alternating with the boys or men through the several verses. The number may also be used effectively as a canon, in which case the first verse only would be used, the second part entering after the first part has sung two measures.

Marseillaise Hymn

(National Hymn of France)

R. DE L. ROUGET DE LISL

Lively march time
f
1. Ye sons of France, a-wake to glo - ry! Hark! hark! what myriads bid you
2. With lux-u - ry and pride sur-round - ed, The vile in - sa-tiate despots
3. O Lib-er - ty! can man re - sign thee, Once hav-ing felt thy gen'rous
mf
p
rise! Your children, wives, and grand-sires hoar-y, Behold their tears and hear their
dare, Their thirst for gold and pow'r un-bound-ed, To mete and vend the light and
flame? Can dungeons, bolts and bars con - fine thee? Or whips thy no-ble spir - it
cries! Be-hold their tears and hear their cries! Shall hateful ty-rants, mischief
air, To mete and vend the light and air. Like beasts of burden would they
tame? Or whips thy no - ble spir - it tame? Too long the world has wept be -
mf
breed-ing, With hireling hosts, a ruf-fian band, Af-fright and deso-late the
load us, Like gods would bid their slaves a-dore; But man is man, and who is
wail-ing That falsehood's dagger ty-rants wield; But free-dom is our sword an
ff
land, While peace and lib-er-ty lie bleed-ing?
more? Then shall they longer lash and goad us?
shield, And all their arts are un a - vail - ing.
To arms, to arms, ye brave! Th'a
veng-ing sword unsheathed! March on, march on! all hearts resolved on vic - to-ry or death.

The Maple Leaf Forever

A. L.
With spirit
ALEXANDER MUIR
1. In days of yore, from Britain's shore, Wolfe the dauntless he-ro came, And planted firm Bri-
2. At Queens-town Heights, and Lundy's Lane, Our brave fa-thers side by side, For freedom, homes, and
3. Our fair Do-min-ion now ex-tends From Cape Race to Nootka Sound, May peace for-ev-er
4. On Mer-ry Eng-land's far famed land May kind Heaven sweetly smile, God bless Old Scotland
tan-ia's flag, On Ca-na-da's fair do-main; Here may it wave, our boast and pride, And
loved ones dear, Firmly stood and no-bly died; And those dear rights which they maintain'd We
be our lot, And plen-teous store a-bound; And may those ties of love be ours, Which
ev-er-more, And Ire-land's Em-'rald Isle; Then swell the song both loud and long, Till
join in love to-geth-er, The This-tle, Shamrock, Rose entwine The Maple Leaf for-ev-er.
swear to yield them never, Our watch word ev-er-more shall be, The Maple Leaf for-ev-er
dis-cord can-not sever, And flour-ish green o'er Freedom's home, The Maple Leaf for-ev-er.
rocks and for-est quiv-er, God save our King, and Heaven bless The Maple Leaf for-ev-er
CHORUS
mf
The Ma-ple Leaf our em-blem dear, The Ma-ple Leaf for-ev-er, God
f
save our King and Heav-en bless The Ma-ple Leaf for-ev-er.

March Of The Men Of Harlech

Welsh Poem translated
by William Duthie

Harmonized
by Joseph Barnb
WELSH AI

mf March time
1. Men of Har-lech! hon-or calls us, No proud Saxon e'er ap-palls us!
2. Tho' our mothers may be weep-ing, Tho' our sisters may be keep-ing
rit.
On we march! whate'er befalls us, Nev-er shall we fly! Forward, lightly
Watch for some who now are sleeping On the bat-tle-field, Still the trumpet'
cresc.
bound-ing, To the trumpet's sounding; Forward ev-er, backward, ne'er, The
bray-ing Sounds on, ev-er say-ing, Let each bow-man pierce a foe, And
haughty foe as-tound-ing; Fight for father, sis-ter, mother, Each is bound to
nev-er stop the slay-ing, Till in-vaders learn to fear us, And no Saxon
ff
each as brother; And with faith in one an-oth-er, We will win or die!
lin-ger near us; Men of Wales! our God doth hear us, Never will we yield!
Dip, Boys, Dip The Oar
F. SARONA
1. 'Tis moon-light on the sea, boys, Our boat is on the strand; She
2. The zeph-yrs woo the spray, boys, Their laughter fills the air; We'll
3. What tho' the dark rocks frown, boys, Their home is on the shore; When

Dip, Boys, Dip The Oar—Continued

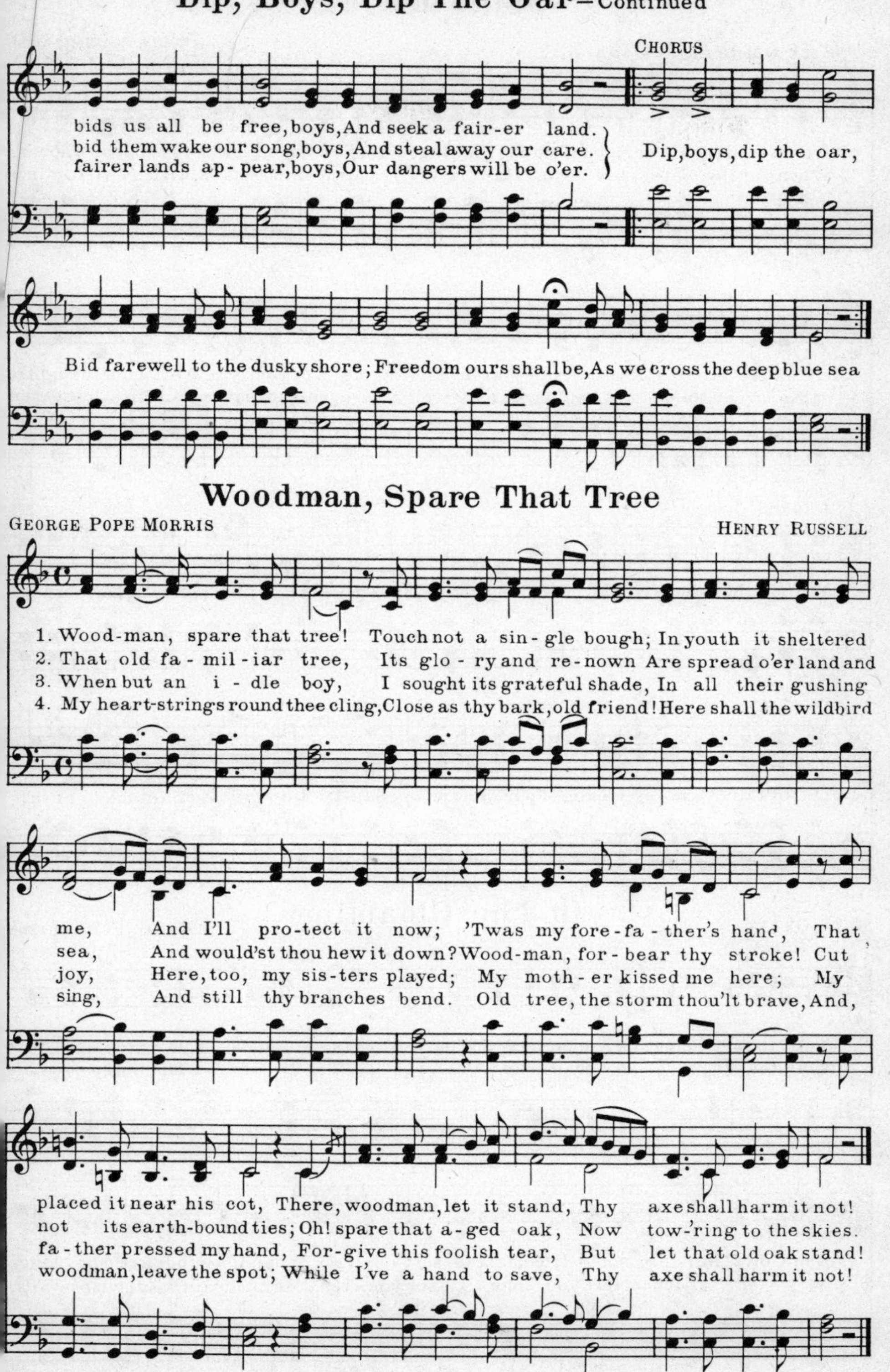
CHORUS
bids us all be free, boys, And seek a fair-er land.
bid them wake our song, boys, And steal away our care.
fairer lands ap-pear, boys, Our dangers will be o'er.
Dip, boys, dip the oar,
Bid farewell to the dusky shore; Freedom ours shall be, As we cross the deep blue sea
Woodman, Spare That Tree
GEORGE POPE MORRIS
HENRY RUSSELL
1. Wood-man, spare that tree! Touch not a sin-gle bough; In youth it sheltered
2. That old fa-mil-iar tree, Its glo-ry and re-nown Are spread o'er land and
3. When but an i-dle boy, I sought its grateful shade, In all their gushing
4. My heart-strings round thee cling, Close as thy bark, old friend! Here shall the wildbird
me, And I'll pro-tect it now; 'Twas my fore-fa-ther's hand, That
sea, And would'st thou hew it down? Wood-man, for-bear thy stroke! Cut
joy, Here, too, my sis-ters played; My moth-er kissed me here; My
sing, And still thy branches bend. Old tree, the storm thou'lt brave, And,
placed it near his cot, There, woodman, let it stand, Thy axe shall harm it not!
not its earth-bound ties; Oh! spare that a-ged oak, Now tow'ring to the skies.
fa-ther pressed my hand, For-give this foolish tear, But let that old oak stand!
woodman, leave the spot; While I've a hand to save, Thy axe shall harm it not!

Santa Lucia

With swinging motion
NEAPOLITAN BOAT SONG
1. Now 'neath the silver moon Ocean is glowing, O'er the calm bil-low Soft winds are blowing
2. When o'er thy waters Light winds are playing, Thy spell can soothe us, All care al-lay-ing;
Here balmy breezes blow, Pure joys invite us, And as we gently row, All things delight us
To thee, sweet Na-po-li, What charms are given, Where smiles creation, Toil blest by heaven
CHORUS
Hark, how the sailor's cry Joyous-ly echoes nigh: San-ta Lu-ci-a! Santa Lu-ci-a,
Home of fair Po-e-sy, Realm of pure Harmony, San-ta Lu-ci-a! Santa Lu-ci-a!
In The Gloaming
META ORRED
ANNIE F HARRISON
Slowly
1. In the gloaming oh, my darling! when the lights are dim and low, And the qui-et
2. In the gloaming oh, my darling! think not bit-ter-ly of me! Though I passed a-
shad-ows, fall-ing, soft-ly come and soft-ly go, When the winds are sob-bing
way in si-lence, left you lone-ly, set you free, For my heart was crushed with

faintly with a gen-tle, unknown woe, Will you think of me and love me, As you did once
longing; what had been could never be. It was best to leave you thus, dear, Best for you and
1
2
rall
cresc.
long a - go?
best for me. It was best to leave you thus, Best for you and best for me.
Last Night The Nightingale Woke Me
Moderately
HALFDAN KJERULF
1. Last night the night-in-gale woke me, Last night when all was still; It
2. I think of you in the day-time, I dream of you by night, I
3. O think not I can for-get you; I could not tho' I would. I
sang in the gold - en moon-light, From out the wood-land hill, I
wake, and would you were here, love, And tears are blinding my sight, I
see you in all a - round me, The stream, the night, the wood, The
o - pened my win-dow so gent - ly, I looked on the dreaming dew, And
hear a low breath in the lime - tree, The wind is float-ing thro' And
flow-ers that slum-ber so gent - ly, The stars a - bove the blue, O
oh, the bird, my dar-ling, Was sing-ing, sing-ing of you, of you.
oh, the night, my dar-ling, Is sigh-ing, sigh-ing for you, for you.
heav'n it - self, my dar-ling, Is pray-ing, pray-ing for you, for you.

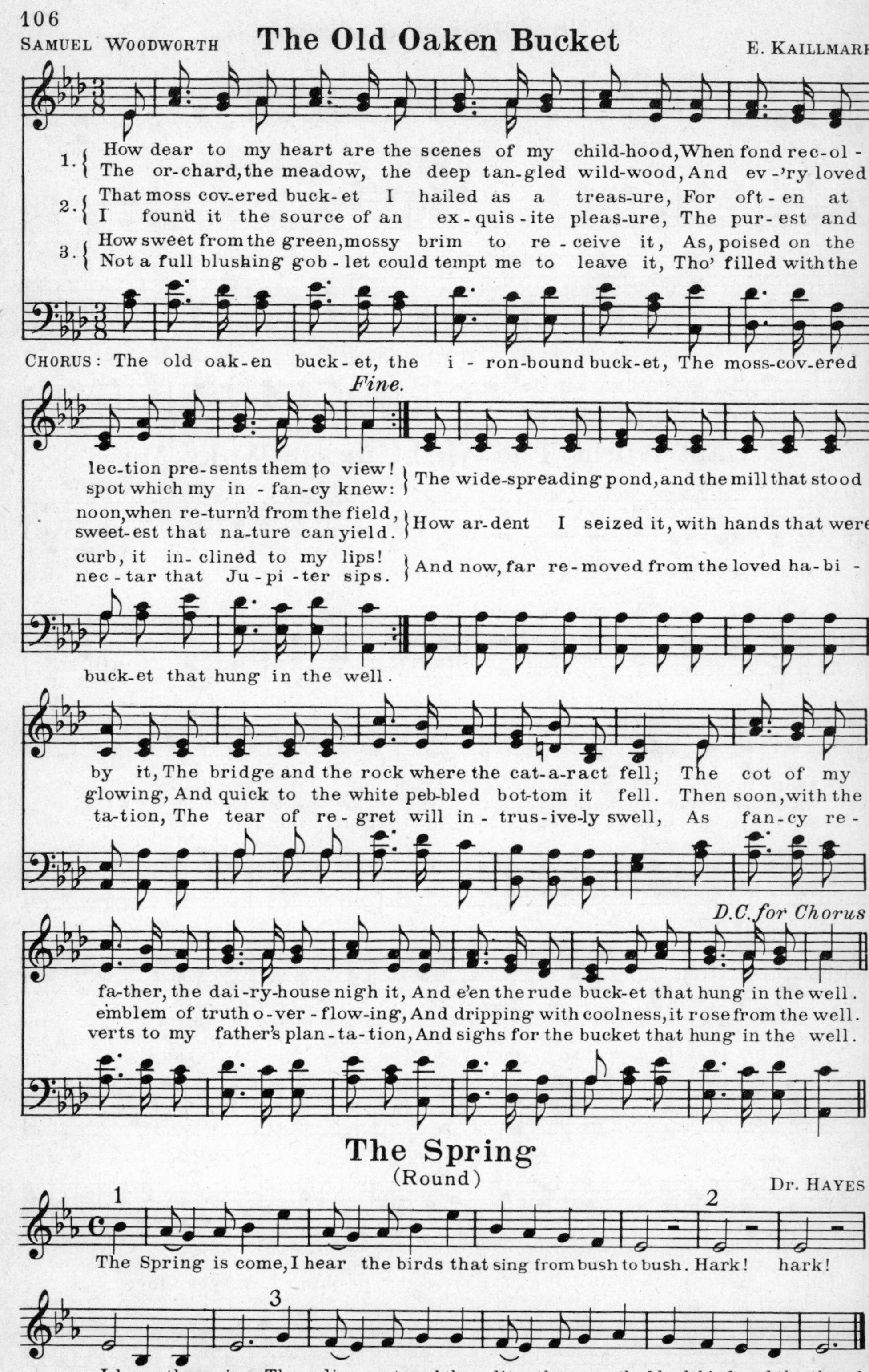
SAMUEL WOODWORTH
The Old Oaken Bucket
E. KAILLMARK
1. How dear to my heart are the scenes of my child-hood, When fond rec-ol -
The or-chard, the meadow, the deep tan-gled wild-wood, And ev-'ry loved
2. That moss cov-ered buck-et I hailed as a treas-ure, For oft-en at
I found it the source of an ex-quis-ite pleas-ure, The pur-est and
3. How sweet from the green, mossy brim to re-ceive it, As, poised on the
Not a full blushing gob-let could tempt me to leave it, Tho' filled with the
CHORUS: The old oak-en buck-et, the i-ron-bound buck-et, The moss-cov-ered
Fine.
lec-tion pre-sents them to view!
spot which my in-fan-cy knew:
The wide-spreading pond, and the mill that stood
noon, when re-turn'd from the field,
sweet-est that na-ture can yield.
How ar-dent I seized it, with hands that were
curb, it in-clined to my lips!
nec-tar that Ju-pi-ter sips.
And now, far re-moved from the loved ha-bi -
buck-et that hung in the well.
by it, The bridge and the rock where the cat-a-ract fell; The cot of my
glowing, And quick to the white peb-bled bot-tom it fell. Then soon, with the
ta-tion, The tear of re-gret will in-trus-ive-ly swell, As fan-cy re -
D.C. for Chorus
fa-ther, the dai-ry-house nigh it, And e'en the rude buck-et that hung in the well.
emblem of truth o-ver-flow-ing, And dripping with coolness, it rose from the well.
verts to my father's plan-ta-tion, And sighs for the bucket that hung in the well.
The Spring
(Round)
Dr. HAYES
1
2
The Spring is come, I hear the birds that sing from bush to bush. Hark! hark!
3
I hear them sing. The lin-net and the lit-tle wren, the black bird and the thrush

Those Evening Bells
THOMAS MOORE
Moderately
Fine.
1. Those evening bells! those eve-ning bells! How man-y a tale their mu-sic tells,
2. Those joy-ous hours have passed a-way; And man-y a heart that then was gay,
3. And so 'twill be when I am gone, That tune-ful peal will still ring on,
D.C.
Of youth and home, and that sweet time When last I heard their soothing chime.
With-in the tomb now dark-ly dwells, And hears no more those evening bells.
While oth-er bards shall walk these dells, And sing your praise, sweet evening bells.
When The Swallows Homeward Fly
CARL HERLOSSOHN
FRANZ ABT
1. When the swallows homeward fly, When the ro - ses scatter'd lie, When from
2. When the white swan southward roves, To seek at noon the orange groves, When the
3. Hush, my heart! why thus complain? Thou must, too, thy woes contain, Tho' on
nei-ther hill nor dale Chants the sil-v'ry nightingale; In these words my bleeding
red tints of the west Prove the sun has gone to rest; In these words my bleeding
earth no more we rove, Loud-ly breathing words of love; Thou, my heart, must find re-
heart Would to thee its grief im-part, When I thus thy im - age lose,
heart Would to thee its grief im-part, When I thus thy im - age lose,
lief, Yield-ing to these words belief; I shall see thy form a - gain,
Can I, ah, can I e'er know re-pose, Can I ah, can I e'er know repose?
Can I, ah, can I e'er know re-pose, Can I ah, can I e'er know repose?
Though to-day we part a-gain, Though to - day we part a - gain.

Go To Sleep, Lena Darling

(Emmet's Lullaby)

J.K.E.
J. K. EMMET
1. Close your eyes, Le - na, my darling, While I sing your lul-la - by; Fear thou no danger, Le-na, Move not, dear Le - na, my darling, For your brother watches nigh you, Lena dear. Angels guide thee, Le-na dear, my darling, Noth-ing e - vil can come near; Brightest flowers blow for thee, Darling ba-by dear to me.
2. Bright be the morn-ing, my darling, When you ope your eyes Sunbeams glow all 'round you, Le-na, Peace be with thee, love, my darling, Blue and cloudless be the sky for Lena dear. Birds sing their bright songs for thee, my darling, Full of sweetest mel - o - dy; An-gels ev - er hov-er near, Darling ba-by dear to me.
CHORUS
Go to sleep, go to sleep, my ba - by, my ba - by, my ba - by, Go to sleep, my ba-by, ba - by, oh, bye, Go to sleep, Le-na sleep.

The Loreley

HEINRICH HEINE
FRIEDRICH SILCHER
With a moderately quick motion
p
1. I know not what it pre - sa - ges, That
2. The most beau - ti - ful maid is re - clin - ing On the
3. It seiz - es with wild - est yearn - ing, The
I am so sad to - day; A leg - end of for - mer
cliff, so won - drous fair; Her glo - ri - ous jew - els are
boat-man, entranc'd in his skiff; He sees not the treach - er - ous
a - ges Will not from my tho'ts a - way The
shin - ing, She is comb - ing her gold - en hair; With a
break - ers, He gaz - es a - lone on the cliff And
dim. e rit.
air is cool and it dar - kles, The Rhine flows calm - ly on, The
gold - en comb she combs it, And sings a song there - by, That
soon will the waves en - gulf them, Both boat and boat - man strong, For
a tempo
rit.
peak of the moun - tain sparkles In the glow of the eve - ning sun.
thrills with its mys - tic mean - ing, And pow - er - ful mel - o - dy.
thus in her toils hath she bound them, The Lore - ley with her song.

The Little Brown Church In The Vale

W. S. P.
WILLIAM S. PITTS
1. There's a church in the valley by the wild-wood, No lov - li - er place in the dale;
2. How sweet on a bright Sabbath morning To list to the clear ringing bell;
No spot is so dear to my child-hood As the lit - tle brown church in the vale.
Its tones so sweet-ly are call - ing, O come to the church in the vale.
rit. a tempo
Come to the church in the wildwood, O come to the church in the
O come, come, come, come, come, come, come, come, come, come, come, come, come, come, come, come,
rit.
dale;
After 2nd verse, repeat Cho. pp
come, come, come, No spot is so dear to my child-hood As the lit - tle brown church in the vale.
Come, With Thy Lute
1. Come, with thy lute, to the fountain; Sing me a song of the mountain; Sing of the hap-py and free,
2. Come, where the zephyrs are straying, Where, mid the flowerbuds play-ing, Rambles the blithe summer bee;
3. Why should we droop in our sadness? Nature, her promise of gladness Sheds o-ver land and o'er sea;
There while the ray is de - clin - ing, While its last ro-ses are shining, Sweet shall our
Let the lone churl, in his sorrow, He who de-spairs of the morrow, Far to his
Come, bring thy lute to the fountain, Sing, love, a song of the mountain; Sweet shall our

Come With Thy Lute—Continued
mel-o-dies be, Un-der the broad lin- den tree, Under the broad lin-den tree.
sol-i-tude flee, Un-der the dark cy-press tree, Under the dark cy-press tree.
mel-o-dies be, Un-der the broad lin - den tree, Under the broad lin-den tree.
Un-der the lin-den tree. Under the lin-den tree.
GEORGE COOPER
Graduation Song
ANCIENT MELODY
Moderately quick
p
1. Our school-days now are past and gone, And yet we fond - ly lin-ger here; For sweet each joy that we have known: 'Tis sad to part from comrades dear. The world before us bright-ly lies, Yet here fond mem'ry loves to dwell; With saddened hearts and dew-y eyes We bid to all a sweet fare-well! Fare - well! Fare - well! We bid to all a sweet fare - well!
2. Long will our hearts re-call each joy That bound us in sweet friendship here; For time can nev - er-more de-stroy The light of mem-'ry burn-ing clear. Of oth-er scenes and oth - er cares Our lips must now their story tell; Each heart your ten-der mem-'ry shares, Teach-ers and comrades, now fare-well! Fare - well! Fare - well! Teach-ers and com-rades, now fare - well!
cresc.
mf

"Ye Olde Folkes' Concertte"

The songs "Revolutionary Tea," "Cousin Jedediah" and "Sound the Loud Timbrel" are examples of those which may be used to advantage in an Old Folks Concert. Programs of this type, made up of songs and recitations selected from among those popular in the days of the old time "Singing School," with the performers appropriately costumed, can be given in any community and are great fun. The more elderly people enjoy them because they bring back memories of an institution which, like the spelling match and husking bee, was important from a social standpoint. The younger people and children will be entertained by taking part in a program similar to one in which their grandparents often participated

Revolutionary Tea

1. There was an old la - dy lived o - ver the sea, And she was an Is - land
2. "Now mother, dear mother," the daughter replied, "I sha'n't do the thing you
3. And so, the old la - dy her servant called up, And packed off a budget of
4. The tea was conveyed to the daughter's door, All down by the o - cean's
Queen, Her daughter lived off in a new countrie, With an o - cean of
ax, I'm will - ing to pay a fair price for the tea, But nev - er the
tea; And ea - ger for three pence a pound, She put in e - nough for a
side; And the bouncing girl pour'd out ev - 'ry pound In the dark and
wa - ter be - tween; The old la - dy's pockets were full of gold, But
three penny tax;" "You shall," quoth the mother, and redden'd with rage, "For
large fam - i - lie, She order'd her ser - vants to bring home the tax, De-
boil - ing tide; And then she called out to the Is - land Queen, "O,
nev - er con - tent - ed was she, So she called on her daughter to
you're my own daughter, you see, And sure, 'tis quite pro - per the
claring her child should o - bey, Or old as she was, and al-
mother, dear moth - er," quoth she, "Your tea you may have when 'tis
pay her a tax, Of three pence a pound on her tea, Of three pence a pound on her tea.
daughter should pay Her mother a tax on her tea, Her moth - er a tax on her tea"
most woman grown, She'd half whip her life away, She'd half whip her life a - way.
steep'd e - nough, But nev - er a tax from me, But nev - er a tax from me."

Cousin Jedediah

H. S. THOMPSON

1. Oh! Jacob, get the cows home and put them in the pen, For the cousins are a-coming to
2. Now, O-bed, wash your face, boy, and tallow up your shoes, While I go to see Aunt Betty, and
3. And, Job, you peel the onions, and wash and fix the 'taters, We'll have them on the table in those
4. Tell Josh to put the colt in the double seated chaise, Let him just card down the cattle, give
see us all a-gain; The dowdy's in the pan, and the tur-key's on the fire,
tell her all the news; And, Kit-ty, slick your hair, and put on your Sunday gown,
shin-y painted waiters; Put on your bran new boots, and those trousers with the straps.
them a lit-tle hay; I'll wear my nice new bell-crown I bought of old U-ri-ah,
And we all must get read-y for Cous-in Jed-e-di-ah.
For Cousin Jed-e-di-ah comes right from Bos-ton town.
Aunt So-phia'll take a shine to you, if you look real slick, per-haps.
And I guess we'll as-ton-ish our Cous-in Jed-e-di-ah.
CHORUS
And Az-a-riah, And Aunt Sophia,
Cousin Jed-e-di-ah, There's Hezekiah,
And Jed-e-di-ah,
All com-ing here to tea; Oh! won't we have a jol-ly time, Oh!
won't we have a jol-ly time! Je-ru-sha, put the ket-tle on, We'll all take tea.

Sound The Loud Timbrel

With spirit

CHARLES AVISON

With spirit

1. Sound the loud tim-brel o'er E-gypt's dark sea; Je - ho - vah has tri-umph'd His
2. Praise to the con-quer-or, Praise to the Lord: His word was our ar-row, His

peo-ple are free; Sing, for the pride of the ty - rant is bro - ken; His
breath was our sword Who shall re - turn to tell E - gypt the sto - ry Of

chari-ots, His horse-men all splen-did and brave; How vain was their boast-ing, the
those she sent forth in the hour of her pride? The Lord hath look'd out from His

Sound The Loud Timbrel–Continued

Lord hath but spoken, And chariots and horsemen are sunk in the wave.
pil-lar of glo-ry, And all her brave thousands are dash'd in the tide.

Sound the loud tim-brel o'er E-gypt's dark sea; ___ Je-ho-vah has tri-umph'd, His
Praise to the Con-quer-or; Praise to the Lord: ___ His word was our ar-row — His

1 2 CODA *f*

peo-ple are free, peo-ple are free, His peo-ple are free, His peo-ple are free.
breath was our sword, breath was our sword, His breath was our sword His breath was our sword

f *tr*

I Cannot Sing The Old Songs
Mrs. C.B.
Mrs. CHARLES BARNARD
Slowly
1. I can-not sing the old songs, I sang long years a-go, For heart and voice would fail me, And fool-ish tears would flow; For by-gone hours come o'er my heart, with each fa-mil-iar strain. I can-not sing the old songs, Or dream those dreams a-gain, I can-not sing the old songs, Or dream those dreams a-gain.
2. I can-not sing the old songs, Their charm is sad and deep; Their melodies would wa-ken Old sor-rows from their sleep, And tho' all un-for-got-ten still, and sad-ly sweet they be, I can-not sing the old songs, They are too dear to me; I can-not sing the old songs, They are too dear to me.
3. I can-not sing the old songs, For vis-ions come a-gain Of gold-en dreams de-part-ed And years of wea-ry pain, Per-haps when earthly fet-ters shall have set my spir-it free, My voice may know the old songs, For all e-ter-ni-ty, My voice may know the old songs, For all e-ter-ni-ty.
Good-night, Ladies
Male Quartette
COLLEGE SONG
1. Good-night, ladies! Good-night, ladies! Good-night, ladies! We're going to leave you now.
2. Fare-well, ladies! Fare-well, ladies! Fare-well, ladies! We're going to leave you now.
3. Sweet dreams, ladies! Sweet dreams, ladies! Sweet dreams, ladies! We're going to leave you now.
Mer-ri-ly we roll along, Roll along, roll along, Merrily we roll along, Over the dark blue sea.

The Bull-Dog

COLLEGE SONG
MALE VOICES
1. Oh! the bull-dog on the bank,
2. Oh! the bull-dog stoop'd to catch him,
3. Says the monkey to the owl:
4. Pharaoh's daughter on the bank,
Oh! the bull-dog on the bank,
Oh! the bull-dog stoop'd to catch him,
Says the monkey to the owl:
Pharaoh's daughter on the bank,
SOLO, FIRST BASS
And the bull-frog in the pool,
And the snapper caught his paw,
"Oh! what'll you have to drink?"
Little Mo - ses in the pool.
CHORUS Lively (MALE QUARTETTE)
Air
Oh! the bull-dog on the bank, And the
Oh! the bull-dog stoop'd to catch him, And the
Says the monkey to the owl: "Oh!
Pharaoh's daughter on the bank, Lit-tle
SOLO, SECOND BASS
rit. ad lib.
And the bull-frog in the pool,
And the snapper caught his paw,
"Oh! what'll you have to drink?"
Little Mo-ses in the pool.
bull-frog in the pool, The bull-dog called the bull-frog, A green old water-fool.
snapper caught his paw, The pol-ly-wog died a laughing, To see him wag his jaw.
what'll you have to drink?" "Why since you are so very kind, I'll take a bottle of ink."
Mo-ses in the pool, She fish'd him out with a telegraph pole, And sent him off to school.
Singing tra la la la la la la, Singing tra la la la la la la, Singing
leil-i - o, leil-i - o,
tra la la la la la, singing tra la la la la la, Tra la la la, tra la la la, tra la la la la la.
leil-i - o.
Repeat pp

Sailing

G.M.
GODFREY MARK
f
1. Y'heave ho! my lads, the wind blows free, A pleas-ant gale is on our lee; An
2. The sail-or's life is bold and free, His home is on the roll-ing sea; An
soon a-cross the o-cean clear Our gal-lant bark shall brave-ly steer But ere we
nev-er heart more true or brave Than his who launches on the wave; A-far he
part from Freedom's shores to-night, A song we'll sing for home and beauty bright. Then here's to
speeds in distant climes to roam, With joyous song he rides the sparkling foam. Then here's to
sail-or and here's to the soldier, too, Hearts will beat for him up-on the waters blue.
sail-or and here's to the soldier, too, Hearts will beat for him up-on the waters blue.

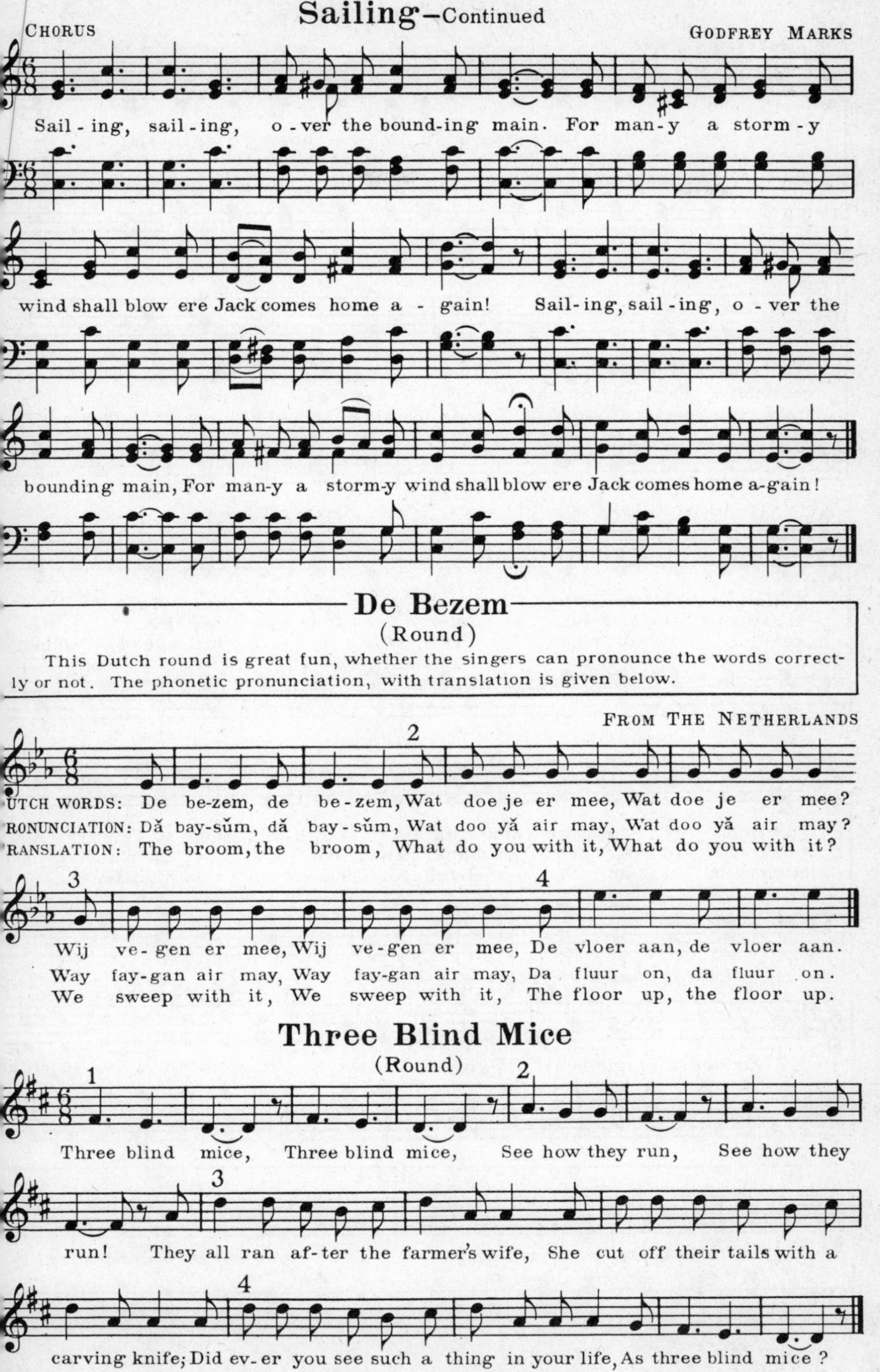
Sailing—Continued
CHORUS
GODFREY MARKS
Sail - ing, sail - ing, o - ver the bound-ing main. For man - y a storm - y
wind shall blow ere Jack comes home a - gain! Sail - ing, sail - ing, o - ver the
bounding main, For man-y a storm-y wind shall blow ere Jack comes home a-gain!
De Bezem
(Round)
This Dutch round is great fun, whether the singers can pronounce the words correctly or not. The phonetic pronunciation, with translation is given below.
FROM THE NETHERLANDS
2
UTCH WORDS: De be-zem, de be - zem, Wat doe je er mee, Wat doe je er mee?
RONUNCIATION: Dă bay-sŭm, dă bay - sŭm, Wat doo yă air may, Wat doo yă air may?
RANSLATION: The broom, the broom, What do you with it, What do you with it?
3
4
Wij ve - gen er mee, Wij ve - gen er mee, De vloer aan, de vloer aan.
Way fay-gan air may, Way fay-gan air may, Da fluur on, da fluur on.
We sweep with it, We sweep with it, The floor up, the floor up.
Three Blind Mice
(Round)
1
2
Three blind mice, Three blind mice, See how they run, See how they
3
run! They all ran af - ter the farmer's wife, She cut off their tails with a
4
carving knife; Did ev - er you see such a thing in your life, As three blind mice?

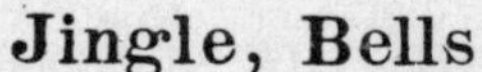

Jingle, Bells

J.P. — J. PIERPONT

Quickly

1. — Dash-ing thro' the snow In a one horse o - pen sleigh, —
2. A day or two a - go I — thought I'd take a ride, And
3. — Now the ground is white, — Go it while you're young, —

O'er the fields we go, — Laugh-ing all the way; —
soon Miss Fan-nie Bright Was seat - ed by my side; The
Take the girls to - night, And sing this sleigh-ing song; Just

Bells on bob - tail ring, — Mak - ing spir - its bright, What
horse was lean and lank, Mis - for - tune seem'd his lot, He
get a bob-tailed nag, Two - for - ty for his speed, Then

fun it is to ride and sing A sleigh-ing song to - night!
got in - to a drift - ed bank, And we, we got up - sot.
hitch him to an o - pen sleigh, And crack! you'll take the lead.

CHORUS (*Accompanied by jingling glasses*)

Jin-gle, bells! jin-gle, bells! Jin-gle all the way! Oh, what fun it is to ride

1. In a one-horse o - pen sleigh!

2. In a one-horse o - pen sleigh!

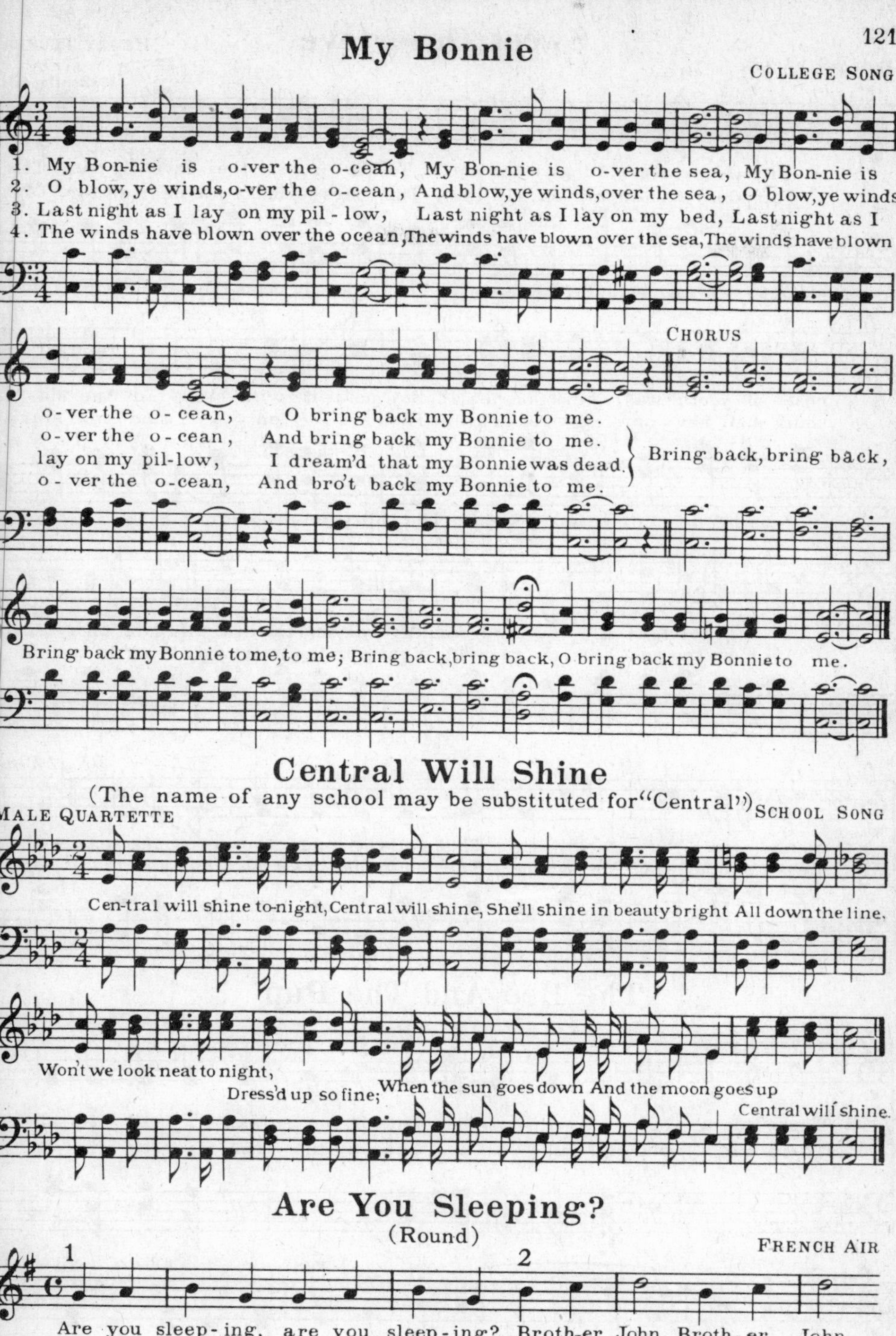
My Bonnie
College Song
1. My Bon-nie is o-ver the o-cean, My Bon-nie is o-ver the sea, My Bon-nie is
2. O blow, ye winds, o-ver the o-cean, And blow, ye winds, over the sea, O blow, ye winds,
3. Last night as I lay on my pil - low, Last night as I lay on my bed, Last night as I
4. The winds have blown over the ocean, The winds have blown over the sea, The winds have blown
o-ver the o-cean, O bring back my Bonnie to me.
o-ver the o-cean, And bring back my Bonnie to me.
lay on my pil-low, I dream'd that my Bonnie was dead.
o-ver the o-cean, And bro't back my Bonnie to me.
Chorus
Bring back, bring back,
Bring back my Bonnie to me, to me; Bring back, bring back, O bring back my Bonnie to me.
Central Will Shine
(The name of any school may be substituted for "Central")
Male Quartette
School Song
Cen-tral will shine to-night, Central will shine, She'll shine in beauty bright All down the line.
Won't we look neat to night,
Dress'd up so fine;
When the sun goes down And the moon goes up
Central will shine.
Are You Sleeping?
(Round)
French Air
1
2
Are you sleep-ing, are you sleep-ing? Broth-er John, Broth-er John,
3
4
Morn-ing bells are ring-ing, Morning bells are ringing: Ding, ding, dong, ding, ding, dong.

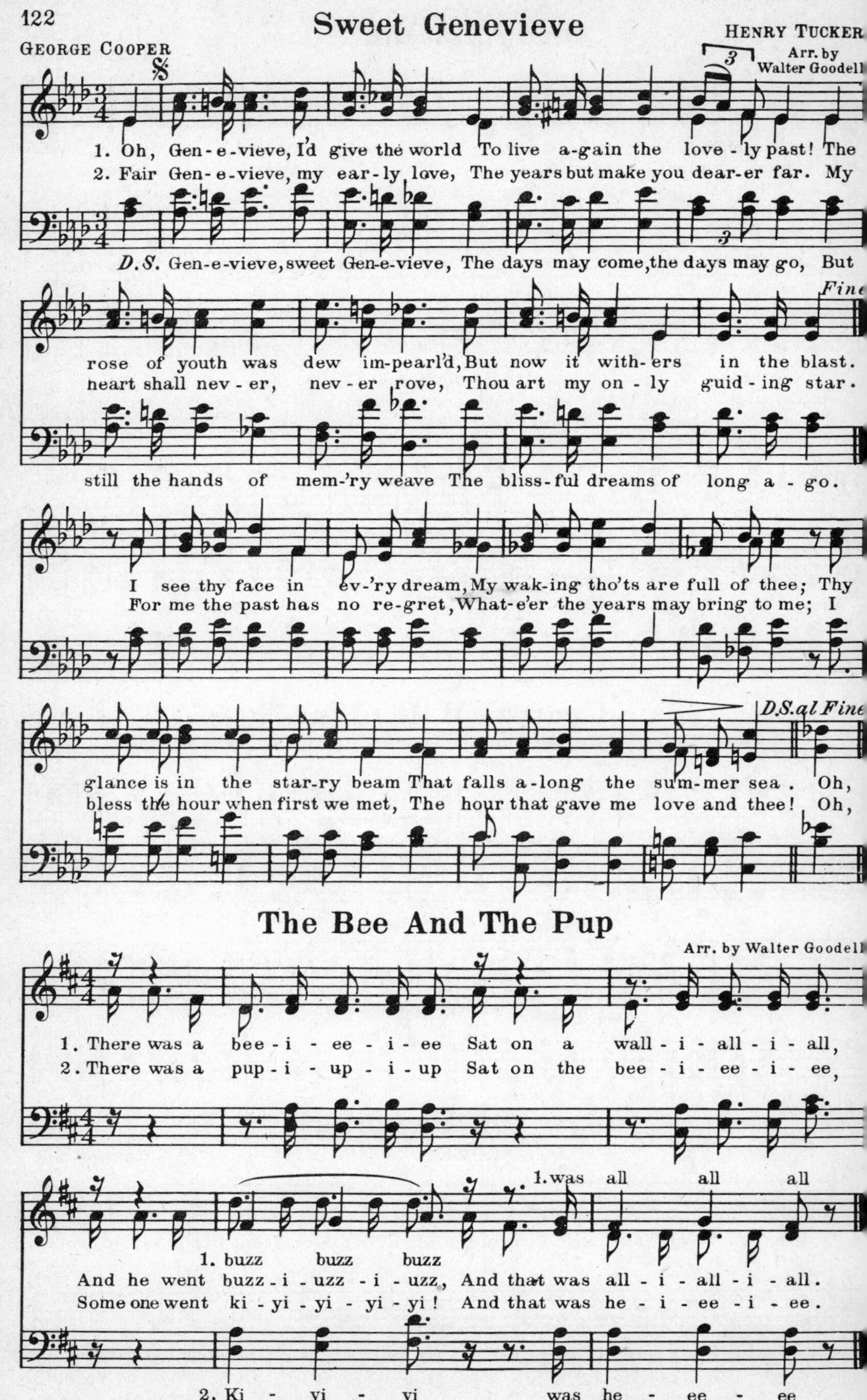
Sweet Genevieve
GEORGE COOPER
HENRY TUCKER
Arr. by Walter Goodell
1. Oh, Gen-e-vieve, I'd give the world To live a-gain the love-ly past! The rose of youth was dew im-pearl'd, But now it with-ers in the blast.
2. Fair Gen-e-vieve, my ear-ly love, The years but make you dear-er far. My heart shall nev-er, nev-er rove, Thou art my on-ly guid-ing star.
D.S. Gen-e-vieve, sweet Gen-e-vieve, The days may come, the days may go, But still the hands of mem-'ry weave The bliss-ful dreams of long a-go.
Fine
I see thy face in ev-'ry dream, My wak-ing tho'ts are full of thee; Thy glance is in the star-ry beam That falls a-long the sum-mer sea. Oh,
For me the past has no re-gret, What-e'er the years may bring to me; I bless the hour when first we met, The hour that gave me love and thee! Oh,
D.S. al Fine
The Bee And The Pup
Arr. by Walter Goodell
1. There was a bee-i-ee-i-ee Sat on a wall-i-all-i-all,
2. There was a pup-i-up-i-up Sat on the bee-i-ee-i-ee,
1. buzz buzz buzz
And he went buzz-i-uzz-i-uzz, And that was all-i-all-i-all.
Some one went ki-yi-yi-yi-yi! And that was he-i-ee-i-ee.
1. was all all all
2. Ki-yi-yi was he-ee-ee

The Spanish Cavalier

W. D. H. WM. D. HENDRICKSON

1. A Span-ish Cav-a-lier stood in his re-treat, And on his gui-tar played a tune, dear; The mu-sic so sweet, Would oft-times re-peat The bless-ing of my coun-try and you, dear
2. I'm off to the war, to the war I must go, To fight for my coun-try and you, dear, But if I should fall, In vain I would call, The bless-ing of my coun-try and you, dear.
3. And when the war is o'er, to you I'll re-turn, A-gain to my coun-try and you, dear; But if I be slain, You may seek me in vain, Up-on the bat-tle-field you will find me.
CHORUS
Oh, say, darling, say, when I'm far a-way, Some-times you may think of me, dear;
Bright sunny days will soon fade away, Re-member what I say, and be true, dear.

The Soldier's Farewell
J. K.
JOHANNA KINKEL
1. Ah, love, how can I leave thee? The sad tho't deep doth grieve me; But know, whate'er befalls me, I go where honor calls me.
2. No more shall I behold thee, Or to my heart enfold thee; In war's array appearing, The foe's stern hosts are nearing.
3. I'll think of thee with longing, When tho'ts with tears come thronging; And on the field, if lying, I'll breathe thy dear name, dying.
Farewell, farewell, my own true love!
Farewell, farewell, my own true love!
The Three Fishermen
COLLEGE SONG
1. O once there were three fishermen, Once there were three fish-er-men, Fisher, fisher, men, men, men Fisher, fisher, men, men, men, O once there were three fisher - men.
2. The first one's name was I - sa - ac, The first one's name was I-sa - ac, I - sa, I - sa, ac, ac, ac I - sa, I - sa, ac, ac, ac The first one's name was I - sa - ac.
3. The second one's name was Ja-a-cob, The second one's name was Ja-a-cob, Ja-a, Ja-a, cob, cob, cob Ja-a, Ja-a, cob, cob, cob The second one's name was Ja-a - cob.
4. The third one's name was Abraham, The third one's name was Abraham, A-bra, A-bra ham, ham, ham A-bra, A-bra, ham, ham, ham The third one's name was A-bra-ham.
5. They all sailed out for Amsterdam, They all sailed out for Amsterdam, Amster, Amster, sh, sh, sh Amster, Amster, sh, sh, sh They all sailed out for Am-ster-dam.
Little Tom Tinker
(Round)
1 Lit tle Tom Tinker got burned with a clink - er And he 2 be-gan to cry. 3 Ma - ma 4 What a poor fel - low am I.

Gaily The Troubadour
T. H. B.
THOMAS. H. BAYLY
1. Gai-ly the Troubadour touch'd his guitar, When he was hastening home from the war.
2. She for the Troubadour hopelessly wept; Sad-ly she tho't of him when others slept.
3. Hark 'twas the Troubadour breathing her name, Under the battlement softly he came,
Singing: "From Pales-tine hith-er I come, La-dy love, la-dy love, welcome me home!"
Singing: "In search of thee would I might roam, Troubadour, Troubadour, come to thy home!"
Singing: "From Pales-tine hith-er I come, La-dy love, la-dy love, welcome me home!"
The Quilting Party
COLLEGE SONG
In the sky the bright stars glit-tered, On the bank the pale moon shone;
Fine.
And 'twas from Aunt Di-nah's quilt-ing par-ty I was see-ing Nel-lie home
CHORUS
D.S. al Fine
I was see-ing Nel-lie home, I was see-ing Nel-lie home;
Merrily, Merrily
(Round)
1
2
Mer-ri-ly, mer-ri-ly, greet the morn; Cheer-i-ly, cheer-i-ly sound the horn.
3
4
Hark! to the ech-oes, hear them play O'er hill and dale, far, far, a-way.

Welcome, Neighbor

Hello Speaker

(Tune for following is first phrase of Twinkle Little Star, page 84.)

Welcome, neighbor, how do you do?
We're mighty glad to meet with you

Hello, speaker, we're your friend.
We'll stay with you until the end.

O Me! O My! (A Toast)

(Substitute any name for the words "the speaker")

O me! O my! We'll get there by and by. If anybody likes the speaker, It's I, I, I, I, I.
O my! O me! We're hap-py as can be. If anybody likes the speaker, It's me, me, me, me, me.

How D'ye Do

(This number may be used at banquets by having various tables compete with one another in improvisin words to suit the melody. Any name may be substituted for "Mister Johnson.")

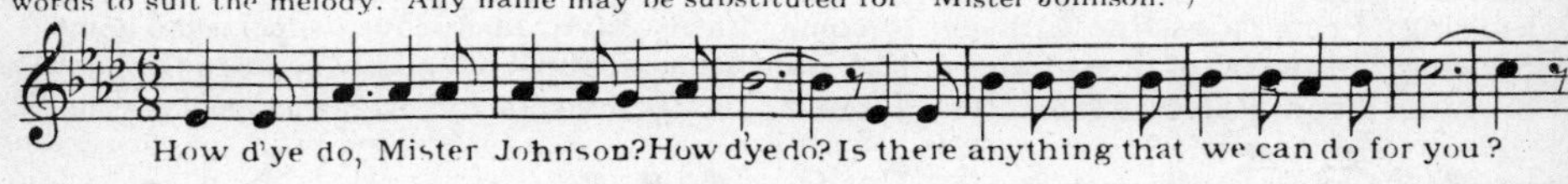
How d'ye do, Mister Johnson? How d'ye do? Is there anything that we can do for you?

We will do it if we can, We'll stand by you to a man. How d'ye do, Mister Johnson? How d'ye do, do, do'

MacDonald's Farm

Old MacDonald had a farm, Ee-i, ee-i-o, And on this farm he had a duck,

Ee-i, ee-i-o, With a quack, quack here and a quack, quack there, Here a quack, there a quac

Here and there a quack, quack, Old MacDonald had a farm, Ee-i-ee-i-o.

Continue indefinitely by using names and sounds of other animals. Do not overlook the Ford, with it "rattle," as a necessary farm adjunct.

ENGLISH FOLK SONG

The Tree In The Wood

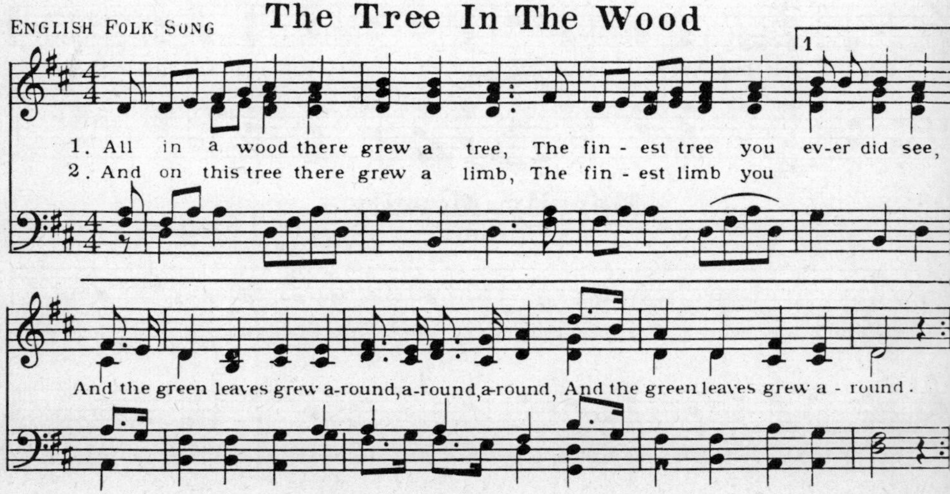
1
1. All in a wood there grew a tree, The fin-est tree you ev-er did see,
2. And on this tree there grew a limb, The fin-est limb you
And the green leaves grew a-round, a-round, a-round, And the green leaves grew a-round.

ever did see; The limb was on the tree, The tree was in the wood,
And the green leaves grew a-round, around, around, And the green leaves grew a round.

3. Branch. 4. Nest. 5. Egg. 6. Yolk. 7. Bird. 8. Wing. 9. Feather.

As each item is added in successive verses, the preceding items are repeated in reverse order. Thus the ast verse would run as follows:

And on the wing there was a feather,
The finest feather you ever did see,
The feather was on the wing,
The wing was on the bird,
The bird was in the yolk,
The yolk was in the egg,
The egg was in the nest,
The nest was on the branch,
The branch was on the limb,
The limb was on the tree,
The tree was in the wood,
And the green leaves grew around, around, around.
And the green leaves grew around.

Alouette

FRENCH CANADIAN FOLK SONG

Fine.
1. A - lou-et - te, gen-tile A-lou-et-te, A - lou-et-te, Je te plu-me-rai.
2. A - lou-et - te, gen-tile A-lou-et-te, A - lou-et-te, Je te plu-me-rai.
Je te plu-me-rai la tete, Je te plu-me-rai la tete, Et la tete,
Je te plu-me-rai la bec, Je te plu-me-rai la bec, Et la bec, Et la tete,
D. C.
Oh!
Et la tete.
Et la bec.
Et la tete.
Le nez. 5. Les pattes.
Le dos. 6. Le cou.

In the measure before the Oh! and the D.C. where the women's voices are echoed by the men's, a word added as each verse is sung and the words of preceding verses are sung in reverse order. Thus, in the last erse, the duet between women and men would run as follows:

Et le cou, et le cou; et les pattes, et les pattes; et le dos, et le dos; et le nez, et le nez; et la bec, et la bec; et la tete, et la tete; Oh! and then back to the beginning ending at the Fine.

Stodola Pumpa

Tr. by Frank Kubina
English version by R.H.

CZECH FOLK SONG
Arr. by Ruth Heller

March tempo.
1. Far in the hills I hear the night-in-gale Sing-ing a song that brings home back to me. Three years a-go at home I left my love. Still she is wait-ing, wait-ing there for me. Hey!
2. Three years to wait is much too long for us. My love and I, we now could mar-ried be. Yes, she and I, we now would have a son, Strong and so hand-some, hand-some just like me! Hey!
3. Son, when you're grown, you must not stay at home. In-to the arm-y you will come with me. Here in the arm-y you will learn to drill. When you are good, then you can march with me! Hey!
(Shout)
REFRAIN
Sto-do-la, sto-do-la, sto-do-la pum-pa. Sto-do-la pum-pa, Sto-do-la pum-pa.
Sto-do-la, sto-do-la, sto-do-la pum-pa, Sto-do-la pum-pa, pum, pum, pum!
AT

After last verse, repeat chorus very softly.

PART TWO

The Gray Book of FAVORITE SONGS

(Selections common to "The Golden Book" and "The Gray Book" omitted)

Selected Readings

Invocation

Almighty and everlasting God, in whom we live and move and have our being; we, thy needy creatures, render thee our humble praises, for thy preservation of us from the beginning of our lives to this day; we bless and magnify thy glorious name; humbly beseeching thee to accept this our morning sacrifice of praise and thanksgiving.

Cleanse the thoughts of our hearts by the inspiration of thy Holy Spirit, that we may perfectly love thee, and worthily magnify thy holy name.

Direct us, O Lord, in all our doings, with thy most gracious favour, and further us with thy continual help; that in all our works begun, continued, and ended in thee, we may glorify thy holy name, and finally, by thy mercy, obtain everlasting life.

Have mercy upon this whole land; and so rule the hearts of thy servants THE PRESIDENT OF THE UNITED STATES, The Governor of this State, and all others in authority, that they, knowing whose ministers they are, may above all things seek thy honour and glory; and that we and all the people, duly considering whose authority they bear, may faithfully and obediently honour them, in thee, and for thee, according to thy blessed word.

O Thou, who hast given us grace at this time with one accord to make our common supplications unto thee; and dost promise that when two or three are gathered together in thy name thou wilt grant their requests; fulfil now, O Lord, the desires and petitions of thy servants, as may be most expedient for them; granting us in this world knowledge of thy truth, and in the world to come life everlasting. *Amen*

Book of Common Prayer

Psalm 96

O sing unto the Lord a new song: sing unto the Lord, all the earth.

Sing unto the Lord, bless his name; show forth his salvation from day to day.

Declare his glory among the nations, his marvelous works among all the peoples.

For great is the Lord, and highly to be praised: he is to be feared above all gods.

For all the gods of the peoples are idols: but the Lord made the heavens.

Honor and majesty are before him: strength and beauty are in his sanctuary.

Give unto the Lord, ye kindreds of the peoples, give unto the Lord glory and strength.

Give unto the Lord the glory due unto his name: bring an offering, and come into his courts.

O worship the Lord in the beauty of holiness; tremble before him, all the earth.

Say among the nations, The Lord reigneth: the world also is established that it cannot be moved:

He shall judge the peoples with equity.

Let the heavens be glad, and let the earth rejoice; let the sea roar, and the fulness thereof; let the field exult, and all that is therein:

Then shall all the trees of the wood sing for joy before the Lord, for he cometh, for he cometh to judge the earth.

He shall judge the world with righteousness, and the peoples with his truth.

Our National Banner

All hail to our glorious ensign! courage to the heart and strength to the hand, to which, in all time, it shall be entrusted! May it ever wave first in honor, in unsullied glory and patriotic hope, on the dome of the Capitol, on the country's stronghold, on the intented plain, on the wave-rocked topmast. Wheresoever on the earth's surface the eye of the American shall behold it, may he have reason to bless it! On whatsoever spot it is planted, there may freedom have a foothold, humanity a brave champion, and religion an altar. Though stained with blood in a righteous cause, may it never, in any cause, be stained with shame. Alike, when its gorgeous folds shall wave in lazy holiday triumphs on the summer breeze, and its tattered fragments be dimly seen through the clouds of war, may it be the joy and pride of the Amrican heart. First raised in the cause of right and liberty, in that cause alone may it forever spread out its streaming blazonry to the battle and the storm. Having been borne victoriously across a mighty continent, and floating in triumph on every sea, may virtue, and freedom, and peace, forever follow where it leads the way!

Edward Everett

America, My Country
Norman H. Hall
Walter J. Goodell
1. A - mer - i - ca, my coun-try, Great na-tion of the world, I love thy peo-ple,
2. A - mer - i - ca, my coun-try, Land that I dear-ly love, For all the bless-ings
3. A - mer - i - ca, my coun-try, Great broth-er-hood of men U - nit - ed 'neath the
hills and plains, I love thy flag un - furl'd; I love thee for thy lof - ty aims, T'ward
of thy laws, I praise the God a - bove; I praise Him for thy gen'rous heart, To
stars and stripes, I hail thee once a - gain. I'll live for thee, A - mer - i - ca, I'll
all hu-man - i - ty, A - mer - i - ca, my coun-try, Fair land of lib - er - ty.
Him I'll bend the knee, A - mer - i - ca, my coun-try, Great land of lib - er - ty.
loy - al be and true, A - mer - i - ca, my coun-try, I pledge my life to you.
My Native Land
Myrtle Koon Cherryman
Edvard Grieg
mf
1. Oh, Na - tive Land, how fair you seem, With lake-lets love-ly as a dream, And,
2. Thy gra-cious farms, with fields un-furl'd, With wealth to feed a hun-gry world; How
3. Oh God of Na-tions, help us grow In kind-ness, as in pow'r, to know The
ff
f
ff
stretch-ing far from sea to sea, Great mountains high in maj - es - ty!
fair thy mis-sion, and how fine, To give thy aid, dear land of mine.
free - dom of true broth-er-hood, And wealth of love the high - est good!

God Of Our Fathers
Daniel C. Roberts
G. W. Warren
Voices alone
Trumpets before each verse.
1. God of our fa-thers, whose al-might-y hand
2. Thy love di-vine hath led us in the past,
3. From war's a-larms, from dead-ly pes - ti-lence,
4. Re-fresh Thy peo-ple on their toil-some way,
Leads forth in beau - ty all the star-ry band
In this free land by Thee our lot is cast;
Be Thy strong arm our ev - er sure de-fense;
Lead us from night to nev-er end-ing day;
Of shin-ing worlds in
Be Thou our Ru - ler,
Thy true re - lig - ion
Fill all our lives with
splen-dor thro' the skies,
Guardian, Guide and Stay,
in our hearts in-crease,
love and grace di-vine,
Our grateful songs be - fore Thy throne a-rise.
Thy word our law, Thy paths our cho - sen way.
Thy bounteous goodness nour - ish us in peace.
And glo - ry, laud and praise be ev-er Thine.
O Worship The King
Sir Robert Grant
Franz Josef Haydn
1. O wor-ship the King all glo-rious a - bove, And grate-ful-ly
2. O tell of His might, and sing of His grace, Whose robe is the
3. Thy boun - ti - ful care what tongue can re-cite? It breathes in the
4. Frail chil-dren of dust, and fee - ble as frail, In Thee do we
sing His won - der - ful love; Our Shield and De - fend-er, the
light, whose can - o - py space; His char-iots of wrath the deep
air, it shines in the light, It streams from the hills, it de -
trust, Nor find Thee to fail; Thy mer - cies how ten - der! how

O Worship The King—Concluded
An-cient of days, Pa - vil-ioned in splen-dor and gird-ed with praise.
thun-der-clouds form, And dark is his path on the wings of the storm.
scends to the plain, And sweet-ly dis-tills in the dew and the rain.
firm to the end! Our Mak-er, De-fend-er, Re-deem-er and Friend.
God Of The Earth, The Sky, The Sea
Samuel Longfellow
Henry J. E. Holmes
1. God of the earth, the sky, the sea! Mak-er of all a - bove, be - low! Cre - a - tion lives and moves in thee, Thy pres-ent life through all doth flow.
2. Thy love is in the sun-shine's glow, Thy life is in the quick-'ning air; When light-nings flash and storm-winds blow, There is thy pow'r; thy law is there.
3. We feel thy calm at ev-'ning's hour, Thy gran-deur in the march of night; And when thy morn-ing breaks in pow'r, We hear thy word, 'Let there be light!'
Refrain
We give thee thanks, thy name we sing, Al-might-y Fa - ther, heavn-ly King. A - men.

Mighty Land, Wondrous Land

CLAIRE GOODELL

CHARLES FRANCOIS GOUNO
Arr. by Walter Goodell

1. Might - y land, won - drous land,
2. Hap - py land, hand in hand,
3. Day by day, this we pray:
Land of peace and plen - ty, Hear our song of praise.
See thy chil - dren bid - ing; Love and friend ship reign.
May thy glo - ries flour - ish. May we e'er be free.
To thee, our be - lov - ed home land, Do we now our voic - es raise.
And we strive that our fore-fa - thers Have not died for us in vain.
Rise, A - mer - i - ca, and lead us On-ward to our des - ti - ny.

To Thee, O Country!

Mrs. John Lane | Julius Eichberg

p
1. To thee O coun-try great and free, With trust-ing hearts we cling; Our
2. For thee we dai-ly work and strive, To thee we give our love; For
Thy pow'r and praises sing Thy
To Him who dwells a-bove To
ff
f
voic-es tuned by joy-ous love, Thy pow'r and prais-es sing Thy
thee with fer-vor deep we pray To Him who dwells a-bove Who
pow'r and prais-es sing.
Him who dwells a-bove.
p
ff
pow'r and prais-es sing. Up-on thy might-y, faith-ful heart, We
dwells a-bove. O God pro-tect our na-tive land, Let
Up-on thy might-y, faith-ful
O God pro-tect our na-tive
lay, we lay our bur-dens down, Thou art the on-ly friend who feels their
Peace, let Peace its ruler be, And let her glo-ry light the way to
heart, We lay our burdens down, Thou art the on-ly friend who feels their
land, Let Peace its rul-er be, And let her glo-ry light the way to
weight with-out a frown. Up-on thy mighty faithful heart, We
make the whole world free! O God pro-tect our native land, Let
weight with-out a frown. Up-on thy mighty faithful
make the whole world free! O God pro-tect our native

To Thee, O Country – Concluded

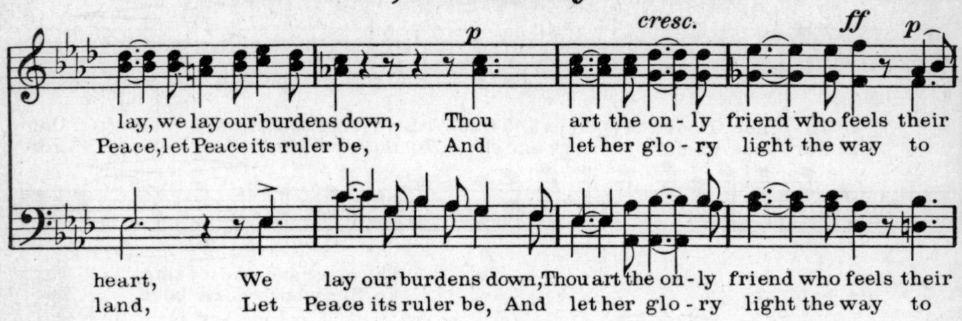
p
cresc.
ff
p
lay, we lay our burdens down, Thou art the on-ly friend who feels their
Peace, let Peace its ruler be, And let her glo-ry light the way to
heart, We lay our burdens down, Thou art the on-ly friend who feels their
land, Let Peace its ruler be, And let her glo-ry light the way to

1
2
cresc.
ff
p
weight with-out a frown.
make the whole world (omit) free, To make the whole world free!
weight with-out a frown.
make the whole world (omit) free, To make the whole world free!

Copyright MCMXIV by Annie E. Lane. Used by permission of Oliver Ditson Co.

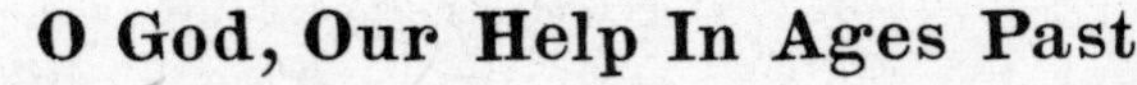

O God, Our Help In Ages Past

ISAAC WATTS — WILLIAM CROFT

Moderately

1. O God, our help in a-ges past, Our hope for years to come,
Our shel-ter from the storm-y blast, And our e-ter-nal home.
2. Un-der the shad-ow of Thy throne, Still may we dwell se-cure;
Suf-fic-ient is Thine arm a-lone And our de-fence is sure.
3. Be-fore the hills in or-der stood, Or earth re-ceived her frame,
From ev-er-last-ing Thou art God, To end-less years the same.
4. A thou-sand a-ges in Thy sight, Are like an eve-ning gone;
Short as the watch that ends the night, Be-fore the ris-ing sun.
5. O God our help in a-ges past, Our hope for years to come,
Be Thou our guard while life shall last, And our e-ter-nal home.

The Spacious Firmament on High

(Creation)

JOSEPH ADDISON — FRANZ JOSEF HAYDN

1.The spa-cious fir - ma - ment on high, With all the blue e -
2.Soon as the eve-ning shades pre - vail The moon takes up the
3.What tho' in sol-emn si - lence all Move round the dark ter-
the - real sky, And span-gled heav'ns, a shin - ing frame, Their
won - drous tale, And night - ly to the list - 'ning earth Re -
res - trial ball? What tho' no re - al voice nor sound A -
great O - rig - i - nal pro-claim. Th'unwearied sun, from day to day,
peats the sto - ry of her birth; While all the stars that round her burn,
mid the ra-diant orbs be found? In rea-son's ear they all re-joice,
Does his Cre - a - tor's pow'rs dis - play, And pub - lish - es to
And all the plan - ets in their turn, Con - firm the ti - dings
And ut - ter forth a glo - rious voice, For - ev - er sing - ing
ev - 'ry land The work of an Al-might - y Hand.
as they roll, And spread the truth from pole to pole.
as they shine, "The hand that made us is di - vine."

Oh Realm of Light

(Creation)

1. Oh realm of light! whose morning star
To Bethl'hem's manger led the way,
Not yet upon our longing eyes
Shines the full splendor of thy day:
Yet still across the centuries fall,
Both strong and sweet, our Lord's command;
And still with steadfast faith we cry,
"Behold, the kingdom is at hand!"

2. Oh realm of peace! whose music clear
Swept through Judea's starlit skies,
Still the harsh sounds of human strife
Break on thy heavenly harmonies:
Yet shall thy song of triumph ring
In full accord, from land to land,
And men with angels learn to sing,
"Behold, the kingdom is at hand!"

EMILY H. MILLER

Still, Still with Thee

HARRIET BEECHER STOWE — E. MOSS

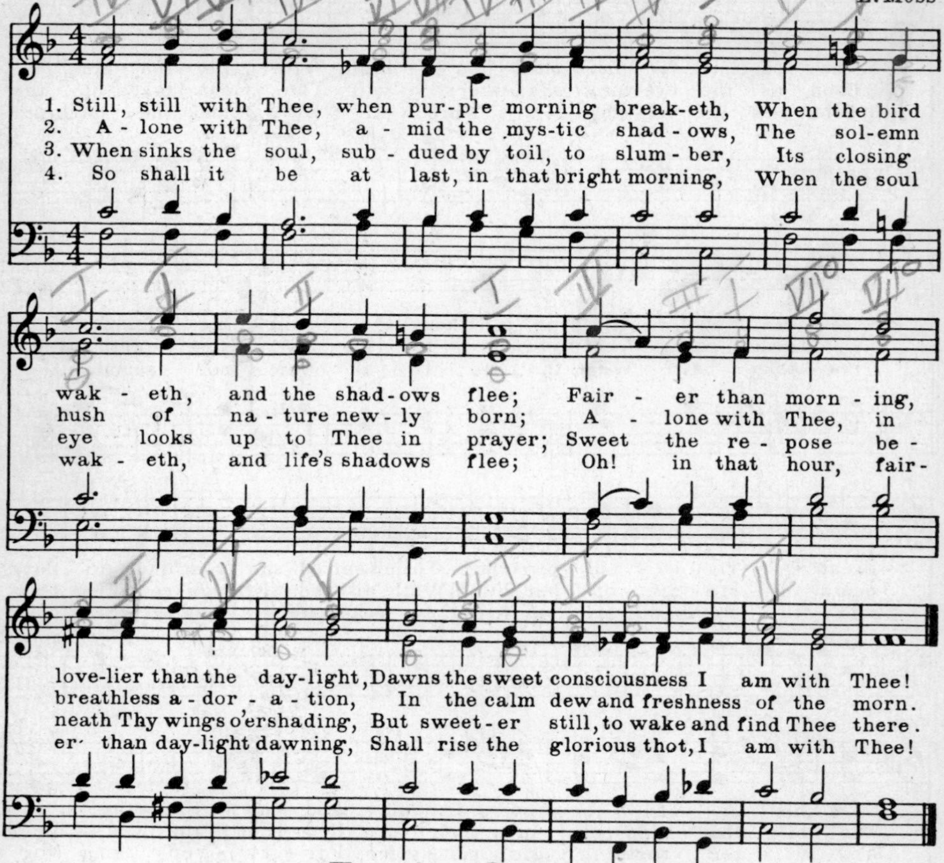

1. Still, still with Thee, when pur-ple morning break-eth, When the bird
2. A - lone with Thee, a - mid the mys-tic shad - ows, The sol-emn
3. When sinks the soul, sub - dued by toil, to slum - ber, Its closing
4. So shall it be at last, in that bright morning, When the soul

wak - eth, and the shad-ows flee; Fair - er than morn - ing,
hush of na - ture new - ly born; A - lone with Thee, in
eye - looks up to Thee in prayer; Sweet the re - pose be -
wak - eth, and life's shadows flee; Oh! in that hour, fair-

love-lier than the day-light, Dawns the sweet consciousness I am with Thee!
breathless a - dor - a - tion, In the calm dew and freshness of the morn.
neath Thy wings o'ershading, But sweet - er still, to wake and find Thee there.
er- than day-light dawning, Shall rise the glorious thot, I am with Thee!

Evening Prayer

CARL MARIA VON WEBER

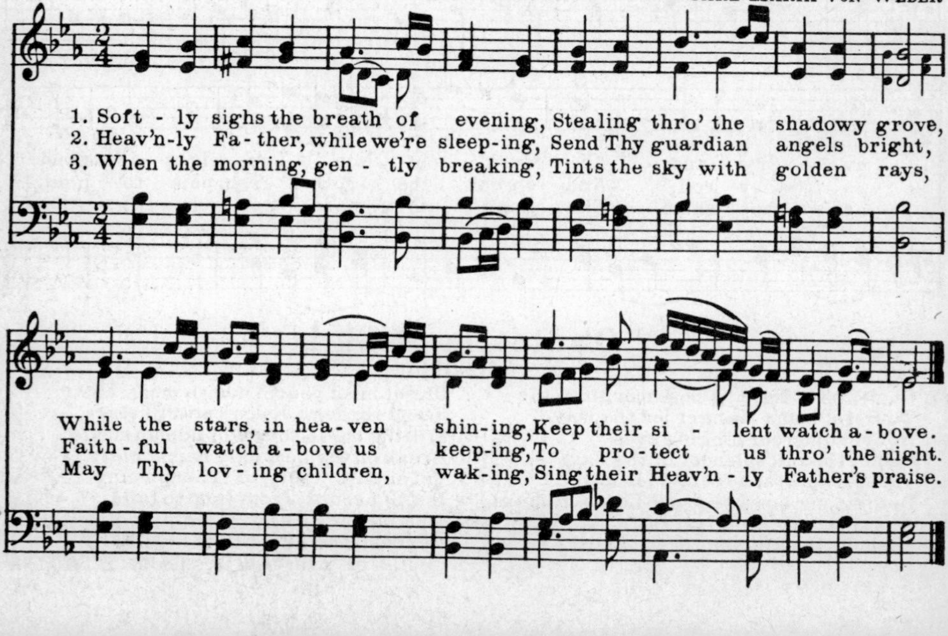

1. Soft - ly sighs the breath of evening, Stealing thro' the shadowy grove,
2. Heav'n-ly Fa - ther, while we're sleep - ing, Send Thy guardian angels bright,
3. When the morning, gen - tly breaking, Tints the sky with golden rays,

While the stars, in hea - ven shin - ing, Keep their si - lent watch a - bove.
Faith - ful watch a - bove us keep - ing, To pro - tect us thro' the night.
May Thy lov - ing children, wak - ing, Sing their Heav'n - ly Father's praise.

Lord of All Being, Throned Afar

OLIVER WENDELL HOLMES — VIRGIL C. TAYLOR

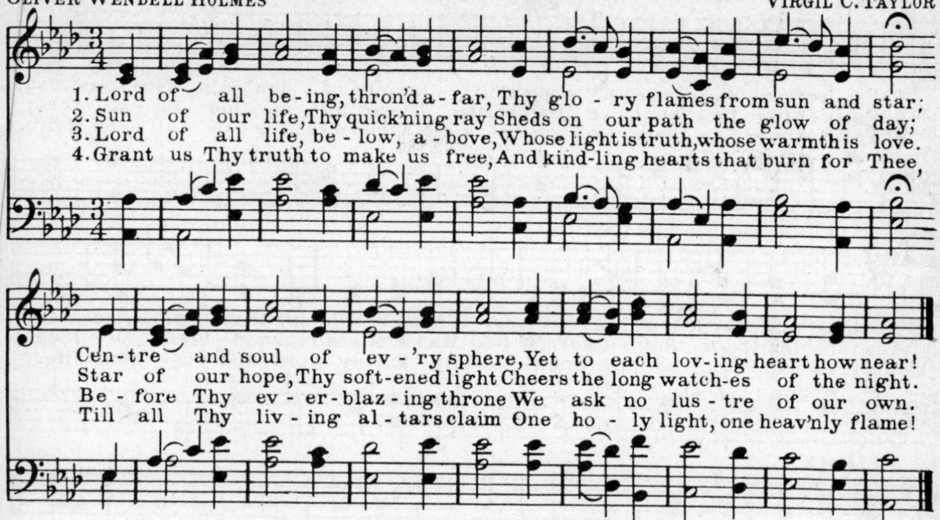

1. Lord of all be-ing, thron'd a-far, Thy glo-ry flames from sun and star;
2. Sun of our life, Thy quick'ning ray Sheds on our path the glow of day;
3. Lord of all life, be-low, a-bove, Whose light is truth, whose warmth is love.
4. Grant us Thy truth to make us free, And kind-ling hearts that burn for Thee,

Cen-tre and soul of ev-'ry sphere, Yet to each lov-ing heart how near!
Star of our hope, Thy soft-ened light Cheers the long watch-es of the night.
Be-fore Thy ev-er-blaz-ing throne We ask no lus-tre of our own.
Till all Thy liv-ing al-tars claim One ho-ly light, one heav'nly flame!

Cast Thy Burden Upon The Lord

(Arr. from Mendelssohn's Oratorio, "Elijah")

Slow and sustained

Cast thy bur-den up-on the Lord; and He shall sus-tain thee;

louder

He nev-er will suf-fer the righteous to fall, He is at thy

He is at thy

right hand.

right hand. Thy mer-cy, Lord, is great, and far a-bove the

louder

softer *p*

heav'ns, Let none be made a-sham-ed, that wait up-on Thee!

Faith of Our Fathers

FREDERICK W. FABER — HENRY F. HEMY and J. G. WALTON

1. Faith of our fa - thers, liv - ing still In spite of dun-geon, fire and sword,
2. Faith of our fa - thers, we will strive To win all na - tions un - to thee;
3. Faith of our fa - thers, we will love Both friend and foe in all our strife,

O how our hearts beat high with joy When-e'er we hear that glo - rious word!
And thro' the truth that comes from God Man-kind shall then in - deed be free.
And preach thee, too, as love knows how, By kind-ly words and vir - tuous life.

REFRAIN

Faith of our fa - thers, ho - ly faith, We will be true to thee till death.

The Lord Is My Shepherd

JAMES MONTGOMERY — THOMAS KOSCHAT
Arr. by W. J. G.

1. The Lord is my Shepherd; no want shall I know. I feed in green pastures, safe
2. Thro' the valley and shadow of death tho' I stray, Since Thou art my Guardian, no
3. In the midst of af-fliction my ta-ble is spread! With blessings unmeasured my
4. Let goodness and mercy, my boun-ti-ful God, Still fol-low my steps till I

fold-ed I rest. He leadeth my soul where the still waters flow, Re-stores me when
e-vil I fear. Thy rod shall de-fend me, Thy staff be my stay, No harm shall be-
cup runneth o'er; With perfume and oil Thou a-nointest my head; O what shall I
meet Thee above. I seek, by the path which my forefathers trod, Thro' the land of their

wand'ring, re-deems when oppress, Re - stores me when wand'ring, re-deems when opprest.
fall me with my Comforter near, No harm shall be-fall me with my Comforter near.
ask of Thy providence more? O what shall I ask of Thy prov - idence more?
so-journ, Thy kingdom of love, Thro' the land of their sojourn, Thy kingdom of love.

In Heavenly Love Abiding

ANNA L. WARING — FELIX MENDELSSOHN

p
cresc.
f
1. In heav'nly love a - bid - ing, No change my heart shall fear, And safe is such con-
2. Where-ev-er He may guide me, No want shall turn me back; My Shepherd is be -
3. Green pastures are be-fore me, Which yet I have not seen; Bright skies will soon be
p
louder
fid - ing, For nothing chang-es here. The storm may roar with-out me,
side me, And nothing can I lack. His wis-dom ev-er wak-eth,
o'er me, Where the dark clouds have been, My life I can-not meas-ure,
The storm may roar with - out me,
His wis-dom ev - er wak-eth,
My life I can - not meas-ure,
The storm may roar without me,
His wis-dom ev-er waketh,
My life I cannot measure,
f
pp
My heart may low be laid; But God is round a - bout me, And can I be dis -
His sight is nev-er dim; He knows the way He tak-eth, And I will walk with
The path of life is free; My Sav - ior has my treasure, And He will walk with
But God is round a - bout me, But
He knows the way He tak - eth, He
My Sav - ior has my treas - ure, My
And can I be dis - may'd?
And I will walk with Him.
And He will walk with me.
louder
f
softer
p
may'd? But God is round a - bout me, And can I be dis - may'd?
Him; He knows the way He tak-eth, And I will walk with Him.
me; My Sav-ior has my treasure, And He will walk with me.
God is round a - bout me, And can I be dis - may'd?
knows the way He tak - eth, And I will walk with Him.
Sav-ior has my treas - ure, And He will walk with me.

Jerusalem The Golden
BERNARD OF CLUNY
Translated by J. M. Neale
G. F. LE JEUNE
1. Je - ru - sa-lem the gold-en! With milk and hon-ey blest; Be-neath thy contem-pla-tion Sink heart and voice oppress. I know not, O I know not, What joys a-wait us there! What radiancy of glo-ry! What bliss beyond compare! Jerusalem the gol-den! With
2. They stand, those halls of Si - on, All ju-bi-lant with song, And bright with many an an-gel, And all the martyr throng. The Prince is ev-er in them, The day-light is se-rene; The pastures of the blessed Are deck'd in glorious sheen. Jerusalem the gol-den! With
3. There is the throne of Da-vid; And there from care releas'd, The shout of them that triumph, The song of them that feast. And they who with their Leader, Have conquered in the fight, For-ev-er and for-ev-er Are clad in robes of white. Jerusalem the gol-den! With
4. O sweet and blessed country, The home of God's e-lect! O sweet and blessed coun-try, That ea-ger heart expect! Je-su, in mer-cy bring us To that dear land of rest! Who art with God the Father, And Spirit ev-er blest. Jerusalem the gol-den! With
Je-ru - - sa-lem the gold-en! Be-neath
milk and honey blest; Be-neath thy contem-pla-tion Sink heart and voice oppress.
Ah, 'Tis A Dream
Translation from HEINE
EDWARD LASSEN
1. My na-tive land, a-gain it meets my eye, The old oaks raise their boughs on high, The vi - o-lets greet-ing seem, Ah! 'tis a dream.
2. And now when far in dis-tant lands I roam My heart will wan-der to my home, But while these fan - cies teem, Ah! 'tis a dream.

Day Is Dying in the West

MARY A. LATHBURY
WILLIAM F. SHERWIN
1. Day is dy - ing in the west; Heav'n is touch - ing earth with rest; Wait and wor - ship while the night Sets her eve-ning lamps a - light Thro' all the sky.
2. Lord of life, be - neath the dome Of the u - ni - verse, Thy home; Gath - er us, who seek Thy face, To the fold of Thy em-brace, For Thou art nigh.
3. While the deep-'ning shad - ows fall, Heart of Love, en - fold - ing all, Thro' the glo - ry and the grace Of the stars that veil Thy face, Our hearts as - cend.
4. When for - ev - er from our sight, Pass the stars the day the night; Lord of an - gels, on our eyes Let e - ter - nal morn - ing rise, And shad - ows end.
CHORUS
p
Ho - ly, ho - ly, ho - ly, Lord, God of Hosts! Heav'n and earth are full of Thee! Heav'n and earth are praising Thee, O Lord most high!

Fairest Lord Jesus, Ruler of All Nature
ANONYMOUS. FROM 12TH CENTURY
(Crusaders' Hymn)
GERMAN AIR
1. Fair-est Lord Je - sus, Ru-ler of all na-ture, O Thou of God and man the Son, Thee will I cher-ish, Thee will I hon-or, Thou, my soul's glory, joy and crown.
2. Fair are the meadows, Fairer still the woodlands, Rob'd in the blooming garb of spring; Je-sus is fair-er, Je-sus is pur-er, Who makes the woeful heart to sing.
3. Fair is the sunshine, Fairer still the moonlight, And all the twinkling star-ry host; Je-sus shines brighter, Je-sus shines purer, Than all the angels heav'n can boast.
Hark! the Vesper Hymn Is Stealing
THOMAS MOORE
Moderately
RUSSIAN AIR
1. Hark! the ves-per hymn is steal-ing O'er the wa-ters soft and clear; Near-er yet and near-er peal-ing, Soft it breaks up-on the ear.
2. Now like moonlight waves re-treat-ing To the shore it dies a-long; Now like an-gry sur-ges meet-ing, Breaks the min-gled tide of song.
f
Ju-bi-la-te, ju-bi-la-te, ju-bi-la-te, A-men.
Ju-bi-la-te, ju-bi-la-te, ju-bi-la-te, A-men.
p
pp
Far-ther now, now far-ther steal-ing, Soft it fades up-on the ear.
Hark! a-gain, like waves re-treat-ing, To the shore, it dies a-long.

Gloria Patri

Palestrina was born in the ancient town of Palestrina, near Rome in about 1524. In 1571 he was appointed chapelmaster of St. Peter's in Rome, and soon after became composer to the Papal choir. Palestrina's work is among the greatest in choral music. A great many of his choruses are used today, but probably the most frequently used one is "Gloria Patri," one of the forms of which is given below.

English adaptation by MYRTLE KOON CHERRYMAN
G. P. PALESTRINA
Quickly with vivacity
Glo-ri-a pa-tri et fi-li-o, glo-ri-a pa-tri et fi-li-o,
Father of Light, we sing in Thy praise. Father of Light, we sing in Thy praise
glo-ri-a pa-tri et fi-li-o, glo-ri-a pa-tri et fi-li-o,
Joy-ful-ly now our voi-ces we raise Joy-ful-ly now our voi-ces we raise
et spi-ri-tu-i sanc - to, spi-ri-tu-i sanc - - to,
May Thy peace come down from above, May thy peace come from a - bove.
et spi-ri-tu-i sanc - to, et spi-ri-tu-i sanc - to.
Fill our hearts with Thy great love. Fill our hearts with Thy great love. A-men.
From Ill Do Thou Defend Me
JOHANN SEBASTIAN BACH
Majestically
1. From ill do Thou de-fend me; Receive me, lead me home; Thy love full oft in
2. New blessings dai-ly send me; From Thee all good things come.
kind - ness hath milk and honey giv'n; O heal my mortal blindness, And fix my heart on Heav'n

Unfold, Ye Portals

(From the oratorio "The Redemption")
ADAPTED FROM PSALM XXIV
CHARLES GOUNOD
Moderately
Un-fold, un-fold, un-fold, ye portals ever
last-ing, un-fold, un-fold, un-fold, ye portals ev-er-
last-ing, With welcome to re-ceive Him as-cend-ing on

Unfold, Ye Portals—Continued

high! ___ Behold the King of Glo - ry! He mounts up thro' the
sky, ___ Back to the heav'nly mansions hast - 'ning. Un-
fold, un - fold, un - fold, ___ for lo, the
8

Unfold, Ye Portals-Continued

1
Fine.
King comes nigh.
nigh.
(Omit 1st time)
But who is
1
Fine.
(Omit 1st time)
pp
He, the King of Glo - ry?
He who Death over
came,
the Lord in battle might - y.

Unfold, Ye Portals-Concluded

pp
f
But who is He,— the King— of Glo - ry? Of
hosts He is the Lord;— of angels and of powers:— the King of
Glo - ry is the King of the saints. Un -
D.C.
cresc.

The Heavens Resound

ANDREAS HOFER

ARRANGED FROM BEETHOVE

1. The heav'ns resound with His prais-es e - ter-nal, In might an
2. The Lord is God! He is King of cre - a-tion; In His righ
glo-ry they com-bine To tell His name thro' earth and the oceans That man ma
hand He holds them all; His chil-dren, we, in love and de - vo-tion, Be-fore His
hear the word di - vine. He holds the suns in the blue vaulted
might and pow-er fall. O Fa-ther, hear! we Thy sons bring ou
f

The Heavens Resound—Concluded

heav - ens, He plants His foot up - on the world;
bless - ings, Our pray'r - ful thanks to Thee we raise;
The myr - iad stars bow in will - ing sub - jec - tion; The u - ni - verse His
The heav'ns re - sound; break, O earth, in - to glo - ry, To serve! a - dore! and
hand un - furl'd, The u - ni - verse His hand un - furl'd.
sing His praise! To serve! a - dore! and sing His praise!

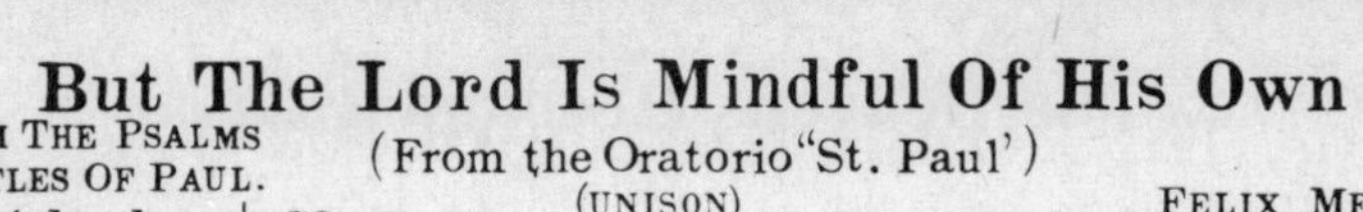
But The Lord Is Mindful Of His Own
(From the Oratorio "St. Paul")

ADAPTED FROM THE PSALMS
AND THE EPISTLES OF PAUL.

(UNISON)

FELIX MENDELSSOH[N]

Moderately slow ♩= 76

But the Lord is mindful of His own, He re - mem-bers His chil - dren. But the Lord is mindful of His own; The Lord remem-bers Hi[s] chil - dren, re - mem - bers His chil - dren.

slower

p *mf*

p

Bow down before Him, ye might - y, for the Lord is

p *fp* *cres[c.]*

But The Lord Is Mindful Of His Own—Concluded

cresc.
near us! Bow down before Him, ye might - y, For the Lord is
f
p
fp
cresc.
f
p
near us! Yea, the Lord is mindful of His own; He re -
f
p
cresc.
mem-bers His chil - dren, Bow down before Him, ye might-y, for the
cresc.
f
f
Lord is near us!

Lift Thine Eyes

Mendelssohn's "Elijah" of which the selection "Lift Thine Eyes" is one of the most popular, was first performed in 1846 at a festival given in Birmingham, England.

The oratorio is divided into two parts. The first tells of the prophet Elijah's experiences up to the time when his offering on Mount Carmel is consumed by fire sent from heaven and the rain falls upon the drought-stricken land. The second part portrays Elijah's life until he is carried to heaven in a fiery chariot. The entire oratorio is intensely dramatic.

Mendelssohn spent many years in its preparation, for, even as he worked upon it, he realized that it was to be his masterpiece. From the composition of the music, he took the keenest pleasure. It was his last great composition, for at the time of its first performance, Mendelssohn was losing strength which led to his death in 1847.

F. M. *With a quick motion* FELIX MENDELSSOHN

p
sf
p
Lift thine eyes, O lift thine eyes to the moun- tains, Whence cometh, whence
Lift thine eyes, O lift thine eyes to the moun-tains, Whence cometh, whence
to the moun-tains, Whence cometh, whence
com-eth, whence com - eth help. Thy help com - eth
com-eth, whence com- eth help, Thy help com - eth, com - eth from the
com-eth, whence com-eth help, Thy help com - eth from the
from the Lord, the ma - ker of heav - en and earth He hath
Lord from the Lord the ma - ker of heav-en and earth He hath
Lord the ma - ker of heav-en and earth He hath

Lift Thine Eyes—Concluded

said, thy foot shall not be mov-ed Thy keep-er will nev-er slum - ber
said, thy foot shall not be mov-ed Thy keep-er will nev-er
said, thy foot shall not be mov-ed Thy keep-er will nev-er
nev-er will nev-er slum - ber, nev-er slum - - ber.
slum - ber nev-er, will nev-er slum - - - - ber
slum - ber nev-er will nev-er slum - ber, will nev - er slum - ber
pp
f
p
sf
Lift thine eyes, O lift thine eyes to the mountains, whence cometh, whence cometh, whence
Lift thine eyes, O lift thine eyes to the mountains, whence cometh, whence cometh, whence
Lift thine eyes, O lift thine eyes to the mountains, whence com-eth, whence
com - eth help, whence com-eth, whence cometh, whence com - eth help.
com - eth help, whence com - eth, whence cometh, whence com - eth help.
com - eth help, whence com - eth, whence cometh, whence com - eth help.

O Rest In The Lord

ADAPTED FROM THE 37th PSALM

(From the oratorio "Elijah")

FELIX MENDELSSO

slowly
p
pp
O rest in the Lord, wait pa-tient-ly for Him and He shall
give thee thy heart's de - sires: O rest in the Lord, wait pa-tient-ly fo
Him, and He shall give thee thy heart's de-sires, and He shall give thee thy heart's
sires. Commit thy way un - to Him, and trust in Him; commit thy way u
to Him, and trust in Him, and fret not thy-self because of e-vil

O Rest In The Lord—Concluded
p
do-ers. O rest in the Lord, wait pa-tient-ly for Him, wait pa-tient-ly for
p
pp
Him; O rest in the Lord, wait pa-tient-ly for Him, and He shall
pp
give thee thy heart's de-sires, and He shall give thee thy heart's de-sires, and He shall
cresc.
sf
p
cresc. sf
give thee thy heart's de-sires. O rest in the Lord, O rest in the
p
p
cresc.
p
Lord, and wait, wait pa-tient-ly for Him.
cresc.
tr

Lovely Appear
Adapted From Isaiah lii:7
(From the oratorio "The Redemption")
With a slow motion
Charles Gouno
mp
Soprano Chorus
Love-ly ap - pear o - ver the mountains The feet of them tha
preach, and bring good news of peace, The feet of them that preach, and
p Alto Chorus
bring good news of peace.__ Love - ly ap - pear__ o - ver the
moun-tains The feet of them that preach,__ and bring good news of peace, The
p
Unison
feet of them that preach, and bring good news of peace,__ Love - ly ap -

pear — o - ver the moun - tains The feet of them that preach, and
pear — o - ver the moun - tains The feet of them that preach, and
pear — o - ver the moun - tains The feet of them that preach, and
louder
p
bring good news of peace, — Love - ly ap - pear — o - ver the
bring good news of peace, — Love - ly ap - pear — o - ver the
bring good news of peace, — Love - ly ap-pear — o - ver the
louder
p
cresc.
dim.
moun - tains The feet of them that preach, and bring good news of peace.
moun - tains The feet of them that preach, and bring good news of peace.
moun - tains The feet of them that preach, and bring good news of peace.
cresc.
dim.

The Lost Chord

Sir Arthur Seymour Sullivan, one of the best known of English composers, was born in London in 1842. His songs and hymns, also his light operas written in conjunction with Sir W S. Gilbert are sung and loved everywhere. "The Lost Chord", "Onward Christian Soldiers" and "The Mikado" are the most popular of his compositions Sullivan was knighted in recognition of his musical work. He died in London in 1900.

ADELAIDE A. PROCTER
SIR ARTHUR SULLIVAN
Moderately quick
TENORS AND BASSES IN UNISON
Seat-ed one day at the Or-gan, I was
wea-ry and ill at ease, And my fingers wandered i-dly O-ver the nois-y
keys. I knew not what I was playing, Or what I was dreaming then; But I

The Lost Chord-Continued

f
struck one chord of mu-sic, Like the sound of a great A-men, Like the
sound of a great A - men.
p
SOPRANOS AND ALTOS
mf
It flood-ed the crim-son twi-light, Like the close of an An-gel's
mf
Psalm, And it lay on my fe-vered spir-it With a touch of in-fi-nite

The Lost Chord-Continued

mf
mp
mf
f
p
calm. It qui-et-ed pain and sorrow, Like love o-ver-coming strife; It
seemed the harmonious ech - o From our dis-cordant life. It linked all perplexed
meanings In-to one perfect peace, And trembled a-way in-to silence, As
if it were loth to cease I have sought, but I seek it vain-ly, That

The Lost Chord-Continued

one lost chord di - vine, Which came from the soul of the Or - gan, And
en - tered in - to mine.
ALL THE VOICES
It may be that Death's bright
an-gel Will speak in that chord a - gain, It may be that on - ly in
heav'n I shall hear that grand A - men; It may be that Death's bright

ff
an - gel will speak in that chord a - gain, It may be that on - ly in
ff
Heav'n I shall hear that grand A - men.
Pilgrims' Chorus
(Tannhauser)
RICHARD WAGNER
Majestically
mf Once more, dear home, I with rapture be-hold thee, And greet the fields that so sweetly enfold thee; Thou, pil - grim staff, may rest thee now, Since I to heav'n have ful-

mf
fill'd my vow By pen - ance sore I have a - toned, And God's pure
mf
law my heart hath owned; My pains hath He with bless - ing crown'd, To
ff
God my song shall aye re - sound, To God my song shall aye re - sound.
ff
3
ff
Once more, dear home, I with rapture behold thee, And greet the fields that so sweetly enfold thee; Thou,
3
pil - grim staff, thy toil is o'er, I'll serve my God for - ev - er-more, Hal-le-lu -
p
rall.
jah! Hal-le-lu - jah! I'll serve my God, I'll serve my God for ev - er - more.

Cantique de Noël
(O Holy Night)
ADOLPHE ADAM
Slowly and majestically
mf
1. O ho - ly night! the stars are bright-ly shin - ing, It is the night of the dear Sav-iour's birth; Long lay the world in sin and er - ror pin - ing, Till He ap-
2. Led by the light of faith se - rene - ly beam - ing, With glow - ing hearts by His cra - dle we stand; So led by light of a star sweet-ly gleam - ing, Here came the
3. Tru-ly He taught us to love one an - oth - er; His law is love, and His gos - pel is peace; Chains shall He break, for the slave is our bro - ther, And in His

Cantique de Noël–Continued

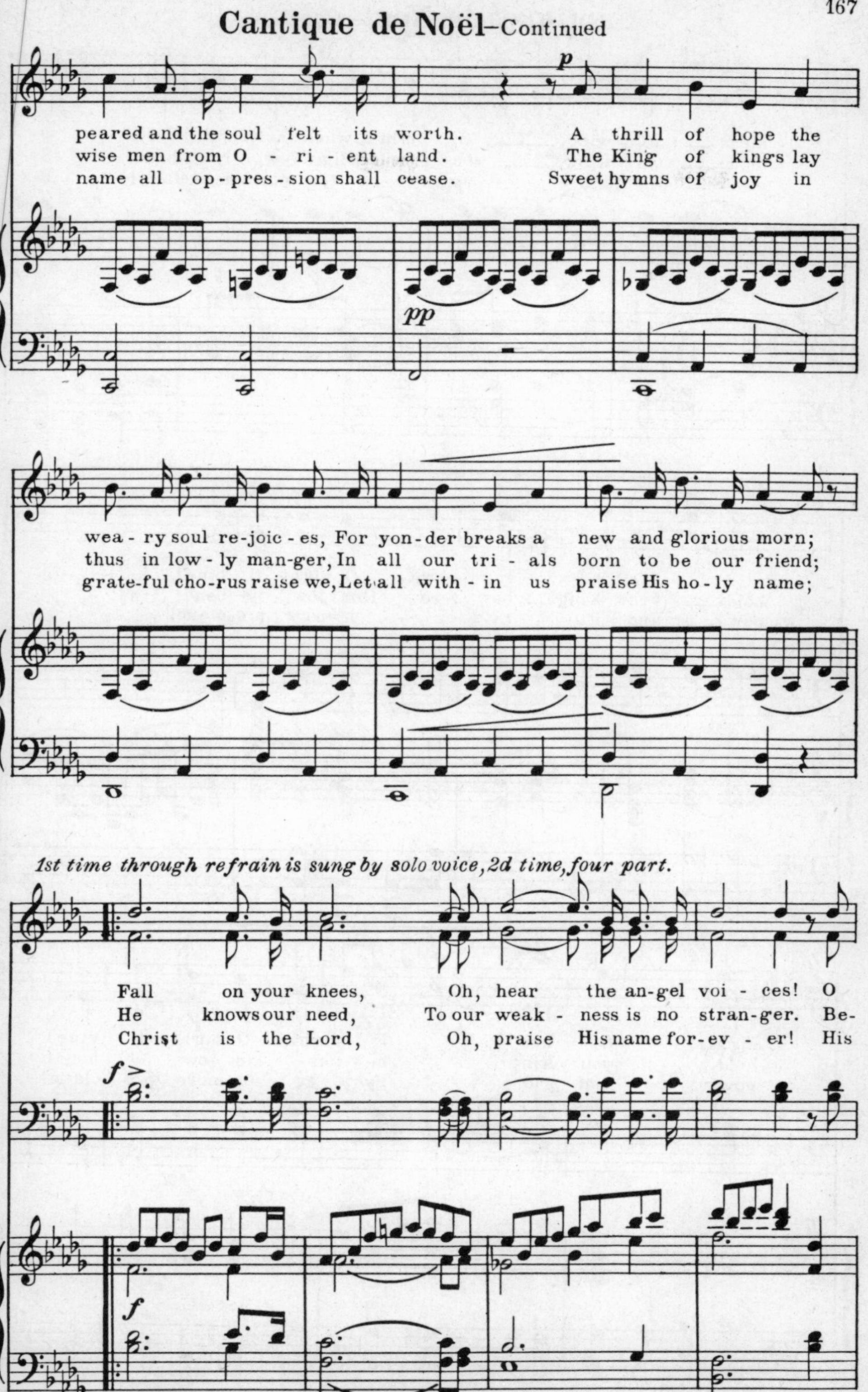
peared and the soul felt its worth. A thrill of hope the
wise men from O - ri - ent land. The King of kings lay
name all op-pres-sion shall cease. Sweet hymns of joy in
pp
wea-ry soul re-joic-es, For yon-der breaks a new and glorious morn;
thus in low-ly man-ger, In all our tri - als born to be our friend;
grate-ful cho-rus raise we, Let all with - in us praise His ho-ly name;
1st time through refrain is sung by solo voice, 2d time, four part.
Fall on your knees, Oh, hear the an-gel voi - ces! O
He knows our need, To our weak - ness is no stran-ger. Be-
Christ is the Lord, Oh, praise His name for-ev - er! His
f
f

Cantique de Nöel—Concluded

night — di - vine, — O night — when Christ was born! O
hold — your King, — be - fore — Him low - ly bend! Be-
pow'r — and glo - - ry ev - er-more pro-claim! His
1
night — O ho - ly night O night di - vine!
hold — your King — be - fore Him low - ly bend!
pow'r — and glo - ry ev - er-more pro-claim!
6
6
2
night, O ho - ly night, O night di - vine!
hold your King be - fore him low - ly bend!
pow'r and glo - ry ev - er-more pro-claim!

Christ, the Lord, Is Risen Today
CHARLES WESLEY
"LYRA DAVIDICA"
1. Christ, the Lord, is ris'n to-day, Al - le - lu - ia! Sons of men and an - gels say: Al - le - lu - ia! Raise your joys and triumphs high; Al - le - lu - ia! Sing, ye heav'ns, and earth, reply. Al - le - lu - ia!
2. Vain the stone, the watch, the seal, Christ has burst the gates of hell: Death in vain for - bids His rise; Christ has opened Par-a-dise.
3. Lives a-gain our glo-rious King: Where, O death, is now thy sting? Once He died our souls to save: Where thy victo-ry, O grave?
4. Soar we now where Christ has led, Fol-lowing our ex - alt - ed Head: Made like Him, like Him we rise; Ours the cross, the grave, the skies.
Hark! Ten Thousand Voices
(St. Oswald)
T. KELLY
JOHN B. DYKES
mf
1. Hark! ten thousand voi-ces sound-ing, Far and wide thro' - out the sky; 'Tis the voice of joy a-bound-ing, Je-sus lives no more to die.
2. Je - sus lives, His con-flict o - ver, Lives to claim His great re-ward; An - gels round the Vic - tor hov-er, Crowding to be - hold their Lord.
3. Yon - der throne for Him e - rect - ed Now becomes the Vic-tor's seat; Lo, the Man on earth re - ject - ed, An-gels wor-ship at His feet!
4. All the pow'rs of heav'n a - dore Him, All o - bey His sovereign word; Day and night they cry be - fore Him, "Ho - ly, Ho - ly, Ho - ly Lord!"

Come Ye Thankful People

HENRY ALFORD | GEORGE J. ELVEY

1. Come, ye thank-ful peo - ple, come, Raise the song of har - vest home:
2. All the world is God's own field, Fruit to His great praise to yield;
3. Ev - en so, Lord, quick-ly come, Hold Thy fi - nal har - vest - home;
All is safe - ly gath - ered in, Ere the win - ter storms be - gin;
Wheat and tares to - geth - er sown, Un - to joy or sor - row grown:
Gath - er Thou Thy peo - ple in, Free from sor - row, free from sin;
God, our Mak - er, doth pro - vide For our wants to be sup - plied;
First the blade, and then the ear, Then the full corn shall ap - pear:
There, for - ev - er pu - ri - fied, In Thy pres - ence to a - bide:

Come Ye Thankful People-Concluded
Come to God's own tem-ple, come, Raise the song of har-vest-home.
Grant, O har-vest Lord, that we Whole-some grain and pure may be.
Come, with all Thine an-gels, come, Raise the glo-rious har-vest-home.
Good King Wenceslas
JOHN NEAL
TRADITIONAL
Moderately quick
CHO. 1. Good King Wences-las look'd out On the Feast of Stephen, When the snow lay round a-bout, Deep and crisp and e-ven; Brightly shone the moon that night, Tho' the frost was cru-el, When a poor man came in sight, Gath'ring win-ter fu - el.
TEN. S. 2. "Hith-er, page, and stand by me, If thou know'st it, tell-ing; Yon-der peas-ant, who is he? Where, and what his dwelling?" "Sire, he lives a good league hence, Underneath the mountain; Right a-gainst the for-est fence, By Saint Ag-nes' foun - tain."
TEN. S. 3. "Bring me flesh, and bring me wine, Bring me pine-logs hith-er; Thou and I will see him dine When we bear them thither." Page and monarch forth they went, Forth they went to-geth-er; Thro' the rude wind's wild lament And the bit-ter weath - er.
TEN. S. 4. "Sire, the night is dark-er now, And the wind blows stronger; Fails my heart, I know not how, I can go no long-er." "Mark my footsteps, my good page Tread thou in them bold-ly: Thou shalt find the win-ter's rage Freeze thy blood less cold - ly."
CHO. 5. In his mas-ter's steps he trod, Where the snow lay din-ted; Heat was in the ver-y sod Which the saint had printed; Therefore, Christian men, be sure, Wealth or rank pos-sess-ing, Ye who now will bless the poor, Shall yourselves find bless - ing.
a little slower

Schubert's Serenade

The name of Franz Peter Schubert, the great Vienna composer, is always associated with song. Other composers of his time gave their thoughts to the composition of operas, oratorios, symphonies, etc., and while Schubert also composed a few of these, he chose the song as the means for expression of his choicest musical thought. During his short lifetime of but thirty-one years (1797-1828), he composed over six hundred songs. His "Serenade" has always been popular. Another of his songs, "The Linden Tree" is given on another page.

TRANSLATION

FRANZ SCHUBERT

1. Thro' the leaves the night winds mov-ing, Mur - mur low and sweet;
2. Moon-light on the earth is sleep-ing, Winds are rus - tling low;
To thy cham - ber win - dow rov - ing
Where the dark - ling streams are creep - ing

3
love hath led my feet.
Dear - est let us go.
3
Si - lent pray'rs of bliss - ful feel - ing
All the stars keep watch in heav - en,
3
Link us tho' a -
While I sing to
3
part, Link us tho' a - part.
thee, While I sing to thee.
3
On the breath of
And the night for
3

Schubert's Serenade-Continued

mu - sic steal - ing To thy dream - ing heart,
love is giv - en Dear - est come to me,
f
To thy dream - ing heart.
Dear - est come to me.
f
pp
Sad - ly in the for - est mourn - ing Wails the whippoor

Schubert's Serenade-Concluded

f
3
will;
And the heart for thee is yearn-ing;
f
f
pp
3
Bid— it, love, be still,
Bid— it, love, be
pp
3
still.
Bid it, love be still.
pp

A Merry Life

(Funiculi, Funicula)

FROM THE ITALIAN
LUIGI DEN
Rapidly and with spirit ♩. = 96
SOLO
1. Some think
2. Ah, me!
— the world is made for fun and frol - ic, — And so do I! —
— 'tis strange that some should take to sigh - ing, — And like it well! —
CHORUS
— And so do I! —
— And like it well! —
SOLO
Some think — it well
For me, — I have n
be all mel - an - chol - ic, — To pine and sigh, —
tho't it worth the try - ing, — So can-not tell! —
CHORUS
To pine an
So can-no

A Merry Life-Continued

SOLO
p
sigh; But I, I love to spend my time in
tell! With laugh, and dance, and song, the day soon
p
sing - ing Some joy - ous song, Some joy - ous song;
pass - es, Full soon is gone, Full soon is gone;
CHORUS
SOLO
To set the air with mu-sic brave-ly ring - ing
For mirth was made for joy-ous lads and lass - es
CHORUS
f
Is far from wrong! Is far from wrong!
To call their own! To call their own!
f

A Merry Life-Concluded

First time Solo, Second time Chorus.

Hark-en! Hark-en! Music sounds a-far! — Hark-en! Hark-en!

Hark-en! Hark-en! Music sounds a-far! — Hark-en! Hark-en!

Mu-sic sounds a-far! Tra-la-la-la, tra-la-la-la, tra-la-la-la, tra-la-la-la

Mu-sic sounds a-far! Tra-la-la-la, tra-la-la-la, tra-la-la-la, tra-la-la-la

Joy is ev-'ry-where, Tra-la-la-la, tra-la-la-la.

Joy is ev-'ry-where, Tra-la-la-la, tra-la-la-la.

The Alphabet

Lively
WOLFGANG MOZART
p
a b c d e f g h i j k l m n o,
a b c d e f g h i j k l m n o,
k l m n o p q, k l m n o p q - r s t u v w
k l m n o p q, k l m n o p q - r s t u v w
mf
x y and z - a b c d
x y and z - a b c d
f
p
e f g h i j k l m n o, k l m n o p q
e f g h i j k l m n o, k l m n o p q,
a b c d e f g h i j k l, k l m m n n o, k l m n o p q,
k l m n o p q, r s t u v w x y and z-.
k l m n o p q, r s t u v w x y and z-.

I Would That My Love

HEINRICH HEINE

FELIX MENDELSSO

With a lively motion

1. I would that my love could si - lent - ly
2. To thee on their wings my fair - est, that
flow in a sin - gle word, I'd give it the mer - r
soul - felt word they would bear, Should'st hear it at ev - 'r
breez - es They'd waft it a-way in sport, I'd
mo - ment, And hear it ev - 'ry where, Should's
give it the mer - ry breez - es, They'd waft it a - way in
hear it at ev - 'ry mo - ment, And hear it ev - 'ry
p
sf
cresc.
f
p

I Would That My Love—Continued

sport; a-way in sport,— a-way in sport,— they'd—
where; and ev-'ry where,— and ev-'ry where,— and—

waft it a-way in sport.
hear— it ev-'ry where.

At night— when thine eye-lids in

slum-ber have clos'd those bright heav'nly beams, Still

I Would That My Love–Concluded
cresc.
there my love — it will haunt — thee e'en in thy deep-est
cresc.
dreams, Still there my love it will haunt thee e'en —
f
e'en in thy deep - est
in thy deepest dreams. thy deepest dreams, E'en —
p
sf
in — thy deep-est, deep - est dreams.
p

Calm as the Night
'ROM THE GERMAN
CARL BOHM
Calmly
slightly slower
p
In time
mf
Calm as the night, Deep as the sea,
p
In time
mf
slower
in time
Thy love for me should be.
p
f
Calm as the night, And deep as the sea,
p
f

Thy love for me, thy love for me—— should be,——

pp *slower*

Thy love, thy love—— should be.

pp *slower* *pp* *in time*

mf *in time*

If thou lov'st me

slower *in time* *mf*

p
slower
in time
As I love thee,— Thine, thine for-e'er—— I'll be.
p
slower
in time

Calm as the Night-Concluded

f faster
ff
Glow - ing as steel And firm as the
f
ff
hills Thy love should be, thy love for me should
p
slower
in time
be, Thy love for me should be.
p
slower
p in time
slower
pp

The Rose of Allandale

SIDNEY NELSON

CHARLES JEFFRY

Arranged by WALTER GOODE[illegible]

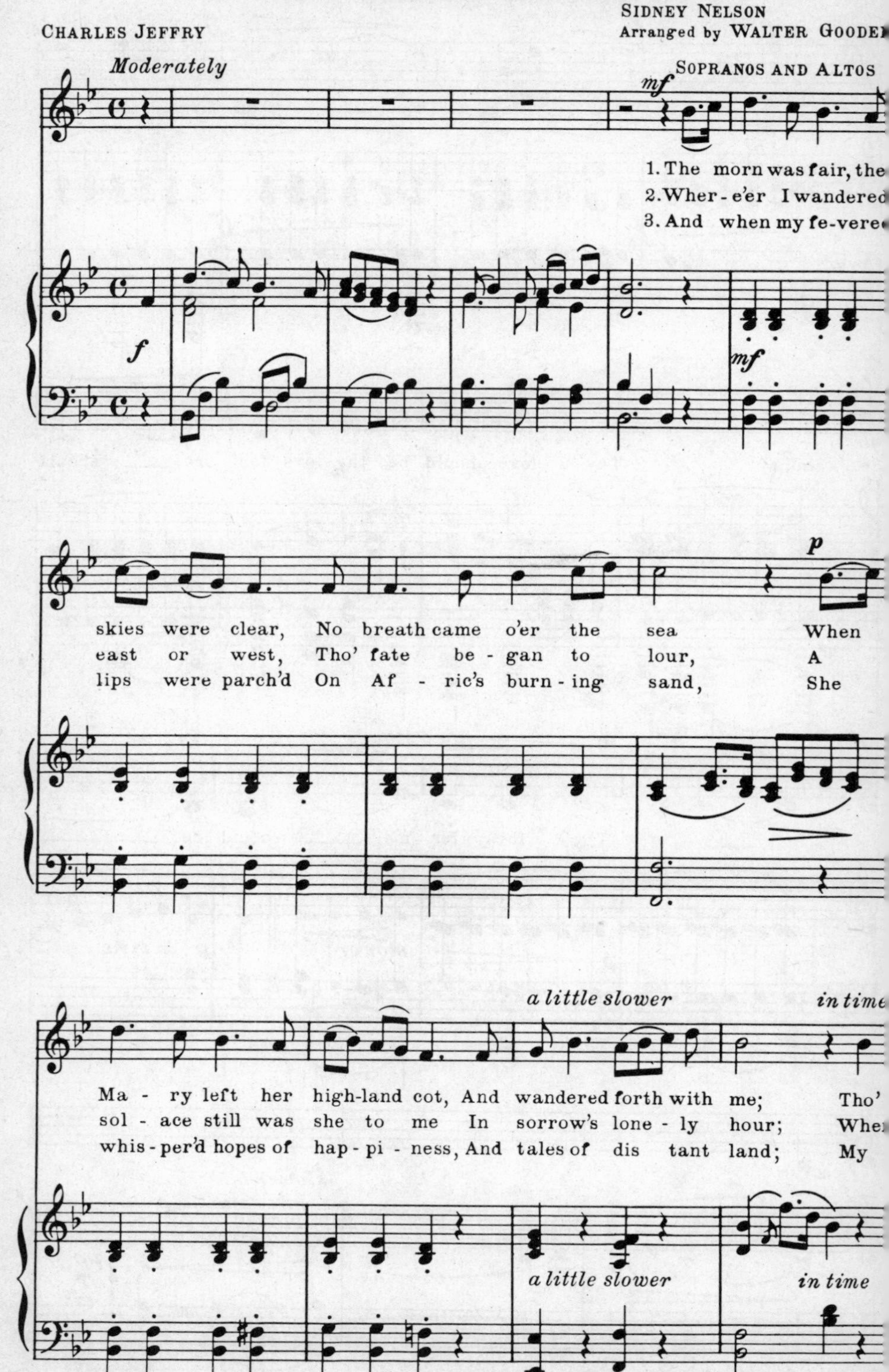
Moderately
SOPRANOS AND ALTOS
mf
f
1. The morn was fair, the skies were clear, No breath came o'er the sea When Ma - ry left her high-land cot, And wandered forth with me; Tho'
2. Wher - e'er I wandered east or west, Tho' fate be - gan to lour, A sol - ace still was she to me In sorrow's lone - ly hour; Whe[illegible]
3. And when my fe-vere[illegible] lips were parch'd On Af - ric's burn - ing sand, She whis - per'd hopes of hap - pi - ness, And tales of dis tant land; My
p
a little slower
in time

The Rose Of Allandale-Concluded

mf a little slower
flow - ers deck'd the moun-tain's side, And fragrance fill'd the vale, By
tem - pests lash'd our gal - lant bark, And rent her shiv-'ring sail, One
life has been a wil - der - ness, Un - blest by for - tune's gale, Had
mf a little slower
faster
mf
far the sweet-est flow-er there Was the Rose of Al - lan - dale.
maid-en form with-stood the storm: 'Twas the Rose of Al - lan - dale.
fate not link'd my lot to hers, The Rose of Al - lan - dale.
p
mf
spirited
a little slower
f
p
The Rose of Al - lan - dale, the Rose of Al - lan - dale, By
f
p
in time
mf
far the sweet est flow-er there Was the Rose of Al - lan - dale.
mf

Come Where My Love Lies Dreaming

S.C.F.

STEPHEN C. FOST
Arr. by Ruth Heller

Moderato
p
p
Come where my love lies dream-ing, Dream-ing the hap-py hours a - way,
vi-sions bright re - deem - ing The fleet-ing joys of day.
Second time a tempo
Dream - ing the hap-py hours,
Come where my love lies dream-ing, Dream-ing the hap-py hours a - way.

poco lento graz.
tempo
My own love is sweet-ly dream-ing
mf
Come where my love lies dream-ing, Dream-ing the hap-py hours a - way.
mf
gräz.
My own love is sweet-ly dream-ing, Her beau-ty
Come where my love lies dream-ing, Come with a lute - toned
8va
beam - ing.
My own love is sweet - ly
lay. (Hm.) Come where my love lies dream-ing, Sweet - ly
melody legato
stacc.
f
My
dream-ing the hap-py hours a - way. Come with a lute, come with a lay,
f

own love is sweet-ly dream-ing, her beau-ty beam-ing,
Come, come, come, come, Come, come, come, come, Come, come, come, come,
lento con grazia tempo
mf
Come where my love lies, My own love is sweet-ly dream-ing the hap-py hours a
Second time to Coda
way.
Soft is her slum - ber, Thoughts bright and free
8va
Dance through her dreams Like gush-ing mel - o - dy;

Come Where My Love Lies Dreaming - Concluded

Light is her young heart, Light may it be;
ritardando
D.S.
Come where my love lies dream ing.
ritardando
CODA
rit.
mf
Dream - ing the hap - py hours a - way.
8va
mf rit.
p

Stephen C. Foster

Stephen Collins Foster, a truly American writer of what may be called the folk songs of America, was born July 4th, 1826 at Lawrenceburg, Pennsylvania, now a part of Pittsburgh, and died in New York in 1864. From an early age he was interested in music. He often attended negro camp meetings and there studied the music of the colored people.

Chief among Foster's characteristics was his tenderness. This quality is reflected in all of his songs.

Gentle Annie
S.C.F.
STEPHEN C. FOSTE
Arr. by J.W.B.
1. Thou wilt come no more, gentle Annie, Like a flow'r thy spir-it did de-part, Thou ar
2. We have roamed in youth 'mid the bowers When thy downy cheeks were in their bloom, Now I
hm
Hm
Hm
hm
hm
gone, a-las, like the many That have bloomed in the summer of my heart.
stand alone 'mid the flowers, While they min-gle their perfume o'er thy tomb.
REFRAI
Shall we
never more be-hold thee, Never hear thy winning voice a-gain, When the
spring time comes, gentle An-nie, When the wild flow'rs are scatter'd o'er the plain?
Fairy-Belle
S.F.C.
Moderately
STEPHEN C. FOSTE
Arr. by J.W.B.
1. The pride of the vil-lage, and the fair-est in the dell, Is the
2. She sings to the meadows, and she car-ols to the streams; She
queen of my song, and her name is Fair-y Belle; The sound of her light step may b
laughs in the sun-light, and smiles while in her dreams; Her hair, like the thistle-down, is

heard up-on the hill, Like the fall of the snow-drops or the dripping of the rill.
borne up-on the air, And her heart like the humming birds is free from ev'ry care.

Fair-y-Belle, gen-tle Fair-y-Belle, The star of the night and the li - ly of the day,

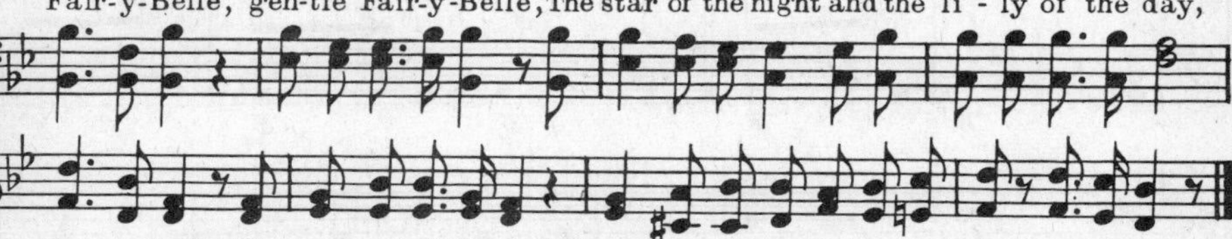
Fair-y-Belle, The queen of all the dell, Long may she revel on her bright, sun-ny way.

Gentle Annie and Fairy-Belle are two of Foster's numbers which are comparatively little known they have been so arranged as to make them useful for either mixed or male quartet. For male voices, have first tenor take the alto part, singing it in the range as written; the second tenor takes the soprano an octave lower than written; the first bass takes the upper part in the bass clef and the second bass the lower.

Sally In Our Alley

Slowly

HENRY CAREY

mp

Of all the girls that are so smart, There's none like pret - ty Sal - ly; She
Her fa-ther he makes cabbage nets, And thro' the streets does cry 'em; Her

mp

is the darling of my heart, And lives in our al-ley; There is no la-dy in the land That's
mother she sells laces long, To such as please to buy 'em; But sure such folk could ne'er beget So

half so sweet as } Sally; She is the darling of my heart, And lives in our al-ley.
sweet a girl as }

Welcome, Sweet Springtime

ANTON RUBINSTEI

1. Wel- come sweet spring time we greet thee in song, Mur-murs of glad- ness fall on the ear; Voi - ces long hush'd now their full notes prolong Ech - o-ing far and near.
Sun - shine now wakes all the flow - 'rets fron sleep, Joy giv - ing in - cense floats on the air; Snow-drop and prim-rose both tim-id-ly peep, Hail we the glad new - year.
D.S. Sing then, ye birds, raise your voi - ces on high Flow'rets a - wake ye! burst in - to bloom! Spring time is come and sweet summer is nigh, Sing, then ye birds, O sing!
Fin
Fin
Balm - y and life breathing breez - es are blow - ing Swift - ly to

na-ture new vig - or be-stow-ing Ah! how my heart beats with rap-ture a-

D. S. al Fine.

new, As earth's fair-est beau-ties a-gain meet my view.

The Bell Is Ringing

(Round)

Lively

1 Hark! the bell is ringing, Call-ing us to sing-ing, Hear the cheerful lay, Come, come, come away!

2 Hark! the bell is ring-ing, Call-ing us to sing-ing, Hear the cheerful lay, Come, come, come away!

3 Hark! Hark! the bell is ringing, Call-ing us to sing-ing, Come, come, come, come away!

Taps

PENN MILITARY COLLEGE U. S. ARMY BUGLE CALL

Day is done, gone the sun, From the lake, from the hill, from the sky, All is well, Safe-ly rest, God is nigh.

Oh, Mistress Shady

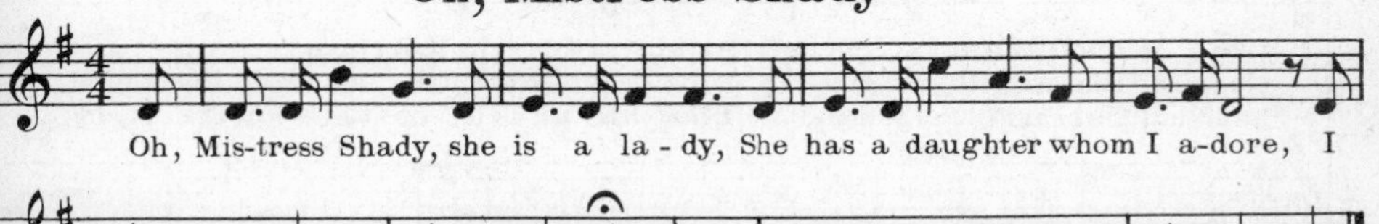
Oh, Mis-tress Shady, she is a la - dy, She has a daughter whom I a-dore, I

go to court her, I mean the daughter, Ev'ry Sunday after-noon at half past four.

2. Monday
3. Tuesday.
4 Wednesday.
5 Thursday
6. Friday.
7. Saturday.

The Blacksmith

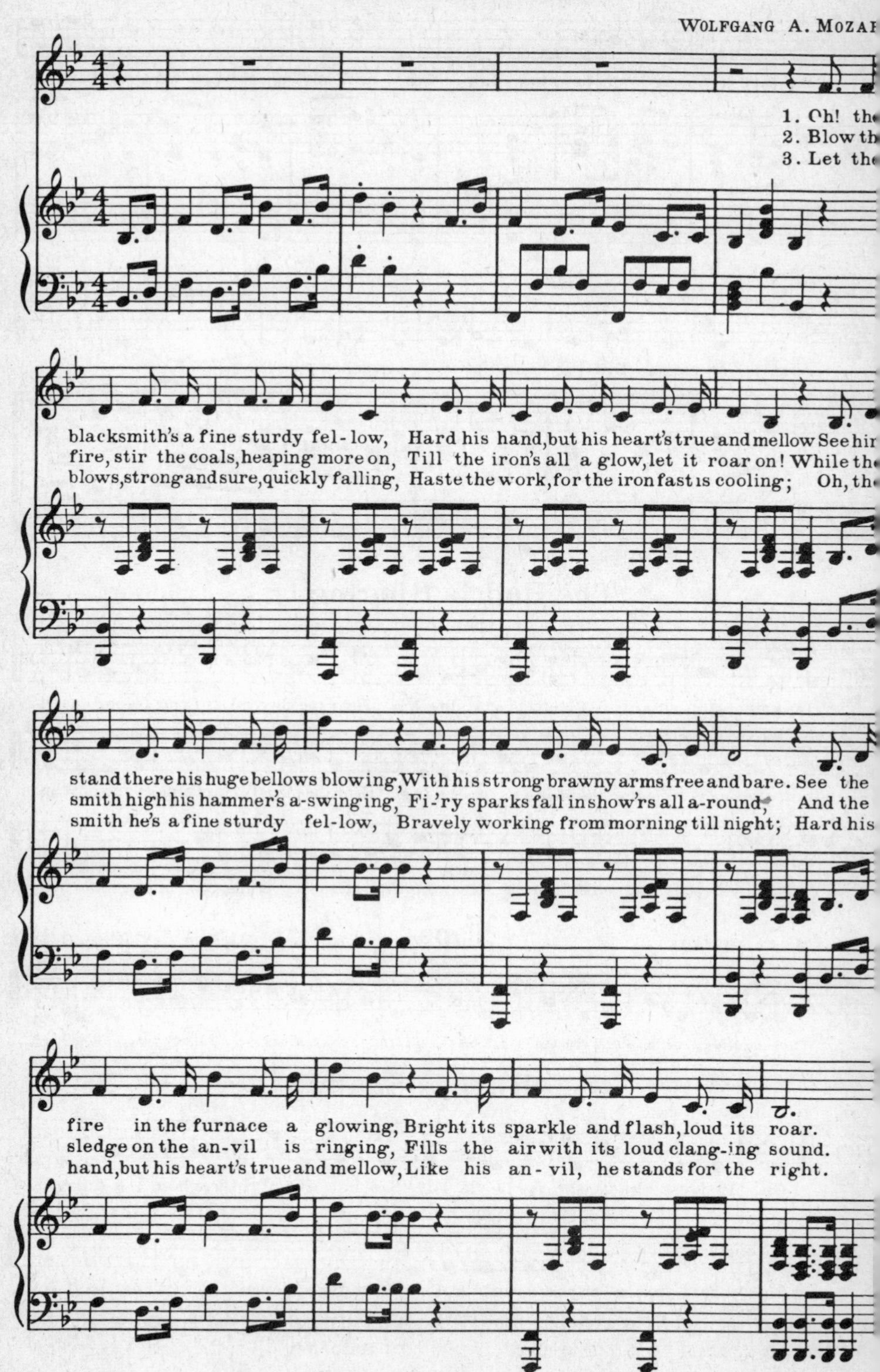
WOLFGANG A. MOZAR
1. Oh! th
2. Blow th
3. Let th
blacksmith's a fine sturdy fel-low, Hard his hand, but his heart's true and mellow See hi
fire, stir the coals, heaping more on, Till the iron's all a glow, let it roar on! While th
blows, strong and sure, quickly falling, Haste the work, for the iron fast is cooling; Oh, th
stand there his huge bellows blowing, With his strong brawny arms free and bare. See the
smith high his hammer's a-swinging, Fi-'ry sparks fall in show'rs all a-round; And the
smith he's a fine sturdy fel-low, Bravely working from morning till night; Hard his
fire in the furnace a glowing, Bright its sparkle and flash, loud its roar.
sledge on the an-vil is ringing, Fills the air with its loud clang-ing sound.
hand, but his heart's true and mellow, Like his an-vil, he stands for the right.

The Low-Backed Car

AMUEL LOVER | OLD IRISH AIR

Moderately fast

1. When first I saw sweet Peggy, 'Twas on a mar-ket day, A low-back'd car she
2. In bat-tle's wild commotion, The proud and mighty Mars, With hostile scythes, de-
3. Sweet Peggy round her car, sir, Has strings of ducks and geese, But the scores of hearts she
4. I'd rath-er own that car, sir, With Peg-gy by my side, Than a coach-and-four and

drove, and sat Up - on a truss of hay; But when that hay was blooming grass, And
mands his tithes Of death, in war-like cars; While Peggy, peace-ful god - dess, Has
slaugh - ters By far out-number these; While she a-mong her poul-try sits, Just
gold galore, And a la-dy for my bride; For the lady would sit for-ninst me, On a

deck'd with flow'rs of spring, No flow'r was there that would compare With the blooming girl I
darts in her bright eye, That knock men down in the market town, As right and left they
like a tur - tle - dove, Well worth the cage, I do engage, Of the blooming God of
cush - ion made with taste, While Peggy would sit be-side me With my arm around her

sing, As she sat in the low-back'd car; The man at the turn-pike bar Nev - er
fly, While she sits in her low-back'd car Than battles more dangerous far For
Love! While she sits in her low-back'd car, The lovers come near and far And
waist, As we drove in a low-back'd car, To be married by Fa-ther Maher*, O, my

ask'd for the toll, But just rubb'd his auld poll, And look'd af-ter the low-back'd car.
the doctor's art Can - not cure the heart That is hit from the low-back'd car.
en - vy the chick-en That Peg-gy is pickin', As she sits in the low-back'd car.
heart would beat high At her glance and her sigh, Tho' it beat in a low-back'd car.

*Pronounced Măr

Nancy Lee

FREDERICK E. WEATHERLY

STEPHEN ADA

With spirit
1. Of all the wives as e'er you know, Yeo
2. The har - bor's past, the breezes blow, Yeo
3. The bo' - s'n pipes the watch be - low, Yeo
ho! lads! ho! Yeo - ho! Yeo - ho! There's none like Nancy Lee, I trow,
ho! lads! ho! Yeo - ho! Yeo - ho! 'Tis long ere we come back, I know,
ho! lads! ho! Yeo - ho! Yeo - ho! Then here's a health before we go,
Yeo - ho! Yeo - ho! Yeo - ho! See there she stands an'
Yeo - ho! Yeo - ho! Yeo - ho! But true an' bright fro
Yeo - ho! Yeo - ho! Yeo - ho! A long, long life to

Nancy Lee—Concluded

waves her hand up - on ___ the quay, An' ev-'ry day when I'm a-way she'll
morn till night my home ___ will be, An' all so neat an' snug an' sweet for
my sweet wife an' mates ___ at sea, An' keep my bones from Da-vy Jones wher-
watch for me, An' whisper low when tempests blow, for Jack at sea; Yeo-
Jack at sea, An' Nancy's face to bless the place, an' wel - come me; Yeo-
e'er we be, An' may you meet a mate as sweet as Nan - cy Lee; Yeo-
ho! lads! ho! Yeo - ho! The sail - or's wife the sail-or's
star shall be, Yeo - ho! we go a - cross the sea; The sail - or's
wife the sailor's star shall be, The sailor's wife his star shall be. ___

The Bonnets of Bonnie Dundee

(Air-"The Band At A Distance")

SIR WALTER SCOTT

Arr. by Sir G. A. MacFarre

With spirit
f
ff
fp
1. To the Lords of Con-ven-tion 'twas Cla-ver-house spoke, Ere the
3. There are hills be-yond Pent-land, and lands be-yond Forth, If there'
King's crown go down there are crowns to be broke; So__ each Cav-a-lier who loves
Lords in the South, there are Chiefs in the North, There are brave Duinewassals, three
hon-our and me Let him fol-low the bon-nets of Bon-nie Dundee.
thousand times three, Will cry "Hey for the bon-nets of Bon-nie Dundee."
Come

The Bonnets Of Bonnie Dundee–Continued

fill up my cup,—come fill up my can, Come sad-dle my hor-ses and
fp
call out my men, Un-hook the West Port and let us go free, For its
f
up wi' the bon-nets o' Bon-nie Dun-dee.
p
ff
2. Dun - dee, he is mount-ed, he rides up the street,–The
4. Then a - wa' to the hills, to the lea, to the rocks, Ere I
fp
bells they ring back-ward the drums they are beat, But the
own a u - surp - er I'll crouch wi' the fox, And—

The Bonnets Of Bonnie Dundee-Concluded

Pro - vost (douce man) said "Just e'en let it be, For the
town is weel rid o' that de'il o' Dundee,"
trem - ble false Whigs, in the midst o' your glee, Ye ha'e
no seen the last o' my bon - nets and me.
Come fill up my cup, come fill up my can, Come sad - dle my horses and call out my men, Un -
hook the West Port and let us go free, For its up wi' the bon - nets o'
Bon - nie Dun - dee.
fp
p
f
ff

Leezie Lindsay

WORDS TRADITIONAL

OLD SCOTCH SONG

Not too slowly
1."Will ye gang to the
2."To gang to the
3. Then up be-spak'
4. She has kilt-ed her
5. He has led her high
p
p
Hie-lands, Lee-zie Lind-say? Will ye gang to the hie-lands wi'
Hie-lands, wi' you, sir! I din-na ken how that may
Lee-zie's best wo-man, A bon-nie young las-sie was
coats o' green sat-in, She has kilt-ed them up to the
up-on a mountain, And bade her look out o'er the
me; Will ye gang to the Hie-lands, Lee-zie Lind-say, My
be; For I ken-na the land that ye live in, Nor
she; "Had I but a mark in my pock-et, It's
knee, And she's aff to the Hie-lands wi' Don-ald, His
sea; "These isles are Lord Ron-ald Mac-Don-ald's, And his
bride and my dar-ling to be?"
ken I the lad I'm gaun wi."
Don-ald that I wad gang wi."
bride and his dar-ling to be.
bride and his dar-ling are ye."

The Midshipmite

FREDERICK E. WEATHERLY
STEPHEN ADAM
Lively
ff
p
1. 'Twas in 'fif - ty-five, on a win-ter's night, Cheer-i - ly, my lads, yo
2. We __ launched the cutter an' shoved her out, Cheer-i - ly, my lads, yo
3. "I'm __ done for now, good - bye!" says he, Stead-i - ly, my lads, yo
p
f
ho! We'd got the __ Roo-shan __ lines in sight, When up comes a lit - tle __
ho! The lub - bers __ might ha' __ heard us shout, As the Mid-dy __ cried, "Now, my
ho! "You make for the boat, never mind for me!" "We'll take 'ee __ back, sir, or
p
Mid - ship-mite, Cheer-i - ly, my lads, yo ho! "Who'll __ go a - shore to -
lads, put a-bout!" Cheer-i - ly, my lads, yo ho! We __ made for the guns, an' we
die," __ says we, Cheer-i - ly, my lads, yo ho! So we hoist-ed him in, in a
8va
mf

The Midshipmite—Concluded

night," says he, "An'— spike their guns a - long wi' me?" "Why bless'ee sir, come a -
rammed them tight, But the musket shots came left and right, An' down drops the poor little
ter - ri - ble plight, An' we pulled, ev'ry man with all his might, An' saved the poor lit-tle
f
long," says we, Cheer - i - ly, my lads, yo ho!— Cheer - i - ly, my lads, yo
Mid-ship-mite, Cheer - i - ly, my lads, yo ho!— Cheer - i - ly, my lads, yo
Mid-ship-mite, Cheer - i - ly, my lads, yo ho!— Cheer - i - ly, my lads, yo
cresc.
f
slower
in time
8
ho! — With a long, long pull, An' a strong, strong pull,
slower
p
slower
Gai - ly, boys, make her go! — An' we'll drink to - night To the Mid - ship -
slower
f
with the voice
last time
mite, Sing-ing cheer - i - ly, lads, yo ho! —
f
ff

A Warrior Bold

The name of the composer, Steven Adams, is a nom-de-plume used by Michael Maybrick: "A Warrior Bold" and "Nancy Lee", which will also be found in this book, are among his most popular songs. Maybrick was born in Liverpool in 1844.

EDWIN THOMAS
STEPHEN ADAM
With Spirit
1. In days of old, when knights were bold, And barons held the
2. So this brave knight, in ar-mor bright, Went gai-ly to the
sway, A war-rior bold, with spurs of gold, Sang mer-ri-ly his lay; Sang
fray; He fought the fight, but ere the night, His soul had pass'd a-way, His
mer-ri-ly his lay: "My love is young and fair, My love hath gold-en
soul had pass'd a - way. The plighted ring he wore Was crush'd and wet with

A Warrior Bold - Concluded

hair, And eyes so blue, and heart so true, That none with her com-pare. So
gore, Yet ere he died, he brave-ly cried, "I've kept the vow I swore. So
what care I tho' death be nigh, I'll live for love or die, So what care I, tho'
what care I tho' death be nigh, I've fought for love and die, So what care I, tho'
1
2
death be nigh, I'll live for love or die."
death be nigh, I've fought for love, for love I die,
I've fought for love, For love, for love I die."

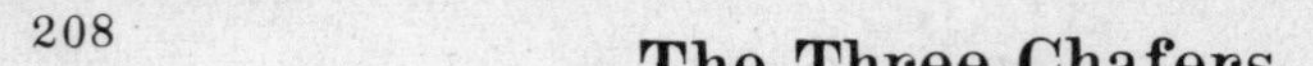

The Three Chafers

(Male Voices)

FRIEDRICH H. TRÜHN

Briskly

1. There were three young and gal - lant chaf - ers, Who with a mer-ry
2. And soon they found a love - ly, love - ly flow'r, As tempt-ing as a
3. The pret - ty flow'r was wide, — so wide — a-wake, And art-ful-ler than
4. Her aunt the spi - der, heard, she heard the call, And came like Fee-faw
5. And while she sat she watch'd, she watch'd her prey, And when she saw them
6. The flow'r, tho' love-ly, had, — she had a heart, As hol-low as a

hum, hum, hum, ★Sum-a,
plum, plum, plum, Sum-a,
some, some, some, Sum-a,
fum, fum, fum, Sum-a,
come, come, come, Sum-a,
drum, drum, drum, Sum-a,
sum, sum, sum, sum, sum, sum, sum, sum, sum, sum, sum, sum,

BASS OR ALTO SOLO.
In dew their nos-es
They all at once were
She call'd her aunt, the
At once her net she
She pounc'd up - on the
She laugh'd and said we've

sum, sum, sum, sum, sum, sum, sum, sum, sum, sum, sum, sum, sum, sum, sum, sum,

dip - ping, In dew their nos-es dip - ping, As tip - sy grew with
bit - ten, They all at once were bit - ten, They all were deep-ly
spi - der, She call'd her aunt, the spi - der, And begg'd she would pro-
spun well, At once her net she spun well, And when she tho't it
chaf - ers, She pounc'd up - on the chaf - ers, And suck'd them thin as
caught ye, She laugh'd and said we've caught ye, Fine chaf-ers and we've

sum, sum, sum, sum, sum, sum, sum, sum, sum,

As tip - sy grew with
They all were deep - ly
And begg'd she would pro-
And when she tho't it
And suck'd them thin as
Fine chaf-ers and we've

sip - ping, As an-y cask of rum, Sum, sum,
smit - ten, Thus chafers can soft be-come, Sum, sum,
vide her A maze to hold like gum, Sum, sum,
done well, With-in it sat quite dumb, Sum, sum,
wa - fers, They nev-er-more could hum, Sum, sum,
taught ye That love is all a hum, Sum, sum,

The Three Chafers-Concluded

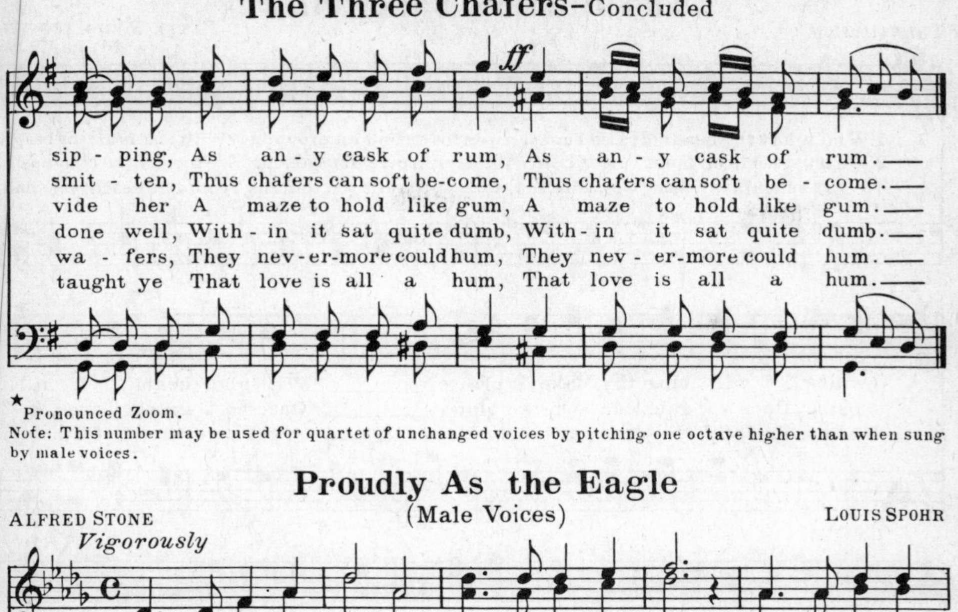
ff
sip - ping, As an - y cask of rum, As an - y cask of rum.
smit - ten, Thus chafers can soft be-come, Thus chafers can soft be - come.
vide her A maze to hold like gum, A maze to hold like gum.
done well, With - in it sat quite dumb, With - in it sat quite dumb.
wa - fers, They nev - er-more could hum, They nev - er-more could hum.
taught ye That love is all a hum, That love is all a hum.

★ Pronounced Zoom.

Note: This number may be used for quartet of unchanged voices by pitching one octave higher than when sung by male voices.

Proudly As the Eagle

(Male Voices)

ALFRED STONE — LOUIS SPOHR

Vigorously

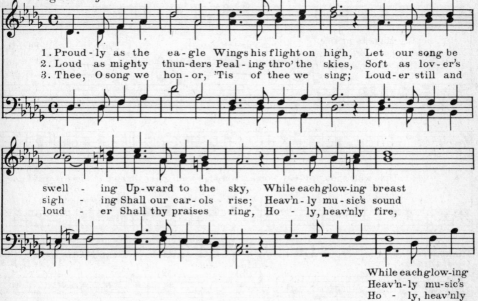

1. Proud - ly as the ea - gle Wings his flight on high, Let our song be swell - ing Up-ward to the sky, While each glow-ing breast Thrills with rapture blest, While each glow-ing breast Thrills with rapture blest.
2. Loud as mighty thun-ders Peal - ing thro' the skies, Soft as lov - er's sigh - ing Shall our car - ols rise; Heav'n - ly mu - sic's sound Spread - ing joy a - round, Heav'n - ly mu-sic's sound Spreading joy a - round.
3. Thee, O song we hon - or, 'Tis of thee we sing; Loud - er still and loud - er Shall thy praises ring, Ho - ly, heav'nly fire, Thou dost e'er in - spire, Ho - ly, heav'nly fire, Thou dost e'er in-spire.

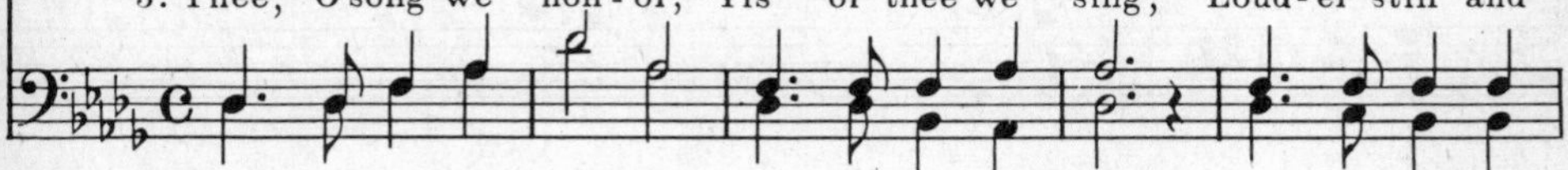

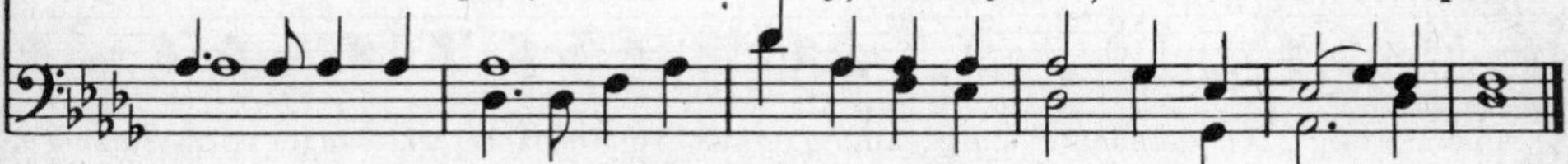

(Bass:)
While each glow-ing breast Thrills with rapture blest, each glowing breast
Heav'n-ly mu-sic's sound Spreading joy a-round, sweet music's sound,
Ho - ly, heav'nly fire, Thou dost e'er in-spire with heav'nly fire,

The Hunter's Farewell
TRANSLATION
(Male Voices)
FELIX MENDELSSOHN
Arr. by J.W.B.
1.Who a-loft thy head did raise, For-est green the mountains crowning? With glad heart thy beauty
2.We must seek our home below, Leave the deer in peace re-pos-ing, Ere for us the chase is
3.What beneath thy shade we swore, In the distant world shall bind us, True to thee each year shall
owning, I will sing thy Maker's praise, With glad heart I will
closing, Once a - gain our horns we blow, Once a - gain, once a -
find us, Faithful chil-dren ev - er - more, ev - er - more, faith-ful
I will sing
sing thy Maker's praise.
gain our horns we blow.
children ev - er - more.
Fare thee well, Fare thee well Fare thee
Fare thee well Fare thee well
well
Fare thee well thou for-est home, Fare thee well, Fare thee well thou for-est home.
Lutzow's Wild Hunt
TRANSLATION
Rapidly
(Male Voices)
CARL MARIA VON WEBER
Arr. by J. W. B.
1.From yonder dark forest what horsemen advance? What sounds from the rocks are re -
2.Why roars in yon val - ley the mer - ci - less fight? What ter - ri - ble sounds are now
ff
p
bound - ing? The sunbeams are gleaming on sword and on lance, And loud the shrill trumpet is
clash - ing? Our true hearted men are maintaining the right, And freedoms bright torch now is

ff
slower
f
sound-ing, And loud the shrill trumpet is sounding. And if you ask what you there be-
flash-ing, The bright torch of freedom is flashing. And if you ask what you there be-
Rapidly
Repeat sung as echo
1
2
hold, These are These are Lutz-ow's hunts-men so free and so bold. bold.
Sleep, Soldier, Sleep
Memorial Day
(Male Voices)
MYRTLE KOON CHERRYMAN
ALPHENS DAVISON
Arr by J.W.B.
1. Sleep, sol-dier, sleep, Sleep, com-rade, 'neath the heav-'ns blue, While on this
2. Sleep, sol-dier, sleep, For you are done with war and fear, Your mem-o-
3. Rest, sol-dier, rest, You faced grim death with cour-age brave, And man-ful-
day we hon-or you, Loy-al and brave, to coun-try true. Sleep, sol-dier, sweetly sleep.
ry to us is dear; The tho't of you brings many a tear. Sleep, sol-dier, gent-ly sleep.
ly your life you gave; Your glo-ry lives be-yond the grave. Rest, sol-dier, gent-ly rest.
The Spider And The Spout
COLLEGE SONG
The blast-ed, bloom-in' spi-der ran up the bloom-in' spout; And then the bloomin'
rain came down and wash'd the spider out; But when the bloom-in' sun ap-peared and
dried up all the rain, Oh, the blast-ed, bloomin', spider, ran up the spout a-gain!

John Peel

ENGLISH HUNTING SONG

With spirit, but not too fast
mf
1. D'ye
2. Yes, I
3. D'ye
mp
ken John Peel with his coat so gay, D'ye ken John Peel at the break o' the day, D'ye ken John Peel when he's far, far a-way With his hounds and his horn in the morn - ing?
ken John Peel and Ru - by too, And Ran - ger and Ring - wood, Bell-man and True; From a find to a check, from a check to a view, From a view to a death in the morn - ing.
ken John Peel with his coat so gay? He lived at Trout - beck once on a day; But now he has gone far a - way, far a - way, We shall ne'er hear his voice in the morn - ing.
louder
louder
softer
softer
CHORUS
f
For the sound of his horn brought
f
f

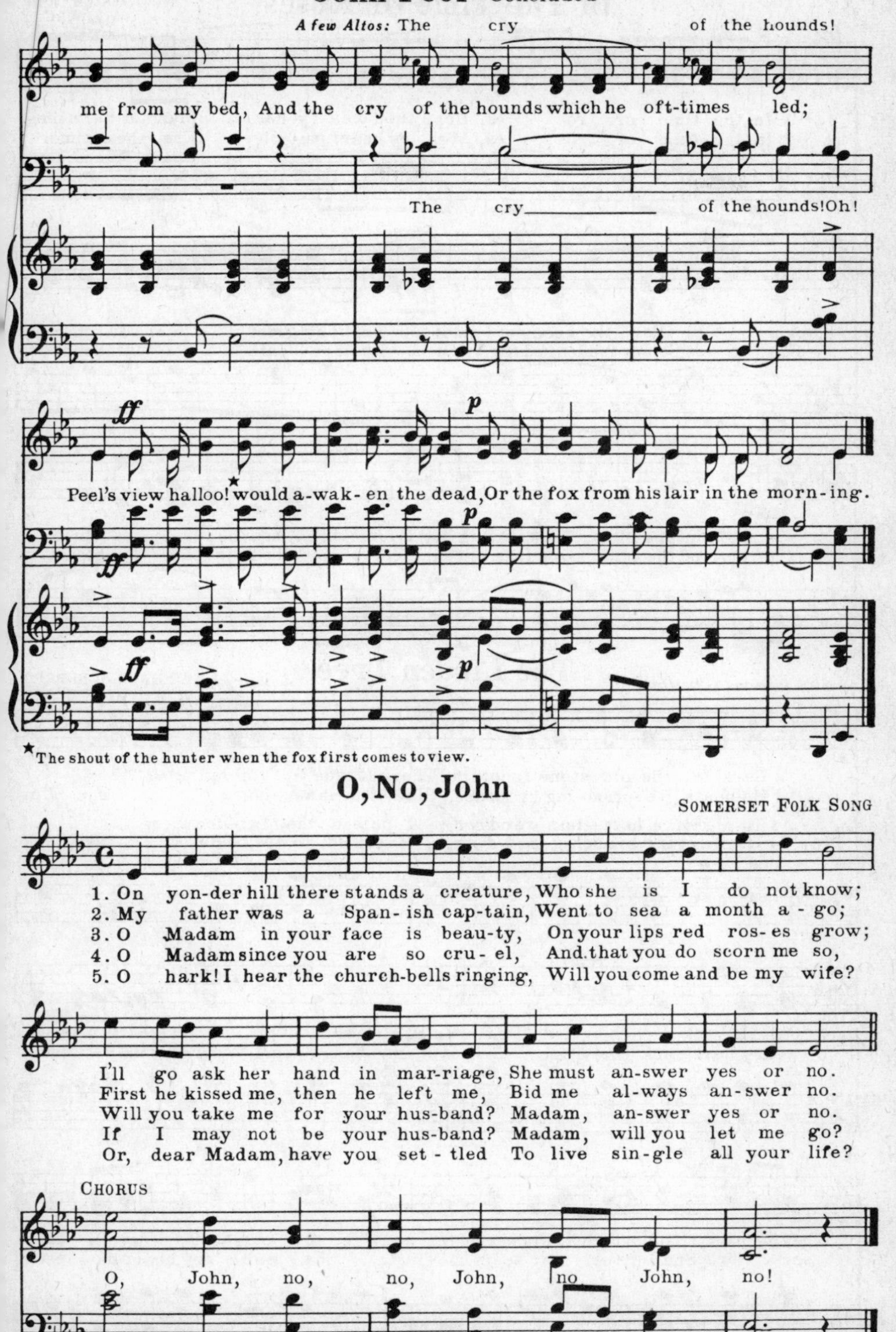
John Peel-Concluded
A few Altos: The cry of the hounds!
me from my bed, And the cry of the hounds which he oft-times led;
The cry of the hounds! Oh!
ff
p
Peel's view halloo! ★ would a-wak-en the dead, Or the fox from his lair in the morn-ing.
ff
p
ff
p
★ The shout of the hunter when the fox first comes to view.
O, No, John
SOMERSET FOLK SONG
1. On yon-der hill there stands a creature, Who she is I do not know;
2. My father was a Span-ish cap-tain, Went to sea a month a-go;
3. O Madam in your face is beau-ty, On your lips red ros-es grow;
4. O Madam since you are so cru-el, And that you do scorn me so,
5. O hark! I hear the church-bells ringing, Will you come and be my wife?
I'll go ask her hand in mar-riage, She must an-swer yes or no.
First he kissed me, then he left me, Bid me al-ways an-swer no.
Will you take me for your hus-band? Madam, an-swer yes or no.
If I may not be your hus-band? Madam, will you let me go?
Or, dear Madam, have you set-tled To live sin-gle all your life?
CHORUS
O, John, no, no, John, no John, no!

In The Time Of Roses
J. REICHARDT
Arr. by W.J.G.
p
1. In the time of ros - es, Hope, thou wea-ry heart! Spring a balm dis-clos - es For the keen-est smart. Tho' thy grief o'er come thee Thro the winter's gloom, Thou shalt thrust it from thee, When the ros - es bloom.
2. In the time of ros - es, Wea-ry heart, re-joice! Ere the summer clos - es Comes the longed for Voice. Let not death ap-pal thee, For, be-yond the tomb, God Him-self shall call thee, When the ros - es bloom.
The Linden Tree
Adapted from the GERMAN
FRANZ SCHUBERT
3
1
2
1. Be-side the old stone fountain, There stands a lin-den tree; Be-neath its spread-ing branches, Glad dreams have come to me. Up-on its bark I chis-eled Dear names so long a - go, I sought its peace in glad - ness, I sought its peace in woe, I sought its peace in woe.
2. To-night, a home-less wand'rer, I passed the lin-den tree; Its wav - ing branches nod-ding, It seemed to speak to me; "Come, weary heart-sick com-rade, Be-neath my shadow rest, Where earth-ly strife or sor - row Shall ne'er thy heart mo-lest, Shall ne'er thy heart mo-lest.
3
This song is complete in three parts and may be used as a trio for girls' voices, the alto taking the tenor with bass omitted.

215
Lovely Night
TRANSLATION
F. H. CHWATAL
Arr. by J. W. B.
1. Love-ly night! O love-ly night! Spreading o-ver hill and meadow, Soft and slow the
2. Ho - ly night! O ho - ly night! Plac - ing brighter worlds before us; Hap - pi-ness thou
haz - y shadow; Soon our wearied eye-lids close, And slumber in thy blest re-pose,
sheddest o'er us; Oh, that we might ne'er re-turn To this dull earth to weep and mourn,
1
2
Soon our wea - ried eye-lids close, And slum-ber in thy blest repose.
Oh, that we might ne'er re-turn To this dull earth to weep and mourn.
WOLFGANG VON GOETHE
The Two Roses
H. WERNER
Moderately slow
mf
louder
1. On a bank two ros - es fair, Wet with morn - ing show - ers,
2. This in leaves of white ar-ray'd, Not a speck to dim them,
3. Like her cheeks, the blush - ing ray Which thy bud en - clos - es;
p
Fill'd with dew, in fragrance grew, As I, pen - sive, full of care, Gather'd two sweet
So I find the spotless mind Which a-dorns my spotless maid, In - no-cen - ce's
Brighter far than you they are, But her charms if I should say, You'd be jeal - ous,
mf
louder
p
flowers.
emblem. Tell me ros - es tru - ly tell, If my fair one loves me well.
ros - es.

Night

MYRTLE KOON CHERRYMAN

FRANZ ABT
Arr. by J. W. B.

1. The sun - set glows in splen - dor To wave a bright fare-well As
2. And now the vel - vet dark - ness Is brightened near and far With
day de-parts in glo - ry All o - ver hill and dell; The shadows lengthen
gleams like ti - ny can - dles, Where many a brilliant star At - tends, in ser-vice
slow - ly And twi-light, hushed and ho - ly, Now dims the sun-set light, Now
loy - al, The moon, se - rene and roy - al, Arrayed in sil - ver bright, Ar-
dims the sun - set light, To greet the night, To greet the night.
rayed in sil - ver bright, The queen of night, The queen of night.

This song is complete in three parts and may be used as a trio for girls voices, the alto taking the tenor, with bass omitted.

Isle Of Beauty

THOMAS H. BAYLY

Moderately

1. Shades of evening close not o'er us, Leave our lone - ly barque a-while;
Morn, a - las! will not re-store us Yon-der dim and dis-tant isle;

2. 'Tis the hour when hap - py fa - ces Smile a - round the ta - per's light;
Who will fill our va - cant pla-ces, Who will sing our songs to - night?

3. When the waves are round me breaking, As I pace the deck a - lone;
And my eye in vain is seek-ing Some green spot to rest up - on:

Isle Of Beauty–Concluded
Still my fan-cy can dis-cov-er Sun-ny spots where friends may dwell;
Thro' the mist that floats a-bove us, Faint-ly sounds the ves-per bell;
What would I not give to wan-der Where my old com-pan-ions dwell;
Dark-er shad-ows round us hov-er, Isle of Beau-ty "fare thee well!"
Like a voice from those a-round us, Breath-ing fond-ly "fare thee well!"
Ab-sence makes the heart grow fon-der, Isle of Beau-ty "fare thee well!"
Steal Away
Slowly
NEGRO "SPIRITUAL"
Steal a-way, steal a-way, steal a-way to Je-sus!
Fine.
Steal a-way, steal a-way home, I ain't got long to stay here.
1. My Lord calls me, He calls me by the thun-der; The
2. Green trees are bend-ing, Poor sin-ners stand trembling; The
3. My Lord calls me, He calls me by the lightning; The
D.C.
trum-pet sounds with-in a my soul: I ain't got long to stay here.

My Lord, What a Mourning
NEGRO "SPIRITUAL"
CHORUS
My Lord, what a mourn-ing, My Lord, what a mourn-ing, My Lord, what a
mourn-ing, When the stars begin to fall.
Fine
LEADER
1. You'll hear the trumpet sound To wake the
2. You'll hear the sinner mourn, To wake the
3. You'll hear the Christian shout, To wake the
CHORUS
D.C.
nations under-ground, Looking to my God's right hand, When the stars begin to fall.
nations under-ground, Looking to my God's right hand, When the stars begin to fall.
nations under-ground, Looking to my God's right hand, When the stars begin to fall.
My Lord Delivered Daniel
NEGRO "SPIRITUAL"
CHORUS
My Lord de-liv-er'd Dan-iel, My Lord de-liv-er'd Dan-iel, My
Lord de-liv-er'd Dan-iel; Why can't he de-liv-er me?
Fine.
LEADER
1. I met a pil-grim on the way, And, I ask him where he's a go-ing. I'm
2. Some say that John the Baptist, Was nothing but a Jew, But the
3. Oh, Dan-iel cast in the li-on's den, He pray both night and day, The
4. He de-liver'd Daniel from the li-on's den, And Jonah from the belly of the whale, And the
5. The rich-est man that ever I saw Was the one that beg the most, His

My Lord Delivered Daniel-Concluded
D.C.
bound for Ca-naan's hap-py land, And this is the shout-ing band. Go on!
Bi - ble doth in - form us That he was a preach-er, too; Yes, he was!
an - gel came from Gal-i-lee, And lock the li - on's jaw. That's so!
He-brew children from the fiery furnace, And why not ev'-ry man? Oh, yes!
soul was filled with Je - sus, And with the Ho - ly Ghost. Yes, it was!
The Old Ark A-Moverin' Along
Leisurely
SPIRITUAL
1. Just wait a lit-tle while I'm gwine to tell you 'bout the ark
2. Then No - ah and his sons they went to work up - on dry land
3. Old No - ah and his sons they went to work up - on the tim - ber
4. And when the ark was fin-ished all ac - cord - ing to the plan
5. Now when the rain be - gan to fall the ark be - gan to rise
6. For for - ty days and for - ty nights the rain it kept a fall - ing
7. That aw-ful rain it stopped at last the wat - ers sub - sid - ed
The old ark a mov - er - in', a mov - er - in' a - long,
1. The Lord He told old No - ah for to build him an old ark.
2. They built that ark ac - cord-ing to the Lord's com - mand.
3. The proud be - gan to laugh, the sil - ly point their fin-ger.
4. Old Mas - ter No - ah took in fam - bly, an - i - mal and man.
5. The wick - ed they hung all a-round with groans and cries.
6. The wick - ed climbed the trees and loud for help they kept a call - ing.
7. And that old ark with all on board on Ar - a - rat rided.
The old ark a mov-er - in', a mov-er - in', a - long. Oh the
Omit in last verse
old ark a mov-er - in', a mov-er - in' a mov-in', The old ark a mover - in', a
D.C.
Last verse only, gradually getting slower.
Fine.
mov-er - in' a - long. Old ark a mov-er - in' a mov-er - in' a - long.

Nobody Knows The Trouble I've Seen
Slowly
mf
NEGRO "SPIRITUAL"
Oh, no-bod-y knows the trouble I've seen, No-bod-y knows but Je-sus!
Fine.
No-bod-y knows the trouble I've seen, Glo-ry Hal-le-lu-jah!
1. Some-times I'm up, some-times I'm down; Oh, yes, Lord; Some-times I'm al-most to the ground, Oh, yes, Lord.
Al-though you see me going along so, Oh, yes, Lord; I have my tri-als here be-low, Oh, yes, Lord.
2. One day when I was walking a-long, Oh, yes, Lord, The element open'd, and the Love came down, Oh, yes, Lord.
I nev-er shall for-get that day, Oh, yes, Lord, When Je-sus wash'd my sins a-way, Oh, yes, Lord.
D.C.
S.C.F.
Oh! Susanna
Moderately
STEPHEN C. FOSTER
1. I came to Al-a-ba-ma wid My ban-jo on my knee, I'm g'wan to Lou-'si-an-a, My true love for to see. It rain'd all night de day I left, De weather it was dry, De sun so hot I froze to death; Su-san-na don't you cry.
2. I had a dream de od-der night, When eb'ry ting was still; I thought I saw Su-san-na, A com-ing down 'de hill. De buck-wheat cake war in her mouth, De tear was in her eye; Says I, I'm com-ing from de South, Su-san-na don't you cry.
3. I soon will be in New Orleans, And den I'll look all 'round, And when I find Su-san-na, I'll fall up-on de ground. But if I do not find her, Dis dark-ey'll sure-ly die; And when I'm dead and bur-ied, Su-san-na don't you cry.

Oh! Susanna—Concluded

CHORUS

Oh! Su-san-na, oh, don't you cry for me, For I goin' to Lou'si-an-a wid my banjo on my knee.

Ring, Ring The Banjo

Paraphase on original Foster text

STEPHEN C. FOSTER
Arr. by J. W. B.

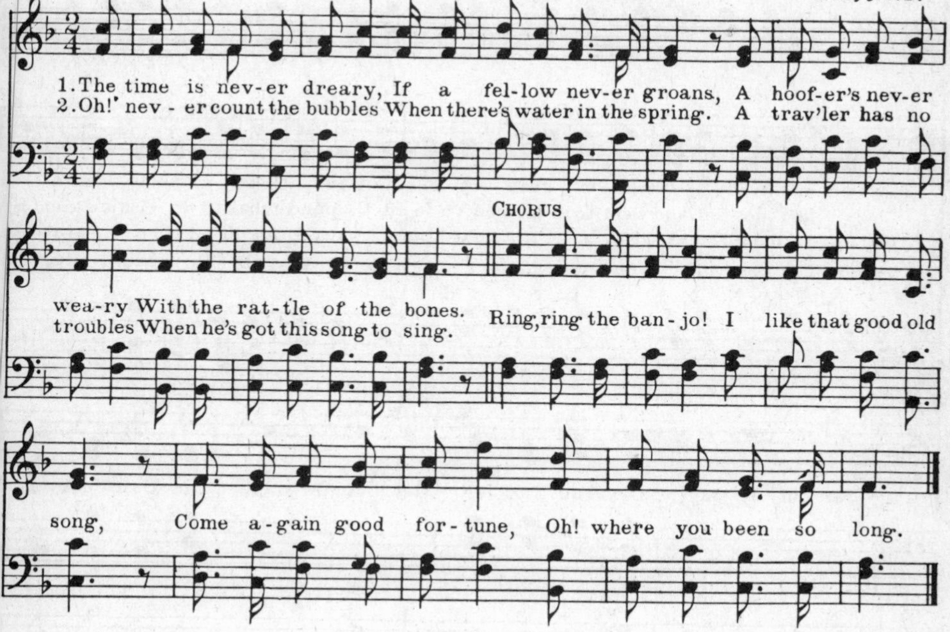

1. The time is nev-er dreary, If a fel-low nev-er groans, A hoof-er's nev-er wea-ry With the rat-tle of the bones.
2. Oh! nev-er count the bubbles When there's water in the spring. A trav'ler has no troubles When he's got this song to sing.

CHORUS

Ring, ring the ban-jo! I like that good old song, Come a-gain good for-tune, Oh! where you been so long.

A "Stunt"

"The Girl I Left Behind Me" may be sung counter to "Ring, Ring The Banjo." A fine assembly "stunt" may be devised by having the girls sing "Ring, Ring The Banjo" while the boys whistle "The Girl I Left Behind Me."

The Girl I Left Behind Me

Briskly

mf

1. I'm lone-some since I cross'd the hill, And o'er the moor and val-ley; Such heav-y thots my
2. Oh, ne'er shall I for-get the night, The stars were bright a-bove me, And gen-tly lent their

heart do fill, Since part-ing with my Sal - ly. I seek no more the fine and gay, For
sil - v'ry light, When first she vow'd she loved me. But now I'm bound to Bright-on camp, Kind

each does but re-mind me How swift the hours did pass away With the girl I've left be-hind me.
Heav'n, may fa-vor find me, And send me safe-ly back a-gain To the girl I've left be-hind me.

Ole Dan Tucker

First Verse—Henry Russel
Other Verses—Myrtle Koon Cherryman
HENRY RUSSEL
mf UNISON
CHORUS
UNISON
1. I come to town de ud-der night, I hear de noise and saw de fight, De
2. Ole Dan he work'd in de cot-ton fiel', But got a stone bruise on his heel, So
3. Ole Dan was hun-gry for to eat Some good corn pone wid chick-en meat, But
4. An' now I thinks dat poor ole Dan, Is git-tin' to be a right ole man, An'
watch-man was a run-nin' roun' Cry-in' "Ole Dan Tucker's come to town." So
he left de fiel' and went troo de wood, To de lit-tle pond whah de fishin's good. So
when he went for to steal a hen, De Mas-sa says, "Don't do dat a-gain!" So
when he dies an goes up high, I hope the an-gels there won't cry, Oh
get out de way, Ole Dan Tuck-er, Get out de way, Ole Dan Tuck-er,
Get out de way, Ole Dan Tuck-er, You're too late to come to sup-per.
Mules
Extended by N.H.H.
(Round)
WALTER GOODELL
1
2
On mules we find Two legs be-hind, And two we find be-fore. We stand be-hind, Be-
3
fore we find What the two be-hind be for. When we're be-hind The two be-hind, We
4
find what these be for. So stand be-fore The two be-hind And be-hind the two be-fore.

Captain Jinks

Lively
1. I'm Cap - tain Jinks, of the Horse Marines; I feed my horse on
2. I joined my corps when twen - ty - one, Of course I thought it
corn and beans, And sport young ladies in their teens, Tho' a cap-tain in the
cap-i-tal fun, When the en-e-my came, of course I run, For I'm not cut out for the
Ar - my. I teach young ladies how to dance, How to dance, How to dance, I
Ar - my. When I left home, mama, she cried, Mama she cried, Mama she cried, When
teach young ladies how to dance, For I'm the pet of the ar - my. I'm
I left home, ma - ma she cried, He's not cut out for the ar - my. I'm
CHORUS
Captain Jinks of the Horse Marines; I feed my horse on corn and beans, And
oft - en live be - yond my means, Tho' a cap-tain in the ar - my.

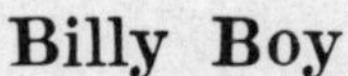

Billy Boy

mf

1. Oh, where have you been, Bil-ly Boy, Bil-ly Boy, Oh, where have you
2. Did she bid you to come in, Bil-ly Boy, Bil-ly Boy, Did she bid you to come
3. Did she set for you a chair, Bil-ly Boy, Bil-ly Boy, Did she set for you a
4. Can she make a cherry pie, Bil-ly Boy, Bil-ly Boy, Can she make a cherry
5. How old is she, Bil-ly Boy, Bil-ly Boy, How old is

been, charming Bil-ly? I have been to seek a wife, She's the
in, charming Bil-ly? Yes, she bade me to come in, There's a
chair, charming Bil-ly? Yes, she set for me a chair, She has
pie, charming Bil-ly? She can make a cher-ry pie, Quick's a
she, charming Bil-ly? Three times six and four times seven, Twenty-

(charming Bil-ly)

joy of my life, She's a young thing and can-not leave her moth-er.
dim-ple in her chin, She's a young thing and can-not leave her moth-er.
ring-lets in her hair, She's a young thing and can-not leave her moth-er.
cat can wink her eye, She's a young thing and can-not leave her moth-er.
eight and e-lev-en, She's a young thing and can-not leave her moth-er.

Blow The Man Down

CHANTEY

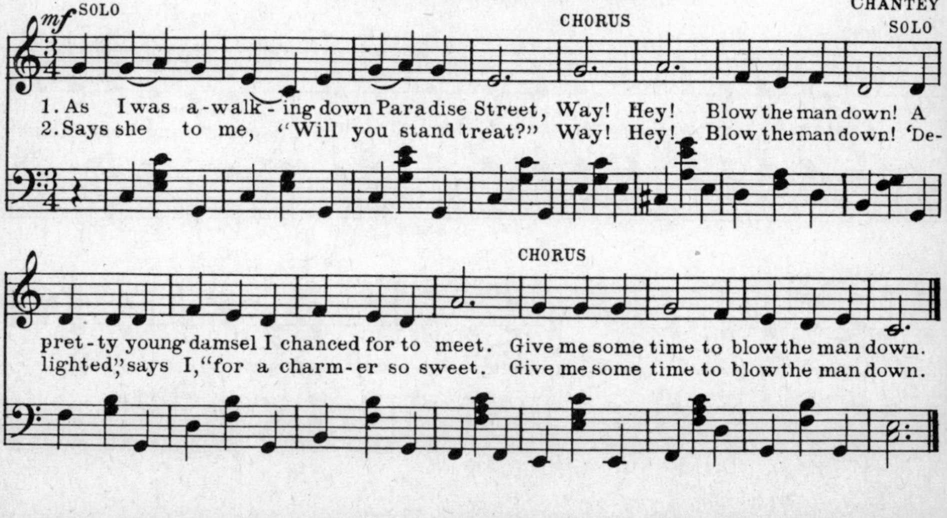

mf SOLO — CHORUS — SOLO

1. As I was a-walk-ing down Paradise Street, Way! Hey! Blow the man down! A
2. Says she to me, "Will you stand treat?" Way! Hey! Blow the man down! 'De-

CHORUS

pret-ty young damsel I chanced for to meet. Give me some time to blow the man down.
lighted," says I, "for a charm-er so sweet. Give me some time to blow the man down.

The Three Sailor Boys
With spirit
THEODORE MARZIALS
f
1. Oh, we're three jol - ly, jol - ly sail - or boys, And we're newly home from
2. There were three pretty girls in merry Portsmouth town, And each one was like a
3. Then up we spoke, we jol - ly sail - or boys, All arm in arm so
South A - mer - i - kee, With our hearts still tingling with the salt, salt wind, And the
po - sy on the tree, There was great eyed Marga - ret, and trim set Sal, And sweet
jol - ly for to see, "There are girls beside the water, at Ja - nei - ro, or Gibraltar, Who can
f
tumble and the tossing of the sea. Oh, honey, we've our pockets full of money; Will you
Kit - ty from the north coun - tree. No, honey, tho' your pockets full of money, We won't
dance right mer - ri - ly as ye;" So, honey, while our pockets full of money, Come and
trip, trip, trip, will you trip it on the Quay? For the wind's in the sail, and the
trip, trip, trip, we won't trip it on the Quay, Till you've set the clerk a - sing - ing, and the
trip, trip, trip, come and trip it on the Quay, For we sail - ors love the o - cean, and the
thun - der in the gale, And our good ship plung - ing to be free.
wed - ding bells a - ring - ing And the par - son has pock - et - ed the fee.
change and the commo - tion, And the good ship plung - ing on the sea.
Haul On The Bowlin'
SOLO
CHORUS
CHANTEY
f
1. Haul on the bow - lin', Our bul - ly ship's a roll - in'! Haul on the bowlin', the bow - lin', haul!
2. Haul on the bow - lin', Our captain he's a - growlin'! Haul on the bowlin', the bow - lin', haul!

They All Love Jack
STEPHEN ADAMS
Arr. by W. J. G.
1. When the ship is trim and read - y, And the jol - ly days are done, When the
2. Where he goes their hearts go with him, E'en his ship he calls her "she", Up a -
3. When he's sail'd the world all o - ver, And a - gain he steps a - shore, There are
last good-byes are whispered, And Jack a - board is gone; The
loft that "lit - tle cher - ub" Sure a maid - en she must be. And as
scores of lass - es wait - ing To love him all the more; He may
lass - es fall a weep - ing, As they watch his ves - sel's track, For
o'er the sea he travels, The mer - maids down be - low Would
lose his gold - en guineas, But a wife he'll nev - er lack, If he'd
all the lands - men lov - ers Are noth - ing af - ter Jack, For
give their crys - tal king - doms For the love of Jack, I trow, Would
wed them all, they'd take him, For they all love Jack, If he'd

They All Love Jack–Concluded

ff

all the lands-men lov - ers___ Are noth - ing af - ter Jack.___
give their crys-tal king - doms For the love___ of Jack, I trow.___
wed them all, they'd take___ him, For they all______ love___ Jack.___

f

For his heart is like the sea, Ev-er o-pen brave and free, And the girls must lone - ly be,___ Till his ship comes back; But if love's the best of all, That can a man be - fall,___ Why, Jack's the king of all,___ For they all love Jack!___

Belle Ob Baltimore
Lively
J. G. Evans
mf
1. I've been thro' Car - o - li - na, I've been to Ten - nes - see, I sail'd the Mis - sis - sip - pi, For mas - sa set me free; I've kiss'd de lub - ly cre - ole On Loui - si - an - a's shore, But I neb - ber found de gal to match De bloom - ing Belle ob Bal - ti - more.
2. My Belle is tall and slen - der, And sings so ber - ry clear, You'd tink she was an owlingale, If once her voice you hear; I walk'd down to her cab - in, And rapp'd up - on de door, I went to gub my dog - ger - type To my sweet Belle ob Bal - ti - more.
Chorus
Oh, boys, Belle's a beau - ty, Eyes so bright and cheek so soot - y; No gal I eb - er seen a - fore, So sweet as Belle ob Bal - ti - more.
The Huntsmen
(Round)
Lively
1 f
A south - er - ly wind and a cloud - y sky Pro - claim it a hunt - ing morn - ing;
2
To horse my brave boys and a - way; Bright Phœ - bus the hill is a - dorn - ing;
3
Hark! hark! for - ward, tan - ta - ra, tan - ta - ra, tan - ta - ra.

Hark! I Hear A Voice
Hark! I hear a voice Way up on the moun-tain top, tip - top,
De-scend-ing down be - low, De-scend-ing down be - low, — low.
CHORUS
Let us all u-nite in love, Trust-ing
Let us all u-nite in love,
in the pow'rs a - bove. Mer-ri-ly now we
Trust-ing in the pow'rs a - bove.
roll, we roll, we roll, we roll, we roll, we roll, Mer-ri-ly now we
roll, we roll, O'er the deep blue sea.
Early to Bed
Round
1.
2.
3.
Ear - ly to bed and ear - ly to rise, Makes a man
health-y and wealthy and wise, Wise, health-y, and wealth - y.

Nut Brown Maiden
(Male Voices)
College Song
Arranged by Walter Goodell
Moderately
1. Nut brown maid-en, Thou hast a bright blue eye for love, Nut brown maiden, Thou
2. Nut brown maid-en, Thou hast a ru - by lip to kiss, Nut brown maiden, Thou
3. Nut brown maid-en, Thou hast a slen-der waist to clasp, Nut brown maiden, Thou
4. Nut brown maid-en, Thou hast such pearly, pearly teeth, Nut brown maiden, Thou
hast a bright blue eye; A bright blue eye is thine, love! The glance in it is mine, love! Nut brown
hast a ru-by lip; A ru - by lip is thine, love! The kissing of it's mine, love! Nut brown
hast a slender waist; A slender waist is thine, love! The arm around it's mine, love! Nut brown
hast such pearly teeth; The pearly teeth are false, love! They rattle when you waltz, love! Nut brown
maid-en, Thou hast a bright blue eye for love, Nut brown maiden, Thou hast a bright blue eye
maid-en, Thou hast a ru - by lip to kiss, Nut brown maiden, Thou hast a ru - by lip.
maid-en, Thou hast a slen-der waist to clasp, Nut brown maiden, Thou hast a slen-der waist.
maid-en, Thou hast such pearly, pearly teeth, Nut brown maiden, Thou hast such pearly teeth.
Where, O Where
Spirited
College Song
1. Where, O where are the verdant Freshmen? Where, O where are the verdant Fresh-men?
2. Where, O where are the gay young Soph'mores? Where, O where are the gay young Soph'mores?
3. Where, O where are the jol - ly Jun-iors? Where, O where are the jol - ly Jun-iors?
4. Where, O where are the grand old Sen-iors? Where, O where are the grand old Sen-iors?
Where, O where are the ver-dant Freshmen? Safe now in the Soph-'more Class.
Where, O where are the gay young Soph'mores? Safe now in the Jun-ior Class.
Where, O where are the jol - ly Jun-iors? Safe now in the Sen-ior Class.
Where, O where are the grand old Sen-iors? Safe now in the wide, wide world.

Where, O Where – Concluded
They've gone out from pre-scribed English, They've gone out from prescribed English,
They've gone out from their old Lat-in, They've gone out from their old Lat-in,
They've gone out from their tough Mathematics, They've gone out from their tough Mathematics,
They've gone out from their Al-ma Ma-ter, They've gone out from their Al-ma Ma-ter,
They've gone out from pre-scribed Eng-lish, Safe now in the Soph'more Class
They've gone out from their old Lat-in, Safe now in the Jun-ior Class.
They've gone out from their tough Mathemat-ics, Safe now in the Sen-ior Class.
They've gone out from their Al-ma Ma-ter, Safe now in the wide, wide world.
Noah's Ark
Lively
College Song
1. Old Noah he built him-self an ark, There's one wide river to cross! He built it all of
2. The animals went in one by one, There's one wide river to cross! And Japhet with a
3. The animals went in two by two, There's one wide river to cross! The Elephant and the
4. The animals went in three by three, There's one wide river to cross! The Hippopotamus and the
5. The animals went in fives by fives, There's one wide river to cross! Shem, Ham, and Japhet,
6. And when he found he had no sail, There's one wide river to cross! He just ran up his
7. And as they talked on this and that, There's one wide river to cross! The ark it bumped on
1. hick-ory bark, There's one wide riv-er to cross!
2. big bass drum, There's one wide riv-er to cross!
3. Kan-ga-roo, There's one wide riv-er to cross!
4. Bum-ble bee, There's one wide riv-er to cross!
5. and their wives, There's one wide riv-er to cross!
6. old coat tail, There's one wide riv-er to cross!
7. Ar-ra-rat. There's one wide riv-er to cross!
Chorus
There's one wide riv-er, and
that wide river is Jor-dan, There's one wide river, There's one wide river to cross.

Rosalie

L. K. LAUNCE KNIGHT

Moderately
1. I'm Pierre de Bon - ton de Par - is, de Par - is, I
2. I go to the fete de Marquise, de Marquise, I
drink my di - vine Eau de vie, Eau de vie. As I ride out each day in my
go and make love at my ease, at my ease. I go to her pere and de -
lit - tle cou - pe, I tell you I'm something to see.
mand for my own The hand of my sweet Ros - a - lie.

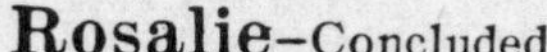

Rosalie–Concluded

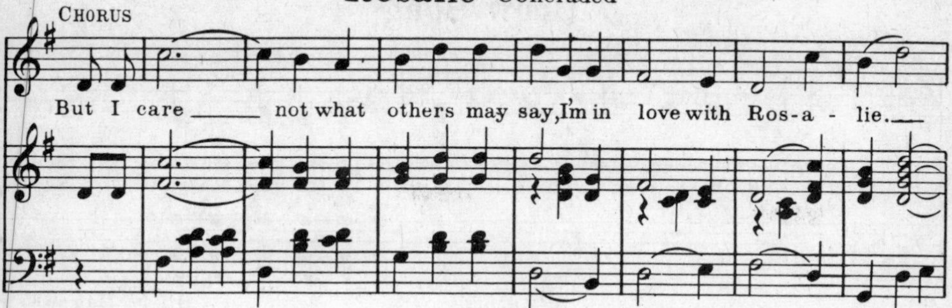

CHORUS

But I care ___ not what others may say, I'm in love with Ros-a - lie. ___

Charming Rose, ___ pretty Rose, ___ I'm in love with my Ros-a - lee. ___

Peter Gray

Quickly
BASS SOLO

COLLEGE SONG

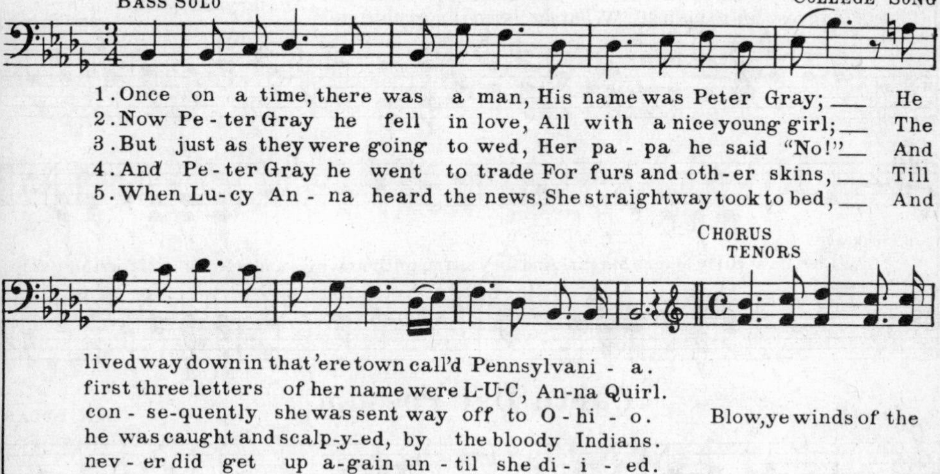

1. Once on a time, there was a man, His name was Peter Gray; ___ He lived way down in that 'ere town call'd Pennsylvani - a.
2. Now Pe-ter Gray he fell in love, All with a nice young girl; ___ The first three letters of her name were L-U-C, An-na Quirl.
3. But just as they were going to wed, Her pa-pa he said "No!" ___ And con - se-quently she was sent way off to O - hi - o.
4. And Pe-ter Gray he went to trade For furs and oth-er skins, ___ Till he was caught and scalp-y-ed, by the bloody Indians.
5. When Lu-cy An - na heard the news, She straightway took to bed, ___ And nev - er did get up a-gain un - til she di - i - ed.

CHORUS
TENORS

Blow, ye winds of the

BASSES

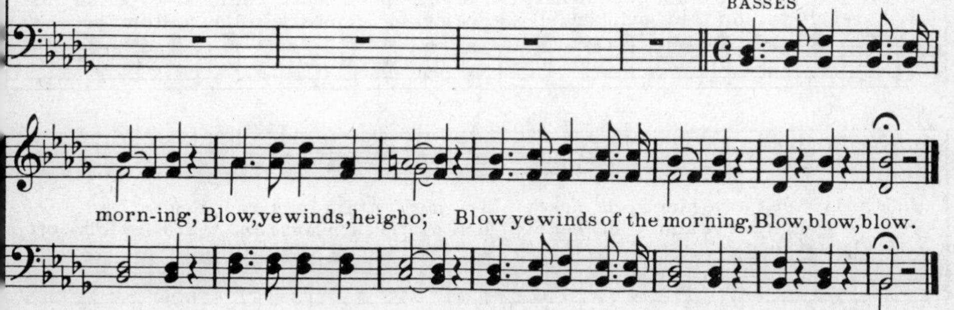
morn-ing, Blow, ye winds, heigho; Blow ye winds of the morning, Blow, blow, blow.

Crow Song

Lively

mf SOLO — CHORUS — SOLO

1. There were three crows sat on a tree, O Bil-ly Ma-gee Ma-gar! There were three crows sat on a tree, O Bil-ly Ma-gee Ma-gar! There were three crows sat on a tree, And they were black as crows could be, And they all flapp'd their wings and cried (Bil-ly Magee! Bil-ly Ma-gee)

2. Said one old crow un-to his mate, O Bil-ly Ma-gee Ma-gar! Said one old crow un-to his mate, O Bil-ly Ma-gee Ma-gar! Said one old crow un-to his mate, "What shall we do for grub to ate?" And they all flapp'd their wings and cried

(Spoken)

Caw, Caw, Caw, Bil-ly Magee Magar! And they all flapp'd their wings and cried Billy Magee Magar!

Carve Dat Possum

Lively — SAM LUCAS

f

1. De pos-sum meat am good to eat, Carve him to de heart; You'll al-ways find him good and sweet, Carve him to de heart; My dog did bark and I went to see,

2. I reached up for to pull him in, Carve him to de heart; De possum he be-gan to grin Carve him to de heart; I carried him home and dressed him off,

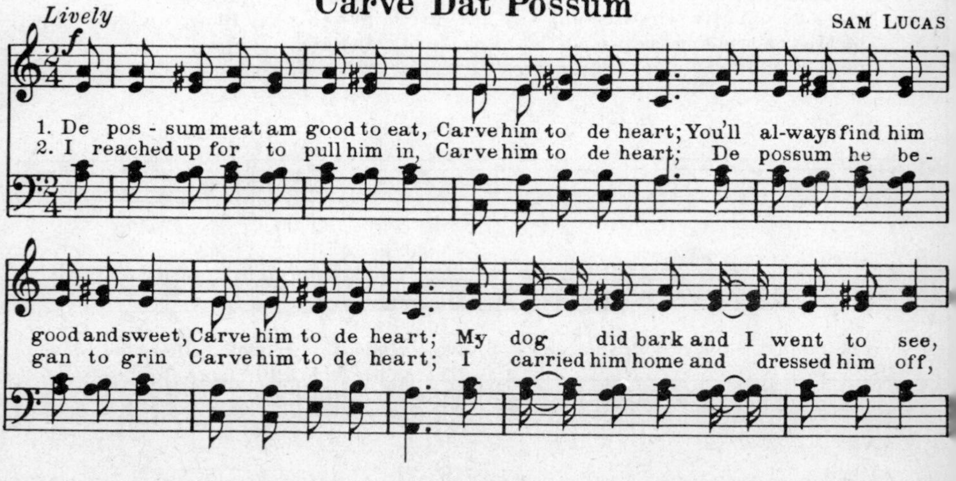

Carve Dat Possum-Concluded

Carve him to de heart; And dar was a pos-sum up dat tree, Carve him to de heart.
Carve him to de heart; I hung him dat night in de frost, Carve him to de heart.
CHORUS
Carve dat possum, carve dat possum, children, Carve dat possum, carve him to de heart; Oh,
carve dat pos-sum, carve dat possum, children, Carve dat possum, carve him to de heart.
Gaudeamus Igitur
(Male Voices)
Arr. by W. J. G.
1. Gau-de-a-mus i-gi-tur, Ju-venes dum sumus; Post jucundam juventu-tem,
2. U-bi sunt, qui an-te nos, In mundo fu-e-re? Transe-as ad su-pe-ros,
3. Vi-vat a-cad-e-mi-a, Vivat profes-so-res, Vi-vat membrum quodlibet,
Post molestam senec-tutem, Nos ha-be-bit hu-mus, Nos ha-be-bit hu-mus.
A-be-us ad in-fe-ros, Qu-os si vis vi-de-re, Qu-os si vis vi-de-re.
Vivant membra quæ-li-bet, Semper sint in flo-re, Semper sint in flo-re

(English Version.)

1. Let us now in youth rejoice,
None can justly blame us;
For when golden youth has fled,
And in age our joys are dead,
Then the dust doth claim us.

2. Where have all our fathers gone?
Here we'll see them never;
Seek the god's serene abode
Cross the dol'rous Stygian flood;
There they dwell forever.

3. Raise we, then, the joyous shout,
Life to Alma Mater!
Life to each professor here,
Life to all our comrades dear,
May they leave us never.

Street Urchins' Medley

(Male Voices)

Arr. by J. W. I
Sing a song of cities, Cities great and small; Rhyming lit-tle ditties
Tell a-bout them all. New-York has her lobsters, Boston has her
beans Bal-timore's the place for oysters, But for 'lasses New Or-leans.
Quickly
Roll dem bones, roll dem bones, Roll 'em on the square; Roll 'em on the sidewalks, the
streets or an-y-where. We roll 'em in the morning, We roll 'em in the night, We
slower
Fine
roll dem bones the whole day long, While the cops are out of sight.
we roll dem bones.

la, la, la, la, la, la, la, la, la, la, la, la, la, la, la, la,
Shine, shine, who wants a shine? My name is Teddy and I'm always ready, my
la, la, la, la, la, la, la, la, la, la, la, la, la, la, la, la,
la, la, la, la, la, la, la, la,
D.S.
brush-es are new, my blacking is fine.
Hi there! mister! Don't you want a shine?
la, la, la, la, la, la, la, la,
Levee Song
1. Oh, I was bo'n in Mo-bile town, A wuk-kin on de lev-ee,
All day I roll de cot-ton down, A wuk-kin on de lev-ee.
2. I use' to have a dawg name' Bill, A wuk-kin on de lev-ee,
He run a-way but I'm here still, A wuk-kin on de lev-ee.
3. Dat li'l ole dawg set up an' beg, A wuk-kin on de lev-ee,
Till I done give him chick-en leg, A wuk-kin on de lev-ee.
wuk wuk wuk wuk wuk wuk
I've been wukkin on de railroad All de live-long day;
(live long day)
I've been wukkin on de railroad, To pass de time a-way.
Doan' yo' hyar de whistle blow-in',
Rise up so ear-ly in de mawn; Doan' yo' hyar de cap'n shout in': "Dinah, blow yo hawn!"
"yo hawn!"

Ducks on a Pond

(Round)

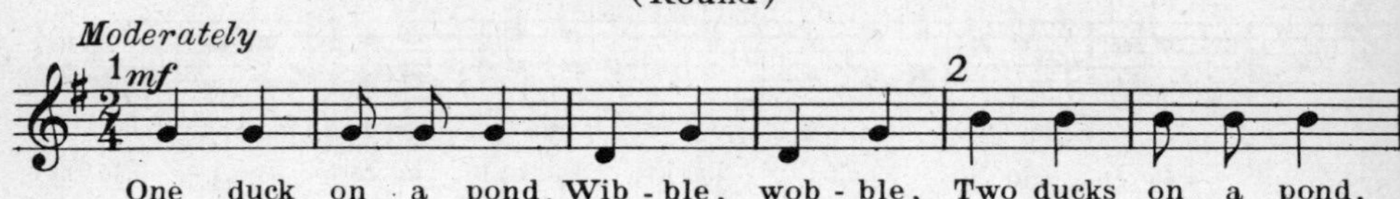
Moderately
1 mf
2
One duck on a pond, Wib-ble, wob-ble, Two ducks on a pond,

3
Wib-ble, wob-ble, wib-ble, wob-ble, Three old la-dies go-ing to mar-ket,

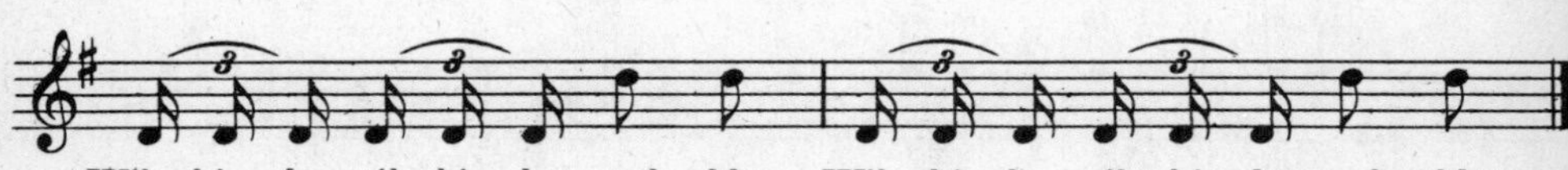
Wib-bi-ly wib-bi-ly wob-ble, Wib-bi-ly wib-bi-ly wob-ble.

Man's Life's a Vapor

(Round)

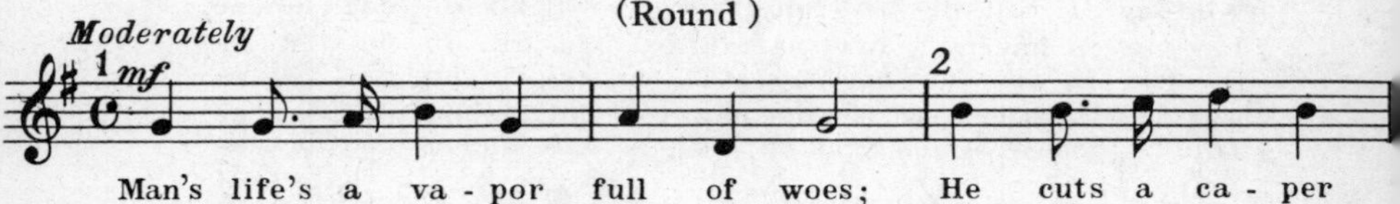
Moderately
1 mf
2
Man's life's a va-por full of woes; He cuts a ca-per

3 f
down he goes, Down he, down he, down he, down he, down he goes.

The Donkey

(Round)

Moderately
1
2
Sweet-ly sings the don-key at the break of day; If you do not feed him,

3
this is what he'll say, "Hee-haw! Hee-haw! Hee-haw! Hee-haw! Hee-haw!"

Add to the fun by using pantomime while singing these rounds.

Style All The While
1.They say that ★ - - he ain't got no style, He's style all the while, He's style all the
2.They say that Miss★ - - she nev-er does smile, She smiles all the while, She smiles all the
while, They say that ★ - - he ain't got no style, He's style all the while, all the while.
while, They say that Miss★ - - she nev-er does smile, She smiles all the while, all the while.
★Supply any name. Make additional verses to suit the occasion.
Information
Adaptation From British Army Song
1. If you want to know where the Sup-er is I know where he's at,
2. If you want to know where the Princ'pal is I know where he's at,
3. If you want to know where the teach-ers are I know where they're at,
4. If you want to know where the stu-dents are I know where they're at,
I know where he's at, I know where he's at. If you want to know where the
I know where he's at, I know where he's at. If you want to know where the
I know where they're at, I know where they're at. If you want to know where the
I know where they're at, I know where they're at. If you want to know where the
Sup-er is I know where he's at; Smok-ing a big ci-gar, I saw him,
Princ'pal is I know where he's at; Tak-ing a lit-tle nap, I saw him,
teachers are I know where they're at; Plan-ning to flunk the class, I saw them,
students are I know where they're at; Up to their necks in work, I saw them,
I saw him, Smok-ing a big ci-gar, I saw him smok-ing a big ci-gar.
I saw him, Tak-ing a lit-tle nap, I saw him tak-ing a lit-tle nap.
I saw them, Plan-ning to flunk the class, I saw them plan-ning to flunk the class.
I saw them, Up to their necks in work, I saw them up to their necks in work.
The Barnyard Family
College Song
1. I have a roost-er, my roost-er loves me. I feed my roost-er on green Bay tree,
2. I have a cat, my cat loves me. I feed my cat on green Bay tree,
Fine.
My lit-tle roost-er goes oo-dle-de-oo, de-oo-dle-de-oo-dle-dee-oo-dle-de-oo.
D.S.
My lit-tle cat goes Me-ow.
D.S.
My lit-tle dog goes Bow-wow.
3. Dog-Bowwow 4. Sheep-Ba-a-a-a 5. Cow-Moo-o-o 6. Crow-Caw-Caw

After third ending with dog call, sing last two measures of cat call and then go back to sign, finishing with rooster call. Any number of verses may be used but in each case after the new animal call has been sung, all preceding endings are sung in inverse order ending with the rooster call. Thus, if six animal calls were used in following order: rooster, cat, dog, sheep, cow, crow, the song would end: My little crow goes, caw-caw; my little cow goes, moo-o; my little sheep goes, Ba-a-a; and so on back to rooster call.

Farewell To Thee

This plaintive melody usually appearing under the title "Aloha Oe," is said to have been written by former Queen Liliuokalani of Hawaii. In the original text, it is a love song of parting.

MYRTLE KOON CHERRYMAN

QUEEN LILIUOKALANI
Arr. by W.J.G.

Moderately with expression

1.Now our gold-en days are at an end; The part-ing hour is coming soon, And we
2.We have felt the thrill of autumn days, And shared the winter's cold as well; When we
3.We have seen togeth-er how the spring Made mir - a-cles of tree and flow'r; But the

think, while swift the moments pass How de-light-ful has been our friendship's boon.
know we now must say good-bye, All our sor-row, no language e'er can tell.
joy that summer bro't to us Led us on t'ward this pensive parting hour.

REFRAIN

Fare-well to thee, fare-well to thee, Our golden days are coming to an end, But

we will hope for bright - er days to come, When friend shall meet with friend.

PART THREE

SUPPLEMENT

Selected and Arranged by
WALTER GOODELL
and
FLORENCE M. MARTIN

Roll, Jordan, Roll

Strongly rhythmic SPIRITUAL

f–p

1. Roll, Jor - dan, roll, roll, Jor - dan, roll, I want to go to hea - ven when I die, To hear Jor - dan roll.

roll

2d Ending *Fine.*

Oh, broth-ers, you ought t' have been there, Yes, yes, my Lord, my Lord! A sit-ting in the king-dom, To hear Jor-dan, Jor-dan roll.

been there, been there,

roll *D. C. al Fine*

roll

2. Oh, preachers, you ought t'have been there, etc.
3. Oh, sinners, you ought, etc.
4. Oh, mourners, you ought, etc.
5. Oh, seekers, you ought t'have been there, etc.
6. Oh, mothers, you ought, etc.
7. Oh, sisters, you ought, etc.

Oh, Wasn't That a Wide River

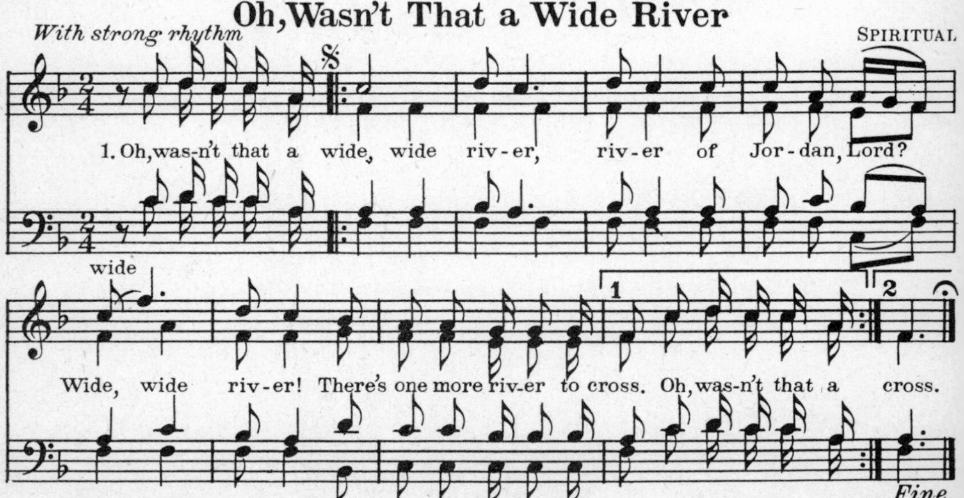

With strong rhythm
SPIRITUAL
1. Oh, was-n't that a wide, wide riv - er, riv - er of Jor - dan, Lord?
wide
Wide, wide riv - er! There's one more riv-er to cross. Oh, was-n't that a cross.
1
2
Fine.

Oh, Wasn't That a Wide River-Concluded
1. Oh, the riv-er of Jor-dan is so wide,
2. I ___ have some friends be-fore you gone,
3. ___ Shout, shout Satan's a-bout,
4. Old Satan is a snake in the grass,
One more riv-er to cross;
I ___ don't know how to get on the oth-er side;
By the grace ___ of ___ God I'll ___ fol-low on;
Shut your door and keep him out;
If ___ you don't mind he'll get you at last;
One more riv-er to cross. Oh was-n't that a -
D. S. al Fine
Down by the River
SPIRITUAL
1. Oh, we'll wait till Je - sus comes Down by the riv - er, We'll wait
we'll wait till Jesus comes Down by the river side.
Fine.
TENOR SOLO
1. Oh, hal-le-lu - jah to that Lamb,
Tenor Solo.
Other voices hum
SOPRANO
Down by the riv-er;
The Lord is on the giv-ing hand,
Down by the riv-er side.
D. C. al Fine

2. Oh, we are pilgrims here below,
Down by the river;
Oh, soon to glory we will go,
Down by the river side.

3. Oh, little did I think that He was so nigh,
Down by the river;
He spake, and made me laugh and cry,
Down by the river side.

Turn Back Pharaoh's Army

SPIRITUAL

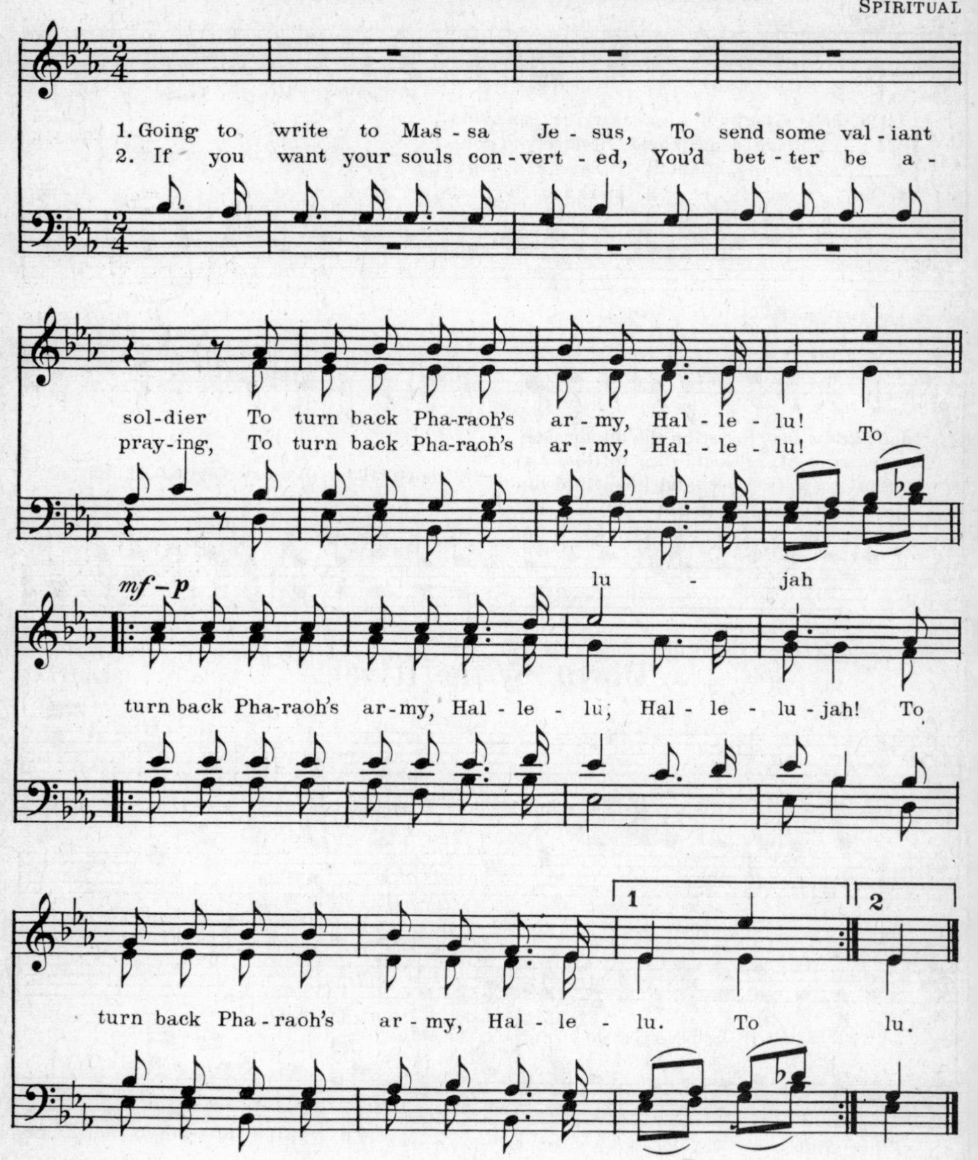
1. Going to write to Mas - sa Je - sus, To send some val - iant sol-dier To turn back Pha-raoh's ar - my, Hal - le - lu!
2. If you want your souls con - vert - ed, You'd bet - ter be a - pray-ing, To turn back Pha-raoh's ar - my, Hal - le - lu!
mf–p
To turn back Pha-raoh's ar-my, Hal - le - lu - jah
Hal - le - lu, Hal - le - lu - jah! To turn back Pha - raoh's ar - my, Hal - le - lu. To
1
2
lu.

3. You say you are a soldier,
Fighting for your Saviour,
To turn back Pharaoh's army, etc.

4. When the children were in bondage,
They cried unto the Lord,
He turned back Pharaoh's army, etc.

5. When Moses smote the water,
The children all passed over,
And turned back Pharaoh's army, etc.

6. When Pharaoh crossed the water,
The waters came together,
And drowned ole Pharaoh's army, etc.

Mary And Martha

SPIRITUAL

mf
1. Mar-y and-a Mar-tha's just gone 'long, Mar-y and-a Mar-tha's just gone 'long.
Mar-y and-a Mar-tha's just gone 'long To ring those charming bells, crying: "Free grace and
Free grace and
dy-ing love, Free grace and dy-ing love, Free grace and dy-ing love," To
Free grace and
ring those charming bells— Oh, way o-ver Jor-dan, Lord, Way o-ver
(Those bells)
Jor-dan, Lord, Way o-ver Jor-dan, Lord, To ring those charming bells.
(lower notes ad lib.) Those bells.

2.
The preacher and the elder's just gone 'long, etc.
To ring those charming bells.—
Cho.—Crying: "Free grace," etc.

3.
My father and mother's just gone 'long, etc.
To ring those charming bells.—
Cho.—Crying: "Free grace," etc.

4.
The Methodist and Baptist's just gone 'long, etc.
To ring those charming bells.—
Cho.—Crying: "Free grace," etc.

Heav'n, Heav'n

SPIRITUAL

1. I've got a robe, you've got a robe, All of God's children got a robe; (a robe)

When I get to Hea-ven, goin' to put on my robe, Goin' to shout all o - ver God's

3rd (sing all o - ver God's)

Repeat ***pp*** *(last time)*

Heav'n, (Heav'n) Heav'n, (Heav'n), Heav'n (Heav'n); Ev-'ry-bod-y talk-in' 'bout

Heav'n ain't goin' there Heav'n Heav'n Goin' to shout all o-ver God's Heav'n (Heav'n).

Heav'n, Heav'n Heav'n, Heav'n

2. I've got a crown — etc.
3. I've got a song — etc. *"sing" instead of "shout"*

Chilly Water

SPIRITUAL

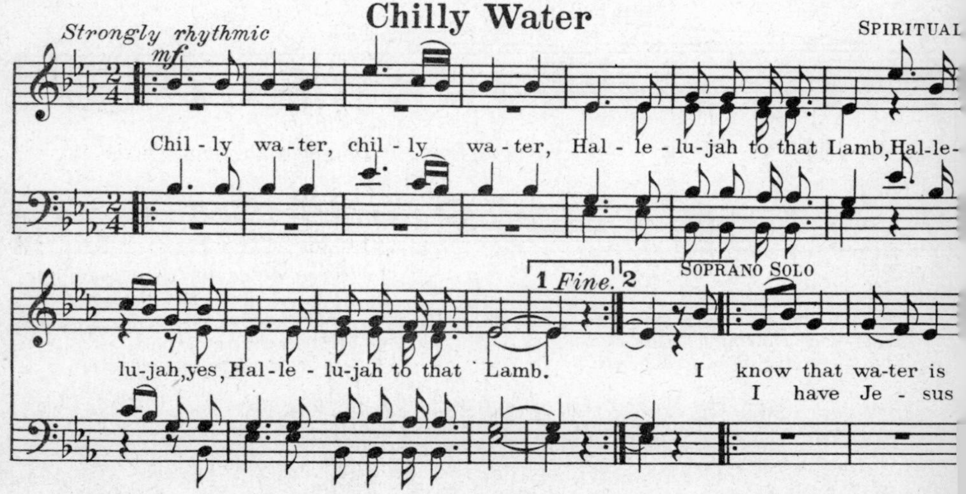
Strongly rhythmic
mf
Chil - ly wa - ter, chil - ly wa - ter, Hal - le - lu - jah to that Lamb, Hal - le -
1 Fine.
2
SOPRANO SOLO
lu - jah, yes, Hal - le - lu - jah to that Lamb. I know that wa - ter is
I have Je - sus

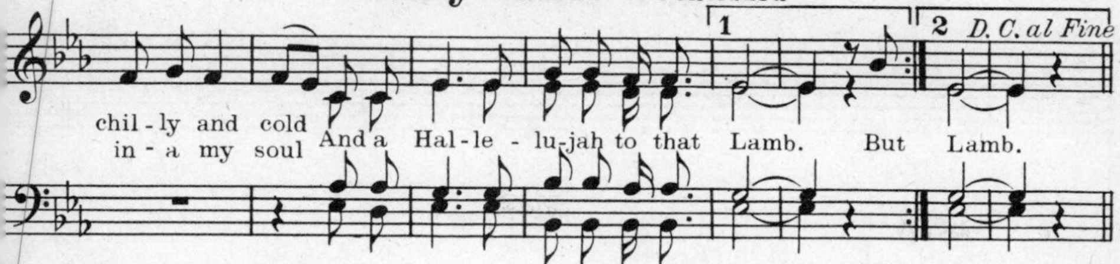

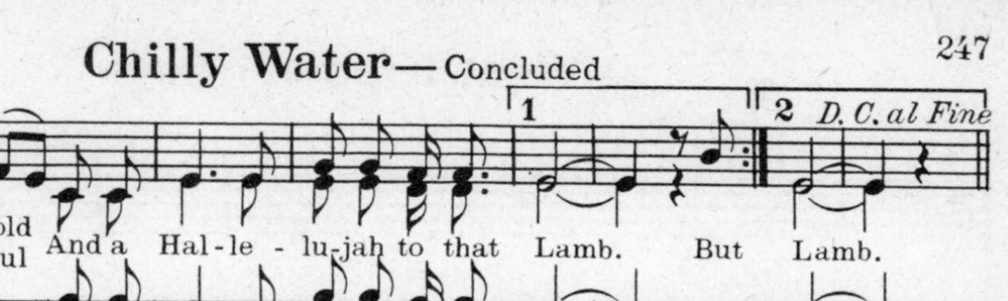
1
2 D. C. al Fine
chil-ly and cold
in-a my soul And a Hal-le-lu-jah to that Lamb. But Lamb.

2. In-a that ark, the little dove mourned,
And hallelujah to that Lamb,
Christ Jesus standing as the corner stone,
And hallelujah to that Lamb.

3. Old Satan's just like a snake in the grass,
And hallelujah to that Lamb,
Watching for to bite you as a-you pass,
And hallelujah to that Lamb.

4. O brothers and sisters, one and all,
And hallelujah to that Lamb,
You had better be ready when the roll is called,
And hallelujah to that Lamb.

O Mary, Don't You Weep

Tenor and Alto duet. Soprano and Bass humming.

SPIRITUAL

Hm Hm

ALTO

O Ma-ry, don't you weep, don't you mourn, O Ma-ry, don't you weep, don't you mourn:

TENOR

Hm Hm

All sing—

1 2

Pha-raoh's ar-my got drown-ded, O Ma-ry, don't you weep! (Mary don't you weep) weep!

Soprano, Alto and Bass Hum—

Hm Hm

1. The way of e-vil do-ing is a-wide and fair, And man-y, man-y, man-y they who per-ish there;
2. There was a mighty man who came on earth to save, Thro' Him we stem the tide of trib-u-la-tion's wave;

All sing— *rall.*

Pha-raoh's ar-my got drown-ded, O Ma-ry, don't you weep.

rall.

What Kind of Shoes

SPIRITUAL

1. What kind of shoes you going to wear? Gold - en slip - pers!
2. What kind of crown you going to wear? Star - ry crown!
What kind of shoes you going to wear? Gold-en slip-pers!
What kind of crown you going to wear? Star-ry crown!
TENOR SOLO
Other voices hum.
Gold - en slip - pers I'm
Star - ry crown I'm
ALL
bound to wear, That out-shines the glit - ter - ing sun.
bound to wear, That out-shines the glit - ter - ing sun.
REFRAIN
Yes, yes,
Yes, yes, my Lord, I'm going to join the heav'n-ly choir,
Yes, yes,
Yes, yes, yes, my Lord, I'm a sol - dier of the cross.
Repeat pp

3.

What kind of robe you going to wear? White robe!
What kind of robe you going to wear ? White robe!
Long white robe I'm bound to wear,
That outshines the glittering sun.

4.

What kind of song you going to sing? New song!
What kind of harp you going to play? Golden harp!
Golden harp I'm bound to play,
That outshines the glittering sun.

It's a-Me, O Lord
(Standin' in the Need of Prayer)
SPIRITUAL
Arr. by WALTER GOODELL
It's a - me It's a - me, O Lord, Stand-in' in the need of
mf - pp - 2nd time
pray'r, yes, Lord! It's a - me It's a me, O Lord,
Fine
Stand-in' in the need of pray'r (of pray'r).
1. Not my broth-er, (no) it's a -
2. Not my fath-er, (no) it's a -
me, O Lord, Not my sis - ter, It's a - me, O Lord,
me, O Lord, Not my moth-er, It's a - me, O Lord,
(no)
D.C.
Stand-in' in the need of pray'r, It's a - me, Stand-in' in the need of pray'r.

250
I Want To Be Ready
SPIRITUAL
Arr. by WALTER GOODELL
1. I want to be read-y, I want to be read-y,— I want to be read-y— To
2. I want to be read-y, I want to be read-y,— I want to be read-y— To
3. I want to be read-y, I want to be read-y,— I want to be read-y— To
Last time molto rall.
Fine.
walk in Je-ru-sa-lem, just like John. John said the cit-y was just four-square, Walk in Jerusalem
walk in Je-ru-sa-lem, just like John. Oh, John! oh, John! what do you say? Walk in Jerusalem
walk in Je-ru-sa-lem, just like John. When Peter was preaching at Pentecost, Walk in Jerusalem
D. C. al Fine
just like John, And he declared he'd meet me there, Walk in Je-ru-sa-lem, just like John.
just like John, That I'll be there at the com-ing day, Walk in Je-ru-sa-lem, just like John.
just like John, He was endowed with the Ho-ly Ghost, Walk in Je-ru-sa-lem, just like John.
Couldn't Hear Nobody Pray
SPIRITUAL
Arr. by WALTER GOODELL
I could-n't hear no-bod-y pray; O I could-n't hear no-bo-dy pray, O
'way down yon-der by my-self O I could-n't hear no-bo-dy pray (all a-lone)
2. (Help me Lord!)
Couldn't hear no-bo-dy pray (Kneelin' down) Couldn't hear no-bo-dy pray.
2. (In my trou-ble)

Deep River
SPIRITUAL
Arr. by WALTER GOODELL
Lento
p-pp
Deep___ Riv-er, my home is o-ver Jor-dan,___ Deep___
p-pp
Stop, last time only.
1
2
Fine.
Riv-er, Lord, I want to cross o-ver in-to camp-ground. camp-ground.
mf
Oh, don't you want to go___ to that gos-pel feast,___ That
prom - is'd land___ where all___ is peace?___ Oh,
D. C. al Fine
don't you want to go to that prom - is'd land where all is peace?

Oh, Peter, Go Ring Dem Bells!

SPIRITUAL

Oh, Pe-ter, go ring dem bells, Pe-ter, go ring dem bells, Pe-ter, go ring dem bells, I heard from Heaven to-day.

Fine.

1. I wonder where my mother has gone, I wonder where my mother has gone, I wonder where my mother has gone, I heard from Heaven to-day

(to-day.)

D. C. al Fine

2. I wonder where sister Mary has gone,
I wonder where sister Mary has gone,
I wonder where sister Martha has gone,
I heard from Heaven to-day.

3. I wonder where brother Moses has gone,
I wonder where brother Daniel has gone,
I wonder where ol' Elijah has gone,
I heard from Heaven to-day.

LAST REFRAIN (ad lib.)
(Repeat pp - ad lib.)
f
I heard from Heav-en to - day, — I heard from Heav-en to - day, — I
thank God, and I thank you too, I heard from Heav-en to - day.
to - day

Home On The Range

COWBOY SONG

Moderately
mf
1. Oh ___ give me a home where the buf - fa - lo roam, Where the deer and the an - te - lope play; Where ___ sel - dom is heard a dis - cour - ag - ing word, And the skies are not cloud - y all day. ___
2. How ___ of - ten at night where the heav - ens are bright With the lights from the glit - ter - ing stars, Have I stood there a - mazed and ___ asked as I gazed If their glo - ry ex - ceeds that of ours. ___
3. Oh, ___ give me a land where the bright dia - mond sand Flows ___ lei - sure - ly down ___ the stream; Where the grace - ful, white swan goes ___ glid - ing a - long Like a maid in a heav - en - ly dream. ___
4. Where the air is so pure, the ___ zeph - yrs so free, The ___ breez - es so balm - y and light, That I would not ex - change my ___ home on the range, For ___ all of the cit - ies so bright. ___
5. Oh, I love those wild flow'rs in this dear land of ours, The ___ cur - lew I love to hear scream, And I love the white rocks and the an - te - lope flocks, That ___ graze on the moun - tain - top's green. ___
EFRAIN
Home, home on the range, Where the deer and the an - te - lope play; ___ Where sel - dom is heard a dis - cour - ag - ing word, And the skies are not cloud - y all day. ___

Praise Ye The Father

Allegretto maestoso M M ♩= 100
CHARLES GOUNO
Praise ye the Fa-ther! Let ev-'ry heart give thanks to Him!
Ev-'ry
Praise ye the Fa-ther, who is ev-er kind and mer-ci-ful!
Praise ye the Fa-ther, Who noteth ev-'ry sparrow's fall!
O King of Glo-ry! Let all earth pro-claim Thy
maj-es-ty! Sing of the Lord, Ev-'ry
Of Him sing praise!
cresc.
dim.
voice pro-claim His pow'r! Who bring-eth joy to the
Pro-claim His pow'r! And peace

cresc. f

world, — And whose mer-cy en-dur-eth ev - er!

cresc. f

to all, — And mer-cy for-ev-er!

p

He — hath made — all the world, and the heav'n a-

p

Our Lord — hath made — all na-ture

bove us! In His strength, in His love, He rul-eth the world, A-

for us! In love He rul-eth the world,

f

rise, and praise ye the Fa-ther! Praise be to the Fa-ther, to the

f

Son, and Ho-ly Spir-it! Praise Him, ev-'ry na-tion, All the

ff

earth shall re-joice in Him! Praise the Fa-ther, Glo-ry to the Lord, our King!

ff

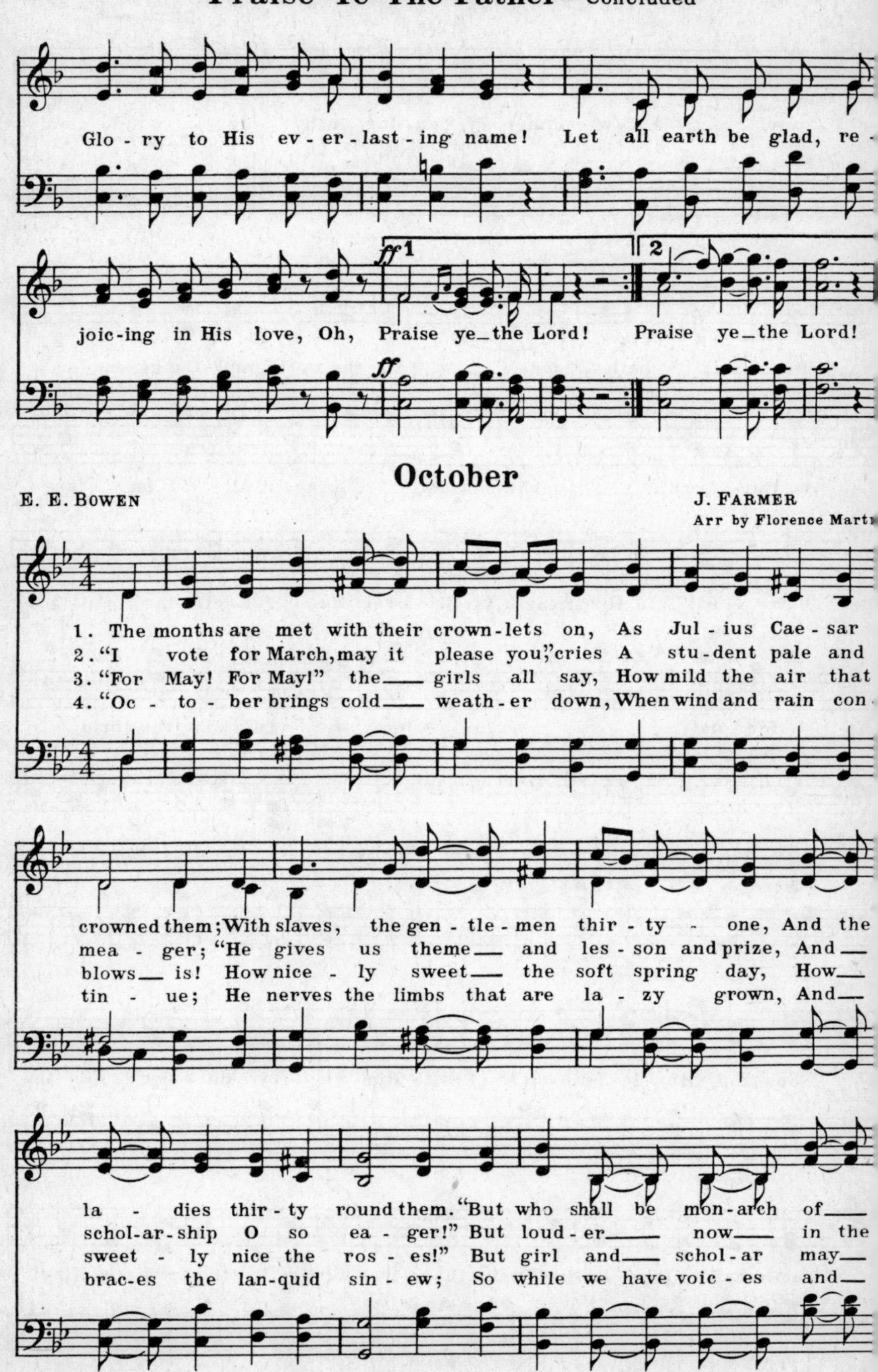
Glo - ry to His ev - er - last - ing name! Let all earth be glad, re -
joic - ing in His love, Oh, Praise ye_the Lord! Praise ye_the Lord!
ff
1
2
October
E. E. Bowen
J. Farmer
Arr by Florence Mart
1. The months are met with their crown - lets on, As Jul - ius Cae - sar
2. "I vote for March, may it please you," cries A stu - dent pale and
3. "For May! For May!" the__ girls all say, How mild the air that
4. "Oc - to - ber brings cold__ weath - er down, When wind and rain con -
crowned them; With slaves, the gen - tle - men thir - ty - one, And the
mea - ger; "He gives us theme__ and les - son and prize, And__
blows__ is! How nice - ly sweet__ the soft spring day, How__
tin - ue; He nerves the limbs that are la - zy grown, And__
la - dies thir - ty round them. "But who shall be mon - arch of__
schol - ar - ship O so ea - ger!" But loud - er__ now__ in the
sweet - ly nice the ros - es!" But girl and__ schol - ar may__
brac - es the lan - quid sin - ew; So while we have voic - es and__

CHORUS
all?" you ask; Go ask of the boys and maid - ens, For
dis - tance floats A choice there is no dis - guis - ing; And you
pray and plead The voice of the lads is clear - er, And
lungs to cheer, And the win - ter frost be - fore us, Come,—
that is the lads' and the lass - ies' task, And they choose him a - far in ca - dence.
hear from man - y heart - y throats The chant of the boys up - ris - ing.
firm and stead - y comes that tread, In time to the mu - sic, near - er!
sing to the king of the mor - tal year, And thun - der him out in cho - rus!"
Oc -
to - ber, Oc - to - ber, March to the dull and
so - ber! The suns of May for the school girls' play, But
give to the boys Oc - to - ber, Oc - to - ber, Oc - to - ber!

God So Loved The World

JOHN 3: 16, 17 JOHN STAINER

p *cresc.*

God so loved the world,— God so loved the world,— that He
that

mf

gave—His on - ly be - got - ten Son, that who - so be - liev - eth, be -

p *cresc.* *f*

liev - eth on Him should not per - ish, should not per - ish but

p

have ev - er - last - ing life. For God sent not His Son in - to the

cresc. *mf*

world to con - demn the world, God sent not His Son in - to the world to con -

p

demn the world; but that the world thru Him might be sav - ed.

pp
cresc.
God so loved the world,— God so loved the world,— that He
that
mf
gave—His on-ly be-got-ten Son, that who-so be-liev-eth, be-
p
cresc.
f
liev-eth on Him should not per-ish, should not per-ish but
have ev-er-last-ing life, ev-er-last-ing life, ev-er-last-ing,
dim. e rall.
ev-er-last-ing
pp
ev-er-last-ing life. God so loved the world,—
ppp
rall.
— God so loved the world,— God so loved the world.

Vilia
From "The Merry Widow"
From the German
New version by
MYRTLE KOON CHERRYMAN
FRANZ LEHAR
Arranged by WALTER GOODEL
Allegretto scherz. M.M. ♩ = 96
mf
(TWO SOLO VOICES)
p
1. One morn-ing a hunts-man all gal-lant and gay, While chas-ing wild
2. The nymph rais'd a cheek that was cool as a leaf, A-las for the
p
boar in the wood cool and gray Es-pied a fair dry-ad a-
kiss both so thrill-ing and brief! As soon as his lips touch'd the
MALE VOICES
Hm

Vilia — Continued
mong the great trees, And soon as he saw her bright hair in the breeze
ex - qui-site face, She van - ish'd, and left but a dim, lone-ly place.
Hm
MIXED VOICES
Hm
Hm
pp rit.
Ten - der thoughts be - gan to throng; Quest of game no more was
Yet, there haunts him, day and night, Ech - oes from that wood - land
TENOR SOLO
Ah
Ah
rit.
rall
strong, For this, straight - way, be - came his hunt - ing song:
sprite: "Dry - ad maid with no mor - tal can u - nite!"
p
MIXED VOICES
Hm
p

Moderato
p
"Vil - ia, fair dry - ad, you rule in the wood, O'er blossoms, bees, and the
Moderato
p
ti - ny bird-brood, Vil - ia, dear maiden, your rule I'll o - bey; Sweet Vil-ia,
love me, I pray. Vil - ia, fair dry - ad, you rule in the

Vilia — Concluded

pp
wood, O'er blossoms, bees, and the ti - ny bird - brood, Hm
TENOR SOLO
Vil - ia, dear
pp
Sweet Vil - ia, love me, I pray,
maid - en, your rule I'll o - bey;
1
2
pray, love me I pray, sweet Vil - i - a!"
8va

Jeanie With The Light Brown Hair

S.C.F.

STEPHEN C. FOSTER
Arr. by Florence Martin

1. I dream of Jean-ie with the light brown hair, Borne like a va - por,
2. I long for Jean-ie with the day dawn smile, Ra-diant in glad-ness,
3. I sigh for Jean-ie, but her light form strayed Far from the fond hearts
on the sum-mer air; I see her trip-ping where the bright streams play,
warm with win-ning guile; I hear her mel - o - dies, like joys gone by,
round her na-tive glade; Her smiles have van-ished and her sweet songs flown,
Hap-py as the dai-sies that dance on her way. Man-y were the wild notes her
Sigh-ing round my heart o'er the fond hopes that die: Sigh-ing like the night-wind and
Flit-ting like the dreams that have cheered us and gone. Now the nod-ding wild flow'rs may
mer - ry voice would pour, Man - y were the blithe birds that
sob - bing like the rain, Wail - ing for the lost one that
with - er on the shore, While her gen - tle fin - gers will
war - bled them o'er: Oh! I dream of Jean - ie with the
comes not a - gain: Oh! I long for Jean - ie and my
cull them no more; Oh! I sigh for Jean - ie with the

light brown hair, Float-ing, like a va-por, on the soft sum-mer air.
heart bows low, Nev-er-more to find her where the bright wa-ters flow.
light brown hair, Float-ing, like a va-por, on the soft sum-mer air.
O Starry Flag
(All Saints)
Norman H. Hall
Henry S. Cutler
1. O star-ry flag of red and white With stars on field of blue,
2. O ban-ner bright with stars and stripes, Re-nowned thru-out the world,
3. May oth-er flags of oth-er lands, Stand by thee in their might,
We hon-or thee, and in our might To thee we'll e'er be true.
Be-cause thou stand-est for the right Wher-e'er thou art un-furled.
As broth-ers with u-nit-ed hands, A broth-er-hood for right.
O glo-rious ban-ner of our land, Our own U-nit-ed States,
Long shalt thou wave thru-out this land, Which gave to thee thy birth,
As em-blems may they ev-er stand With thee, for what is just,
For right and jus-tice shalt thou stand, Midst world as-so-ci-ates.
And hon-ored shalt thou ev-er be In ev-'ry land on earth.
For free-dom, lib-er-ty and faith, That all in them may trust.

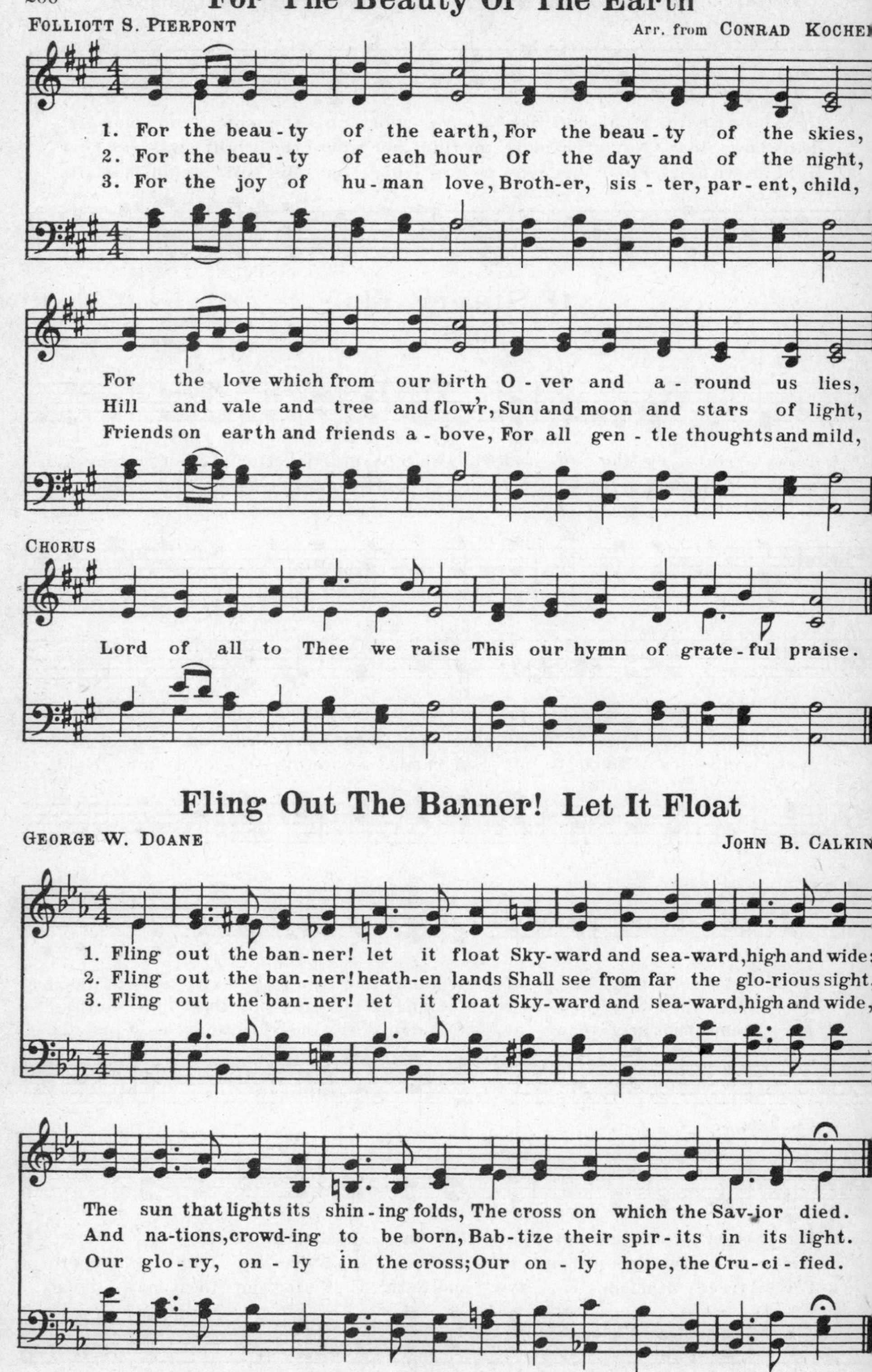
For The Beauty Of The Earth
Folliott S. Pierpont
Arr. from Conrad Kocher
1. For the beau-ty of the earth, For the beau-ty of the skies,
2. For the beau-ty of each hour Of the day and of the night,
3. For the joy of hu-man love, Broth-er, sis-ter, par-ent, child,
For the love which from our birth O-ver and a-round us lies,
Hill and vale and tree and flow'r, Sun and moon and stars of light,
Friends on earth and friends a-bove, For all gen-tle thoughts and mild,
Chorus
Lord of all to Thee we raise This our hymn of grate-ful praise.
Fling Out The Banner! Let It Float
George W. Doane
John B. Calkin
1. Fling out the ban-ner! let it float Sky-ward and sea-ward, high and wide:
2. Fling out the ban-ner! heath-en lands Shall see from far the glo-rious sight,
3. Fling out the ban-ner! let it float Sky-ward and sea-ward, high and wide,
The sun that lights its shin-ing folds, The cross on which the Sav-ior died.
And na-tions, crowd-ing to be born, Bap-tize their spir-its in its light.
Our glo-ry, on-ly in the cross; Our on-ly hope, the Cru-ci-fied.

The Meeting Of The Waters

'HOMAS MOORE

IRISH AIR

Arr. by Florence Martin

1. There is not in the wide world a val - ley so sweet As the
2. Yet it was not that Na - ture had shed o'er the scene Her
3. 'Twas that friends, the be - lov'd of my bos - om, were near, Who made
vale in whose bos - som the bright wa - ters meet, Oh, the
pur - est of crys - tal and bright - est of green; 'Twas
ev - 'ry dear scene of en - chant - ment more dear, And who
last rays of feel - ing and life must de - part, Ere the
not her soft mag - ic of stream - let or rill, Oh!
felt how the best charms of Na - ture im - prove, When we
bloom of that val - ley shall fade from my heart, Ere the
no it was some - thing more ex - qui - site still, Oh!
see them re - flect - ed from looks that we love, When we
bloom of that val - ley shall fade from my heart.
no it was some - thing more ex - qui - site still.
see them re - flect - ed from looks that we love.

Beautiful Dreamer
S. C. F.
STEPHEN C. FOSTER
Arr. by Florence Martin
1. Beau-ti-ful dream-er, wake un-to me, Star-light and dew-drops are wait-ing for
2. Beau-ti-ful dream-er, out on the sea, Mer-maids are chant-ing the wild lo-re-
thee, Sounds of the rude world heard in the day,
lei; O - ver the stream-let va-pors are borne,
Lulled by the moon-light have all passed a-way! Beau-ti-ful dream-er,
Wait-ing to fade at the bright com-ing morn. Beau-ti-ful dream-er,
queen of my song, List while I woo thee with soft mel-o-dy;
beam on my heart, E'en as the morn on the stream-let and sea;
Gone are the cares of life's bus-y throng, Beau-ti-ful dream-er, a-wake un-to
Then will all clouds of sor-row de-part, Beau-ti-ful dream-er, a-wake un-to
me! Beau-ti-ful dream-er, a-wake un-to me!
me! Beau-ti-ful dream-er, a-wake un-to me!

Bonny Eloise

C. W. ELLIOTT

J. R. THOMAS
Arr. by Florence Martin

1. O sweet is the vale where the Mo-hawk gen-tly glides On its clear wind-ing way to the sea, And dear-er than all sto-ried streams on earth be-sides, Is this bright roll-ing riv-er to me;
2. O sweet are the scenes of my boy-hood's sun-ny years, That be-span-gle the gay val-ley o'er, And dear are the friends seen thru mem-o-ries' fond tears That have lived in the blest days of yore;
REFRAIN
But sweet-er dear-er, yes, dear-er far than these Who charm where oth-ers all fail Is blue-eyed, bon-ny, bon-ny E-lo-ise, The belle of the Mo-hawk Vale.

Wait For The Wagon

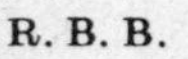

R. B. B.

R. B. BUCKLEY
Arr. by Florence Martin

1. Will you come with me, my Phyl-lis dear, To ___ yon blue moun-tain free? Where the blos-soms smell the sweet-est, Come rove a-long with me. It's ev-'ry Sun-day morn-ing, When you are by my side, We'll jump in-to the wag-on, And all take a ride.

2. Where the riv-er runs like sil-ver, ___ And the birds they sing so sweet, I ___ have a cab-in, Phyl-lis, And some-thing good to eat. Come lis-ten to my sto-ry, It will re-lieve my heart, So jump in-to the wag-on, And off we will start.

REFRAIN

Wait for the wag-on, Wait for the wag-on, Wait for the wag-on And we'll all take a ride.

Send Out Thy Light

PSALM XLIII and XX

CHARLES GOUNOD

Adagio molto
fff
Moderato
pp
Send out Thy light, send out Thy light! Send out Thy light and Thy
cresc.
dim.
truth, let them lead me, And let them bring me to Thy ho - ly hill;
p
f
Send out Thy light and Thy truth, let them lead me, And let them
O let them lead me,
bring me to Thy ho - ly hill, un - to Thy ho - ly hill, let them
O let them lead me,
rit.
lead, let them lead me, And let them bring me to Thy ho - ly hill.
O
ff
O God, then will I go un - to Thine al - tar, On the

Send Out Thy Light—Continued

harp we will praise Thee, O Lord our God! O God,— then will I
Prais - ing Thee,
go un - to Thine— al - tar, And we will praise Thee,
cresc. molto ff
and we will praise Thee, praise Thee, praise Thee on the harp, O our
God! on the harp, O our God! on the harp, O our God!
fff
pp
Send out Thy light and Thy truth, let them lead me, And let them
bring me to Thy ho - ly hill. Send out Thy light and Thy
dim. p cresc.

f rit. dim.
truth, let them lead me, And let them bring me to Thy ho - ly hill.
f rit. dim.
p p
Why, O soul, art thou sor - row - ful, And why cast down with - in me?
p p
cresc.
Still trust the lov - ing kind - ness of the God of thy strength,
cresc.
And my tongue yet shall praise Him, and my tongue yet shall praise Him,
f ff
and my tongue yet shall praise Him, Who hath plead - ed my cause!
f ff
p cresc. f rit.
Send out Thy light and Thy truth, let them lead me, And let them
p cresc. f rit.

bring me to Thy ho - ly hill, Lord — our — God! — Lord our God! Thou wilt save Thine a - noint - ed, Thou wilt hear us from heav - en; Some in char - i - ots put their faith! Our trust is in Thee! — They are brought down and fall - en, they are brought down and fall - en, But the Lord is our help - er, we shall not be a - fraid, But the Lord is our help - er, we shall not be a - fraid. —
dim.
p
f
cresc.
cresc. molto
ff
pp
rit.

ppp
Send out Thy light and Thy truth, let them lead me,
cresc.
dim.
p
And let them bring me to Thy ho - ly hill;
p
cresc.
f
Send out Thy light and Thy truth, let them lead me, And let them
dim.
p
O let them
bring me to Thy ho - ly hill, un - to Thy ho - ly
lead me, O
O let them
f
rit.
dim.
hill, let them lead, let them lead me, And let them bring me to Thy
lead me, O
fff
ppp
ho - ly hill; Send out Thy light, O Lord our God!

And the Glory of the Lord

From "The Messiah"

ISAIAH 40:5

GEORGE FREDERICK HANDEL
Arranged by WALTER GOODELL

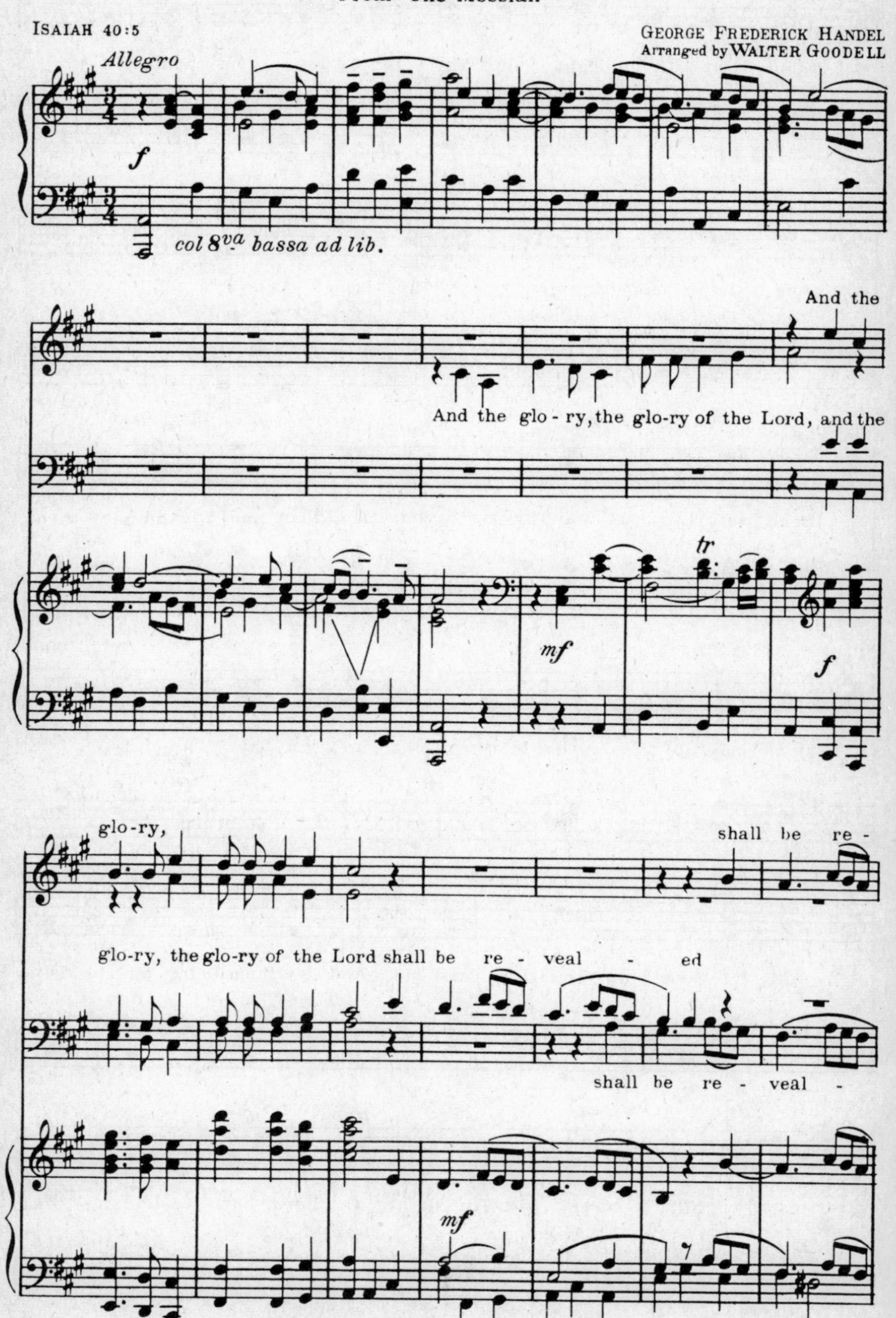
Allegro
f
col 8va bassa ad lib.
And the
And the glo - ry, the glo-ry of the Lord, and the
tr
mf
f
glo-ry,
shall be re -
glo-ry, the glo-ry of the Lord shall be re - veal - ed
shall be re - veal -
mf

veal - ed.
And the glo - ry, the glo - ry of the
Shall be re - veal - ed,
And the glo - ry, the glo - ry of the Lord
- ed. Shall be re - veal - ed
Lord. shall be re - veal'd,
be re - veal - - - - ed, and the
Shall be re - veal - - ed.
f
glo - ry, the glo - ry of the Lord shall be re - veal - ed.

And The Glory Of The Lord—Continued

And all flesh shall see it to - geth-er. And all

flesh shall see it to - geth-er; and all flesh shall

For the mouth of the

For the mouth of the Lord hath

see it to - geth - er, and all flesh shall see it to -

Lord hath spo-ken it;

spo - ken it,
and all flesh
and all flesh shall see it to-geth-er
geth - er;
and all flesh shall see it to-geth - er:
For the
mf
f
and all flesh shall see it to-geth - er;
mouth of the Lord hath spo - ken it.
f
and all flesh shall
And the glo-ry, the glo-ry of the Lord, and all flesh shall see it, shall
and all flesh shall

And The Glory Of The Lord—Continued

see it to-geth-er; the mouth of the Lord hath spo-ken it,
it to-gether
see it
and the glo-ry, the glo-ry of the Lord, shall
see it to-geth-er

for the
be re - veal-ed
and all flesh and all flesh shall see it to-
and all flesh shall see it to-

mouth of the Lord hath spo - ken it, hath
geth-er: for the mouth of the Lord
the glo-ry, the glo-ry of the Lord shall be re - veal -
geth-er: And the glo-ry, the glo-ry of the

And The Glory Of The Lord—Continued
spo - ken it
hath spo-ken it; and all flesh shall
- - - - ed and all flesh
Lord shall be re-veal - ed, and all flesh shall
mf
and the glo-ry, the glo-ry, the glo-ry of the Lord, shall
see it to-geth-er and the glo-ry, the
be re-veal - ed,
shall be re-veal - ed, re-veal-ed
glo-ry of the Lord
shall be re-
shall be re-veal - ed re-

And The Glory Of The Lord—Concluded

and all flesh shall see it to - geth-er, to - geth -
and all flesh shall
see it to - geth-er, to - geth -
veal - ed, and all flesh shall
veal - ed, for the mouth of the Lord hath spo-ken
er; For the mouth of the Lord
er; For the mouth of the Lord hath spoken it, For the mouth
it. for the
Adagio
of the Lord hath spo - ken it.
mouth of the Lord, the mouth of the Lord.
Adagio

ALPHABETICAL INDEX

Abide With Me 59
Adeste Fidelis 72
Ah, Love, How Can I Leave Thee 124
Ah, 'Tis A Dream 142
All The Birds Are Here Again 91
All Through The Night 41
Aloha Oe 240
Alouette 127
Alphabet, The 179
America 3
America, My Country 131
America, The Beautiful... 7
And The Glory Of The Lord 276
Annie Laurie 39
Anvil Chorus 20
Are You Sleeping 121
At Pierrot's Door 86
Auld Lang Syne 37
Away in a Manger 72

Baa! Baa! Black Sheep... 76
Barnyard Family, The.... 239
Battle Cry of Freedom, The 16
Battle Hymn Of The Republic, The 12
Beautiful Dreamer 268
Bee and The Pup, The.... 122
Believe Me, If All Those Endearing Young Charms.. 46
Bell Doth Toll, The....... 24
Belle Ob Baltimore....... 228
Bell Is Ringing, The...... 195
Billy Boy 224
Birds' Return, The........ 91
Blacksmith, The.......... 196
Blest Be The Tie That Binds 60
Blow The Man Down...... 224
Blue-Bells Of Scotland, The 38
Bonnets of Bonnie Dundee, The 200
Bonny Eloise 269
Bull Dog, The.......... 117
But The Lord Is Mindful Of His Own 152
By Thy Rivers Gently Flowing 99
By Yon Bonnie Banks..... 36

Calm As The Night....... 183
Cantique De Noel........ 166
Capital Ship, A.......... 94
Captain Jinks 223
Carry Me Back To Old Virginny 32
Carve Dat Possum....... 234
Cast Thy Burden Upon The Lord 139
Central Will Shine........ 121

Chilly Water 246
Christ, The Lord, Is Risen Today 169
*Close Your Eyes, Lena, My Darling 108
*Columbia, The Gem Of The Ocean 6
*Come, Thou Almighty King 56
Come Where My Love Lies Dreaming 188
*Come, With Thy Lute..... 110
Come, Ye Thankful People. 170
*Comin' Thro' The Rye.... 37
Couldn't Hear Nobody Pray 250
*Cousin Jedediah 113
*Cradle Song 81
Creation 137
Crow Song 234
Crusader's Hymn 144
*Cuckoo, The 85

*Darling Nelly Gray....... 31
Day Is Dying In The West. 143
*Dearest Spot, The........ 52
*Dear Little Robin........ 89
*De Bezem 119
*Deck The Hall 66
Deep River 251
*Dickory, Dickory, Dock.... 76
*Dip, Boys, Dip The Oar.... 102
*Dixie 10
Donkey, The 238
Down By The River...... 243
*Doxology, The 65
*Drink To Me Only With Thine Eyes 46
Ducks On A Pond 238

Early To Bed 229
*Emmet's Lullaby 108
Evening Prayer 138

Fairest Lord Jesus, Ruler Of All Nature 144
Fairy-Belle 192
Faith Of Our Fathers..... 140
*Farewell To Summer...... 91
Farewell To Thee........ 240
*Farmer In The Dell, The.. 92
Farmer, The 92
*Farmyard, The 93
*Father In Heaven........ 23
*Father, We Thank Thee... 88
*Fath'r And I Went Down To Camp 8
*First Noel, The.......... 67
*Flag Of The Free......... 5
Fling Out The Banner, Let It Float 266
*Flow Gently, Sweet Afton. 35

*Flow'rets All Sleep Soundly, The 96
For The Beauty Of The Earth 266
*From Every Spire On Christmas Eve.......... 70
From Ill Do Thou Defend Me 145
From Yonder Dark Forest. 210
Funiculi, Funicula 176

*Gaily The Troubadour.... 125
Gaudeamus Igitur........ 235
Gentle Annie............ 192
Girl I Left Behind Me, The. 221
*Glad Christmas Bells..... 69
Gloria Patri 145
*God Be With You Till We Meet 62
*God Bless Our Native Land 3
*God Of Our Fathers...... 132
God Of The Earth, The Sky, The Sea 133
*God Of The Nations....... 20
God So Loved The World.. 258
*Go Down, Moses.......... 97
Goin' To Shout All Over God's Heaven 246
*Gone Are The Days....... 25
*Good-bye, Good-bye To Summer 80
Good King Wenceslas..... 171
*Good Morning To You.... 82
Good Night 31
*Good Night, Ladies....... 116
*Go To Sleep, Lena Darling. 108
*Graduation Song......... 111
*Gwine To Lay Down My Burden 97

*Hail, Columbia.......... 9
*Hail To The Chief........ 40
*Hard Times, Come Again No More 28
Hark! I Hear A Voice.... 229
Hark! Ten Thousand Voices 169
*Hark! The Herald Angels Sing 68
Hark! The Vesper Hymn is Stealing 144
*Harp That Once Through Tara's Halls, The...... 47
Haul On The Bowlin'..... 225
*Heart Bowed Down, The.. 49
Heavens Resound, The.... 150
Heav'n, Heav'n 246
Hello, Speaker 126
*Hey, Diddle, Diddle...... 76
*Holy Ghost With Light Divine 64

*Complete orchestral and band parts for all the selections marked with asterisks are included in the Instrumentation of the Golden Book of Favorite Songs. Send for information regarding this instrumentation.

HALL & McCREARY COMPANY, CHICAGO

ALPHABETICAL INDEX—Continued

*Holy, Holy, Holy 56
Holy Night 67
Home On The Range 253
*Home, Sweet Home 24
*Hop, Hop, Hop! 85
*How Can I Leave Thee 30
*How Dear To My Heart ... 106
*How D'ye Do 126
How Firm A Foundation .. 72
Hunter's Farewell, The ... 210
Huntsmen, The 228

*I Ain't Gwine Study War No More 97
I Came To Alabama 220
*I Cannot Sing The Old Songs 116
I Come To Town De Udder Night 222
*If A Body Meet A Body 37
*I Heard The Bells On Christmas Day 71
*Illinois 99
I'm Lonesome Since I Cross'd The Hill 221
I'm Pierre de Bonton 232
In Days Of Old 206
*In Days Of Yore 101
*Indian Lullaby 78
Information 239
In Heavenly Love Abiding. 141
*Integer Vitae 23
*In The Gloaming 104
*In The Prison Cell I Sit ... 14
In The Time Of Roses 214
Isle Of Beauty 216
*Italian Hymn 56
*It Came Upon The Midnight Clear 68
*I Think, When I Read That Sweet Story 62
It's A-Me, O Lord 249
I've Been Thro' Carolina .. 228
*I Wandered Today To The Hill, Maggie 50
I Want To Be Ready 250
*I Will Sing A Lullaby 85
I Would That My Love 180

*January And February 90
Jeannie With The Light Brown Hair 264
Jerusalem The Golden 142
*Jesus, Lover Of My Soul .. 61
*Jesus Loves Me 63
*Jesus, Tender Shepherd, Hear Me 58
*Jingle, Bells 120
*John Brown's Body 13
John Peel 212
*Jolly Old Saint Nicholas ... 75
*Joy To The World 71
*Juanita 52

*Just Before The Battle, Mother 16

*Kathleen Mavourneen 48
Keep The Home Fires Burning 19
*Keller's American Hymn .. 14
*Killarney 43

*Largo 54
*Last Night The Nightingale Woke Me 105
*Last Rose of Summer, The. 41
*Lead Kindly Light 64
Leezie Lindsay 203
Levee Song 237
Lift Thine Eyes 154
*Lightly Row 86
Linden Tree, The 214
*Little Bo-Peep 77
*Little Brown Church in The Vale, The 110
*Little Dustman, The 96
*Little Jack Horner 77
*Little Man, A 84
*Little Tom Tinker 124
*Little White Snowdrop 83
*Loch Lomond 36
*Long, Long Ago 34
Lord Is My Shepherd, The. 140
Lord Of All Being, Thron'd Afar 139
*Loreley, The 109
Lost Chord, The 160
Lovely Appear 158
Lovely Evening 70
Lovely Night 215
*Love's Old Sweet Song 45
Low-Backed Car, The 197
*Lullaby And Good Night ... 81
*Luther's Cradle Hymn 72
Lutzow's Wild Hunt 210

*MacDonald's Farm 126
Man's Life's A Vapor 238
*Maple Leaf Forever, The .. 101
*March Of The Men of Harlech 102
*Marseillaise Hymn 100
Mary and Martha 245
*Massa's In The Cold Ground 30
*Materna 7
*Maxwelton's Braes Are Bonnie 39
Meeting Of The Waters, The 267
*Men Of Harlech 102
*Merrily, Merrily 125
Merry Life, A 176
*Michigan, My Michigan ... 98
*Mid Pleasures And Palaces 24

Midshipmite, The 204
Mighty Land, Wondrous Land 134
*Mine Eyes Have Seen The Glory 12
*Minstrel Boy, The 51
*Morning Prayer 88
Morn Was Fair, The 186
Mules 222
*My Bonnie 121
*My Country, 'Tis Of Thee .. 3
*My Faith Looks Up To Thee 59
My Lord Delivered Daniel .. 218
My Lord, What A Mourning 218
My Native Land 131
*My Old Kentucky Home ... 26

Nancy Lee 198
*Nearer, My God, To Thee .. 61
Night 216
Noah's Ark 231
Nobody Knows The Trouble I've Seen 220
*Now 'Neath The Silver Moon 104
Now Our Golden Days Are At An End 240
*Now Thank We All Our God 65
*Now The Day Is Over 57
Nut Brown Maiden 230

*O Beautiful For Spacious Skies 7
*O Come, All Ye Faithful ... 72
October 256
Of All The Wives 198
*O God, Beneath Thy Guiding Hand 22
O God, Our Help In Ages Past 136
*Oh Jacob, Get The Cows ... 113
Oh, Mistress Shady 195
O Holy Night! 166
*Oh, Paddy, Dear 44
Oh Peter, Go Ring Dem Bells 252
Oh Realm Of Light 137
*Oh Say! Can You See 4
Oh! Susanna 220
Oh, Wasn't That A Wide River 242
*Oh, Wert Thou In The Cauld Blast 38
Old Ark A-Moverin Along, The 219
*Old Black Joe 25
*Old Dog Tray 28
*Old Folks At Home 27
*Old Hundredth 65
*Old Oaken Bucket, The ... 106
Ole Dan Tucker 222
*O Little Town of Bethlehem 73
O Mary, Don't You Weep .. 247
*O Me! O My! 126

*See note on page 283.

ALPHABETICAL INDEX—Concluded

Once In The Dear Dead Days ... 45
O, No, John ... 213
Onward, Christian Soldiers 57
On Yonder Hill ... 213
O Rest In The Lord ... 156
O Starry Flag ... 265
Our School Days Now Are Past ... 111
O Where, And O Where ... 38
O Worship The King ... 132

Patriots, The ... 96
Peter Gray ... 233
Pilgrim's Chorus ... 164
Praise For Peace ... 23
Praise God From Whom All Blessings Flow ... 65
Praise Ye The Father ... 254
Pride Of The Village, The .. 192
Proudly As The Eagle ... 209

Quilting Party, The ... 125

Reuben And Rachel ... 99
Revolutionary Tea ... 112
Ring, Ring The Banjo ... 221
Robin Adair ... 39
Robin And Chicken, The .. 79
Robin Redbreast ... 80
Robin, The ... 89
Rock-a-bye, My Little Owlet 78
Rocked In The Cradle Of The Deep ... 53
Roll, Jordan, Roll ... 242
Rosalie ... 232
Rose Of Allandale, The ... 186
Round De Meadows ... 30
Row, Row, Row Your Boat . 50

Safely Through Another Week ... 60
Sailing ... 118
Sally In Our Alley ... 193
Santa Lucia ... 104
Scale Song ... 79
Schubert's Serenade ... 172
Scotland's Burning ... 36
Seeing Nellie Home ... 125
See-Saw, Margery Daw ... 77
Send Out Thy Light ... 271
Shades Of Evening ... 216
Should Auld Acquaintance. 37
Silent Night ... 67
Sing A Song Of Cities ... 236
Singing In The Rain ... 82
*Sleep, My Child ... 41
Sleep, Soldier, Sleep ... 211
*Slumber Song ... 91
*Softly Now The Light Of Day ... 66
Softly Sighs The Breath Of Evening ... 138
*Soft O'er The Fountain ... 52
*Soldier Boy ... 88
*Soldier's Farewell, The ... 124
*Sound The Loud Timbrel .. 114
Spacious Firmament On High ... 137
*Spanish Cavalier, The ... 123
*Speed Our Republic ... 14
Spider And The Spout, The. 211
Spring, The ... 106
Standing In The Need Of Prayer ... 249
*Stars Of The Summer Night 27
*Star-Spangled Banner, The 4
Steal Away ... 217
Still, Still With Thee ... 138
Stodola Pumpa ... 128
Street Urchin's Medley ... 236
Style All The While ... 239
Sunset Glows In Splendor, The ... 216
*Sun Shines Bright, The ... 26
*Susy, Little Susy ... 87
*Sweet And Low ... 42
Sweet Genevieve ... 122
*Swing Low, Sweet Chariot. 95

Taps ... 195
*Tell Me The Tales ... 34
*Tenting On The Old Camp Ground ... 15
*There Are Many Flags In Many Lands ... 98
*There's A Church In The Valley ... 110
*There's A Low Green Valley 31
*There's Music In The Air .. 34
*There Was An Old Darkey. 29
*There Was An Old Lady .. 112
They All Love Jack ... 226
*Those Evening Bells ... 107
*Three Blind Mice ... 119
Three Chafers, The ... 208
*Three Fishermen, The ... 124
Three Sailor Boys, The ... 225
Thro' The Leaves The Night Wind's Moving ... 172
'Til The Boys Come Home 19
Time Is Never Dreary, The 221
*'Tis Here We Are Pledging 96
*'Tis Moonlight On The Sea. 102
*'Tis Springtime ... 90
To Thee, O Country! ... 135
To The Lords Of Convention 200
*Tramp! Tramp! Tramp! .. 14
*Tree In The Wood, The ... 126
Turn Back Pharaoh's Army 244
'Twas In Fifty-five ... 204
*Twinkle, Little Star ... 84
Two Roses, The ... 215

*Uncle Ned ... 29
Unfold, Ye Portals ... 146
*Up On The House-Top ... 75

*Vacant Chair, The ... 13
Vilia ... 260

Wait For The Wagon ... 270
*Waiting To Grow ... 83
Warrior Bold, A ... 206
*Way Down Upon De Swanee River ... 27
*Wearing Of The Green ... 44
Welcome, Neighbor ... 126
Welcome, Sweet Springtime 194
*We're Tenting Tonight ... 15
*We Shall Meet ... 13
*We Three Kings of Orient Are ... 74
What Kind Of Shoes ... 248
*What's This Dull Town To Me ... 39
When First I Saw Sweet Peggy ... 197
*When Israel Was In Egypt's Land ... 97
*When I Was A Lady ... 87
*When Johnny Comes Marching Home ... 18
*When The Corn Is Waving. 33
*When The Nights Grow Cold 91
When The Ship Is Trim And Ready ... 226
*When The Swallows Homeward Fly ... 107
*When You And I Were Young, Maggie ... 50
Where, O Where ... 230
*Where The Elm Tree Branches ... 82
*While Shepherds Watched Their Flocks ... 74
Who Aloft Thy Head Did Raise ... 210
Will Ye Gang To The Hielands ... 203
*With The Moon's Pale Shimmer ... 86
*Woodman, Spare That Tree 103
*Work For The Night Is Coming ... 58

*Yankee Doodle ... 8
*Years Of Peace ... 22
*Ye Sons Of France ... 100
*Yes, We'll Rally Round The Flag ... 16

*See note on page 283.

Classified List of Songs

For page numbers see Alphabetical Index immediately preceding.

CHANTEYS AND SEA SONGS

Blow the Man Down
*Capital Ship
*Dip, Boys, Dip the Oar
Haul on the Bowlin'
Midshipmite
Nancy Lee
*Sailing
They All Love Jack
Three Sailor Boys

CHILDREN'S SONGS

*At Pierrot's Door
*Baa! Baa! Black Sheep
*Birds' Return
*Cuckoo
*Dickory, Dickory, Dock
*Farewell to Summer
*Farmer
*Farmer in the Dell
*Good Morning to You
*Hey, Diddle, Diddle
*Hop, Hop, Hop
*Indian Lullaby
*January and February
*Lightly Row
*Little Bo-Peep
*Little Jack Horner
*Little Man
*Morning Prayer
*Robin
*Robin and Chicken
*Robin Redbreast
*Scale Song
*See-Saw, Margery Daw
*Singing in the Rain
*Soldier Boy
*Susy, Little Susy
*'Tis Springtime
*Twinkle, Little Star
*Waiting to Grow
*When I Was a Lady

CHRISTMAS SONGS

*Away in a Manger
Cantique De Noel
*Deck the Hall
*First Noel
*From Every Spire on Christmas Eve
*Glad Christmas Bells
*Hark! the Herald Angels Sing
*I Heard the Bells on Christmas Day
*It Came Upon the Midnight Clear
*Jolly Old Saint Nicholas
*Joy to the World
*Luther's Cradle Hymn
*O, Little Town of Bethlehem
*Silent Night
*Up on the House-Top
*We Three Kings
*While Shepherds Watched Their Flocks

COLLEGE SONGS

Blacksmith
*Bull-Dog
Captain Jinks
Carve Dat Possum
*Central Will Shine
Gandeamus Igitur
*Good-Night, Ladies
*Graduation Song
Hark! I Hear a Voice
*Integer Vitae
*Jingle, Bells
Lutzow's Wild Hunt
Merry Life
*My Bonnie
Noah's Ark
Nut Brown Maiden
October
Peter Gray
Proudly As the Eagle
*Quilting Party
Rosalie
*Three Fishermen
Where, O Where

FOLK AND HOME SONGS

*All Through the Night
*Auld Lang Syne
*Believe Me, if All Those Endearing
*Blue-Bells of Scotland
Bonny Eloise
*Brahm's Lullaby
*Carry Me Back to Old Virginny
*Comin' Thro' the Rye
*Cradle Song
*Dearest Spot
*Drink to Me Only with Thine Eyes
*Gaily the Troubadour
Girl I Left Behind Me
*Hard Times Come Again No More
*Harp That Once Through Tara's Halls
Home on the Range
*Home, Sweet Home
*I Cannot Sing the Old Songs
In the Time of Roses
Isle of Beauty
*I Will Sing a Lullaby
John Peel
*Juanita
*Killarney
*Last Rose of Summer
Leezie Lindsay
Levee Song
*Little Brown Church in the Vale
*Little Dustman
*Loch Lomond
*Long, Long Ago
Lovely Night
Low-Backed Car
*Massa's in the Cold Ground
Meeting of the Waters, The
*Minstrel Boy
*My Old Kentucky Home
Night
*Old Black Joe
*Old Dog Tray
*Old Folks at Home
*Old Oaken Bucket
Ole Dan Tucker
O, No, John
Ring, Ring the Banjo
*Robin Adair
*Slumber Song
Stodola Pumpa
*There's Music in the Air
*Those Evening Bells
*Uncle Ned
*Vacant Chair
*Wearing of the Green
*When You and I Were Young, Maggie

NATIONAL AND PATRIOTIC

*America
America, My Country
*America, the Beautiful
*Battle Cry of Freedom
*Battle Hymn of the Republic
Bonnets of Bonnie Dundee
*Columbia, the Gem of the Ocean
*Dixie
*Flag of the Free
*God Bless Our Native Land
*Hail, Columbia!
*Hail to the Chief
*Illinois
*John Brown's Body
*Just Before the Battle, Mother
Keep the Home Fires Burning
*Keller's American Hymn
*Maple Leaf Forever
*March of the Men of Harlech
*Marseillaise Hymn
*Michigan, My Michigan
Mighty Land Wondrous Land
My Native Land
O Starry Flag
*Patriots
Sleep, Soldier, Sleep
*Star-Spangled Banner
Taps
*Tenting on the Old Camp Ground
*There Are Many Flags in Many Lands
To Thee, O Country!
*Tramp! Tramp! Tramp!
*When Johnny Comes Marching Home
*Yankee Doodle

NEGRO SPIRITUALS

Chilly Water
Couldn't Hear Nobody Pray
Deep River
Down By the River
*Go Down, Moses
Heav'n, Heav'n
*I Ain't Gwine Study War No More
It's a-Me, O Lord
I Want to Be Ready
Mary and Martha
My Lord Delivered Daniel
My Lord, What a Mourning
Nobody Knows the Trouble I've Seen
Oh, Peter, Go Ring Dem Bells!
Oh, Wasn't That a Wide River
Old Ark a-Moverin Along
O Mary, Don't You Weep
Roll, Jordan, Roll
Steal Away
*Swing Low, Sweet Chariot
Turn Back Pharaoh
What Kind of Shoes

OLD FOLKS' SONGS

*Cousin Jedediah
*Revolutionary Tea

OPERATIC SONGS

*Anvil Chorus
*Heart Bowed Down
Largo—Handel
Pilgrims' Chorus

PEACE SONGS

*Praise for Peace
*Years of Peace

SACRED SONGS

*Abide with Me
*Adeste Fideles
And the Glory of the Lord
*Blest Be the Tie
But the Lord Is Mindful of His Own
Cast Thy Burden
Christ, the Lord, Is Risen Today
*Come, Thou Almighty
Come Ye Thankful
Creation
Crusaders' Hymn
Day Is Dying in the West
*Doxology
Evening Prayer
Fairest Lord Jesus
Faith of Our Fathers
Fling Out the Banner, Let It Float
For the Beauty of the Earth
From Ill Do Thou Defend Me
Gloria Patri
*God Be with You Till We Meet Again
God of the Earth
*God of Our Fathers
God So Loved the World
Good King Wenceslas
Hark! Ten Thousand Voices
Hark! the Vesper Hymn
Heavens Resound
*Holy Ghost! with Light Divine
*Holy, Holy, Holy
How Firm a Foundation
In Heavenly Love Abiding
Italian Hymn
*I Think, When I Read That Sweet Story
Jerusalem, the Golden
*Jesus Loves Me
*Jesus, Lover of My Soul
*Jesus, Tender Shepherd, Hear Me
*Largo
*Lead, Kindly Light
Lift Thine Eyes
Lord Is My Shepherd
Lord of All Being
Lost Chord
Lovely Appear
*My Faith Looks Up to Thee
*Nearer, My God, to Thee
*Now Thank We All
*Now the Day Is Over
*O Come All Ye Faithful
*O God, Beneath Thy Guiding Hand
O God, Our Help in Ages Past
Oh Realm of Light
*Old Hundredth
*Onward Christian Soldiers
O Rest in the Lord
O Worship the King
Pilgrims' Chorus
*Praise God, from Whom All Blessings Flow
Praise Ye the Father
*Rocked in the Cradle of the Deep
*Safely Through Another Week
Send Out Thy Light
*Softly Now the Light of Day
*Sound the Loud Timbrel
Spacious Firmament
Still, Still with Thee
Unfold, Ye Portals
*Work, for the Night Is Coming

ROUNDS

Are You Sleeping?
Bell Doth Toll
Bell Is Ringing
*De Bezem
Donkey
Ducks on a Pond
Early to Bed
Good Night
Huntsmen
*Little Tom Tinker
Lovely Evening
Man's Life's a Vapor
*Merrily Merrily
Mules
Row, Row, Row Your Boat
Scotland's Burning
Spring
*Three Blind Mice

SONGS OF SENTIMENT

Ah, 'Tis a Dream
Aloha Oe
*Annie Laurie
Beautiful Dreamer
Belle ob Baltimore
Bonny Eloise
Calm As the Night
Come Where My Lov
*Come, with Thy Lut
*Darling Nelly Gray
*Emmet's Lullaby
Fairy-Belle
Farewell to Thee
*Flow Gently, Sweet Afton
Gentle Annie
*Go to Sleep, Lena Darling
*How Can I Leave Th
Hunter's Farewell
*In the Gloaming
I Would That My Love
Jeannie with the Light Brown Ha
*Kathleen Mavourne
*Last Night the Nigh ingale Woke Me
Linden Tree
*Loreley
*Love's Old Sweet So
Meeting of the Wate
Oh! Susanna
*Oh, Wert Thou in t Cauld Blast
Rose of Allandale
Sally in Our Alley
*Santa Lucia
Schubert's Serenad
*Soldier's Farewell
*Spanish Cavalier
*Stars of the Summe Night
*Sweet and Low
Sweet Genevieve
Two Roses
Vilia
Wait for the Wagon
Warrior Bold
Welcome, Sweet Springtime
*When the Corn Is Waving
*When the Swallows Homeward Fly
*Woodman, Spare That Tree

STUNT SONGS

*Alouette
Alphabet
Barnyard Family
Bee and the Pup
Billy Boy
Crow Song
*Farmyard
Hello Speaker (words only)
*How D'ye Do
Information
*MacDonald's Farm
Oh, Mistress Shady
*O Me! O My!
*Reuben and Rachel
Sing a Song of Citie
Spider and the Spo
Street Urchins' Medley
Style All the While
Three Chafers
*Tree in the Wood
*Welcome, Neighbor

**Orchestral and band parts for the titles starred are in the Instrumentation of "The Golden Book"*